Analytic
Geometry

Analytic Geometry

William K. Smith

New College

The Macmillan Company, New York

Collier-Macmillan Limited, London

The Macmillan Company
866 Third Avenue, New York, New York 10022

Collier-Macmillan Canada, Ltd., Toronto, Ontario

American Mathematical Society subject classification number : 50–XX–01
Library of Congress catalog card number : 77–160372

First Printing

To the Memory of My Father and My Mother

Preface

Without suggesting that this book will be all things to all students, I believe nevertheless that the claim can justly be made that it has considerable flexibility.

First, with regard to the textual material itself, all of the usual topics for a traditional course in plane analytic geometry will be found in Chapters 1 through 6 and (for the use of a parameter) the last part of Chapter 7. Thus, a one-term course in this subject can be based on all or selected parts of these chapters. Vectors in the plane, introduced in Chapter 7, appear initially as an obvious extension of the concept of line segment, which is defined and used extensively in the early chapters. However, the analytic representation of a vector as an ordered pair of real numbers is quickly obtained and subsequently emphasized. Vector functions and the geometric representation of their ranges lead in a direct way to parametric representation of curves in the plane.

The standard material of three dimensional analytic geometry—lines, planes, cylinders, surfaces of revolution, and quadric surfaces—is given full coverage in Chapter 8. At the same time the discussion of vectors in 3-space provides a review of the properties described in Chapter 7 and permits the use of vectors in finding analytic representations of lines and planes in three dimensions. A careful and complete treatment of the vector product appears in Section 8.3.

Chapter 9, to some extent lagniappe, is nevertheless an important and natural extension to the world of linear algebra of some of the concepts and techniques which were introduced previously. The solution of systems of linear equations by means of elementary row operations on matrices is applied to the finding of the inverse of an invertible matrix and to the finding of eigenvectors of a matrix. Finally, the simplification of a quadratic form by a coordinate transformation is obtained in terms of the diagonalization of a symmetric matrix and its eigenvalues. The relation of this material to the usual rotation-of-axes technique for simplifying the equations of the conic section curves is clearly brought out.

In order not to interrupt unnecessarily often the flow of geometric ideas, appendices on sets, the sigma notation, determinants, and the trigonometric functions appear at the end of the book. These topics could be assigned, as needed, for advance reading or for independent study.

The flexibility provided by the rather large number of choices available in selecting topics for study is augmented by the arrangement and variety of the exercises. Three classes of exercises appear: The A exercises are routine drill problems of the sort needed to gain the necessary skills and techniques for working in the subject. The B exercises are almost entirely of a theoretical nature, *and the theory they include is an essential part of the book*. Thus, at the very least, *all of the B exercises should be read*. Extensive and detailed hints are given for most of the more difficult problems. The C exercises are in some cases theoretical and in some cases not; in any event, these problems are intended to be somewhat more challenging, although not required for the sequel. Thus, by a judicious use of the exercises, an instructor can achieve considerable variety in his course and accommodate students in all segments of the ability spectrum.

The third support on which the claim for flexibility rests is the exposition. Every attempt has been made to achieve clarity and comprehensibility (there are, for instance, numerous worked examples). At the same time the approach is modern and rigorous and is intended to guide the student in a natural way from the elementary mathematics of his previous experience toward the more abstract realms for which he may be headed. Clearly, of course, an aim of this sort is never perfectly attained; it is hoped, though, that the result is within a reasonably small neighborhood of the goal.

The numbering system is complete within each chapter. Thus, the second definition in Chapter 7 would be referred to in Chapter 7 as Definition 2. But a reference in Chapter 7 to the third definition of Chapter 2 would be to Definition 2.3, and similarly for theorems, examples, etc.

I am deeply indebted to my daughter Annette for her typing of the manuscript. In her first endeavor of this sort she produced work of such high quality it *almost* makes one want to start another book.

W. K. S.
Sarasota

Contents

9 Matrices 234

A Few Preliminaries

1.1 Introduction

The classical Greek numeral system was not satisfactory for arithmetic calculations; it was, in fact, in this respect roughly comparable to the Roman numeral system. As a consequence, when Euclid and his predecessors developed the study of geometry they made relatively little use of numbers and relied on methods intrinsic to geometry. When such is the case the term *synthetic* is sometimes used to distinguish this approach from that which we shall be using.

With the introduction of the Arabic numeral system into Western culture and, in particular, with the development of the real numbers, making possible the establishment of a one-to-one correspondence between the set of real numbers and the set of points on a straight line, the stage was set for a marriage joining geometry and analysis, the branch of mathematics that is based on the real numbers. René Descartes (1596–1650) was the first to exploit this union in his *Discours de la méthode pour bien conduire sa raison et chercher la vérite dans les sciences*, published in 1637. This marked the beginning of *analytic geometry*.

The preceding paragraph suggests, and correctly so, that we shall need some knowledge of sets and of the real numbers. Because the study of sets is now included in practically all mathematics curricula (sometimes beginning very early in the program), we shall here omit the exposition of the basic ideas; even so, we do present in Appendix 1 a brief summary of definitions, fundamental relations, and notation.

We cannot, however, afford to be so presumptuous about the set of real numbers, and we shall, in Section 1.2, describe in some detail the properties of this system that are essential for our purposes.

Before turning to this project, though, we pause to make a few remarks which are appropriate at this time. The first concerns the subject matter of analytic geometry. We shall not, in general, be proving with our new techniques those same theorems of Euclidean geometry already studied. For one thing this would be wasteful, and for another, the difference in technique suggests—indeed, almost requires—a difference in subject matter. (An analogy can be given by considering the type of building constructed by the classical Greeks and that constructed by means of modern techniques.)

Nevertheless, there will be some intersection between the two sets of geometrical systems, and this brings us to our second remark. Ideally we should develop analytic geometry independently of synthetic geometry, and logically this is possible. But a few occasions arise where, for reasons of pedagogy or expedience, it becomes advisable to draw on a theorem or two from synthetic geometry. We shall do this, but minimally. For a hint at why we shall, compare the derivation of Equation 2.8 as given in the text and as outlined in Exercise C6 after Section 2.3. In Appendix 2 we list the theorems from synthetic geometry that will be used. (Interesting research project: determine where these theorems have been used and rewrite these portions of the text without using the theorems from synthetic geometry.)

Our third remark is related to the second one. In the second paragraph of this section we referred to the one-to-one correspondence between the set of real numbers and the set of points on a straight line. This correspondence is *the* basic building block of analytic geometry and, as its formulation is in terms of a straight line, making use of it almost requires us to take *straight line* as an undefined term. Almost, but not quite: logically, one can avoid this step, but pedagogically it is wiser for us not to avoid it. This is a statement of opinion, but we have at least made it explicit.

1.2 The Real Numbers

We shall refer to the set of real numbers by the symbol **R**. There are three properties that characterize **R**, i.e., which distinguish it from all other number systems.

1. First of all, **R** is a *field*, which we now describe precisely.

DEFINITION 1. *A field F is a set with at least two elements and with two binary operations, addition and multiplication, defined on it satisfying the following axioms (a, b, and c are arbitrary elements of F):*

A_1. $a + b \in F$ *(closure)* M_1. $a \cdot b \in F$.

A_2. $b + a = a + b$ *(commutativity)* M_2. $b \cdot a = a \cdot b$.

A_3. $a + (b + c) =$ M_3. $a \cdot (b \cdot c) = (a \cdot b) \cdot c$.
$(a + b) + c$ *(associativity)*

A_4. There exists an   *(identity)* M_4. There exists an element
element $0 \in F$ such that $1 \in F$, $1 \neq 0$, such that
$a + 0 = a$, all $a \in F$. $a \cdot 1 = a$, all $a \in F$.

A_5. For every $a \in F$ there exists M_5. For every $a \in F$, $a \neq 0$,
an element $-a$ *(inverse)*   there exists an element
such that $a + (-a) = 0$. a^{-1} such that $a \cdot a^{-1} = 1$.

D. $a \cdot (b + c) = a \cdot b + a \cdot c$ *(distributivity)*.

The axioms of Definition 1 provide the basis for almost all the "rules" of elementary algebra. It would not be wise for us to pursue this point too far, but as illustrations we prove two properties.

THEOREM 1.   *The additive inverse is unique.*

PROOF.   Suppose the element $a \in F$ has two inverses, i.e., suppose $a + (-a) = 0$ and $a + b = 0$, for some b. We now show that $b = -a$. For

$$
\begin{aligned}
b &= b + 0 & & A_4 \\
&= b + (a + (-a)) & & \text{supposition} \\
&= (b + a) + (-a) & & A_3 \\
&= (a + b) + (-a) & & A_2 \\
&= 0 + (-a) & & \text{supposition} \\
&= -a & & A_2 \text{ and } A_4. \quad \blacksquare
\end{aligned}
$$

THEOREM 2.   *For every $a \in F$, $a \cdot 0 = 0$.*

[*Remark:* This theorem concerns a *multiplicative* property of the *additive* identity 0. The only axiom connecting addition and multiplication is **D**; the proof of the assertion must use **D**.]

PROOF.   Let $a \in F$; then

$$
\begin{aligned}
a &= a \cdot 1 & & M_4 \\
&= a \cdot (1 + 0) & & A_4 \\
&= a \cdot 1 + a \cdot 0 & & D \\
&= a + a \cdot 0 & & M_4.
\end{aligned}
$$

We now add $-a$ to both sides:

$$
\begin{aligned}
(-a) + a &= (-a) + (a + a \cdot 0) & & ? \\
a + (-a) &= ((-a) + a) + a \cdot 0 & & A_2 \text{ and } A_3 \\
0 &= 0 + a \cdot 0 & & A_2 \text{ and } A_5 \\
0 &= a \cdot 0 & & A_4. \quad \blacksquare
\end{aligned}
$$

Notice that subtraction and division, not referred to in the axioms, can be introduced as follows:

$$a - b = a + (-b)$$
$$a \div b = a/b = a \cdot b^{-1}.$$

As support for our assertion that the rules of algebra follow from the axioms of Definition 1 we state an omnibus theorem, all parts of which can be proven from these axioms. However, we are not going to demonstrate this fact.

THEOREM 3. *The field axioms imply the following for a, b, c, d arbitrary elements of F:*

1. $(-a)b = -(ab)$.
2. $a(-b) = -(ab)$.
3. $-(-a) = a$.
4. $(-a)(-b) = ab$.
5. $-a = (-1)a$.
6. $-(b + c) = (-b) + (-c)$.
7. $a - (-b) = a + b$.
8. $a - (b + c) = a + (-b) + (-c)$.
9. $a - (b - c) = a + (-b) + c$.
10. $a(b - c) = ab - ac$.
11. $a = b \Rightarrow a - c = b - c$.
12. $1/(1/a) = a$.
13. $(a/c) \pm (b/c) = (a \pm b)/c \qquad (c \neq 0)$.
14. $\left.\begin{array}{l} a = b \\ c \neq 0 \end{array}\right\} \Rightarrow a/c = b/c$.
15. $a(b/c) = (ab)/c \qquad (c \neq 0)$.
16. $(1/c)(1/d) = 1/(cd) \qquad (cd \neq 0)$.
17. $(ac)/(bc) = a/b \qquad (bc \neq 0)$.
18. $(a/b)(c/d) = (ac)/(bd) \qquad (bd \neq 0)$.
19. $(a/b)/(c/d) = (a/b)(d/c) = (ad)/(bc) \qquad (bcd \neq 0)$.
20. $a/b = c/d \Leftrightarrow ad = bc \qquad (bd \neq 0)$.
21. $(a/b) \pm (c/d) = (ad \pm bc)/bd \qquad (bd \neq 0)$.
22. $(-a)/b = -(a/b) = a/(-b) \qquad (b \neq 0)$.
23. $(-a)/(-b) = a/b \qquad (b \neq 0)$.
24. $(a/b)/c = a/bc \qquad (bc \neq 0)$.

There are many fields, some having only a finite number of elements. The student is most likely to be familiar with **R** and with the field **Q** of *rational numbers*, i.e., the numbers that can be expressed exactly as the *ratio* of two integers. Further, there are two sets of numbers that will be important to us that are not fields. They are the set **N** of *natural numbers*:

$$\mathbf{N} = \{1, 2, 3, \ldots\},$$

and the set **Z** of integers:

$$\mathbf{Z} = \{\ldots, -3, -2, -1, 0, 1, 2, 3, \ldots\}.$$

2. We next mention the second distinguishing property of **R**: it is an *ordered field* in the sense of the following definition.

DEFINITION 2. *A field F is ordered if there is a binary relation $<$ defined on it that satisfies the following axioms:*

O_1. For every $a, b \in F$ exactly one of the following holds:

$$\left.\begin{array}{l} (i) \ a < b \\ (ii) \ a = b \\ (iii) \ b < a \end{array}\right\} \quad (trichotomy).$$

O_2. $\left.\begin{array}{l} a < b \\ b < c \end{array}\right\} \Rightarrow a < c \quad (transitivity).$

O_3. $\left.\begin{array}{l} a < b \\ c \in F \end{array}\right\} \Rightarrow a + c < b + c \quad (relation \ of \ < \ to \ +).$

O_4. $\left.\begin{array}{l} a < b \\ 0 < c \end{array}\right\} \Rightarrow ac < bc \quad (relation \ of \ < \ to \ \cdot).$

[*Note:* In the statement of the O axioms we have used the symbol $\Rightarrow$. If S_1 and S_2 are statements, then $S_1 \Rightarrow S_2$ means S_1 implies S_2, or from the validity of S_1 must follow that of S_2; sometimes for purposes of syntax, it is convenient to verbalize $\Rightarrow$ as "it is true that." We shall also use $S_1 \Leftrightarrow S_2$ to mean that $S_1 \Rightarrow S_2$ and $S_2 \Rightarrow S_1$; in other words, the statements S_1 and S_2 are *logically equivalent*. The assertion $S_1 \Leftrightarrow S_2$ is often verbalized as "S_1 if and only if S_2"; some writers symbolize this as "S_1 iff S_2."]

We shall use $a \leqslant b$ to mean that either $a < b$ or $a = b$. Also, we shall use $b > a$ to mean that $a < b$. If $a > 0$, we shall say that a is *positive*; if $a < 0$, then a is *negative*. Thus the set **N** of natural numbers can also be called the set of *positive integers*.

Both **R** and the field **Q** of rational numbers are ordered. The field of complex numbers is not ordered, nor is any finite field (see Exercise B13).

3. As already stated, the sets of rational and real numbers are both ordered fields. They are, however, not the same ($\sqrt{2} \in \mathbf{R}$, $\sqrt{2} \notin \mathbf{Q}$—see Exercise B14) and we must distinguish between them. The third characterizing property of **R** is, it turns out, the deepest and most difficult to describe precisely. We shall not attempt to do so here. For our purposes it will be sufficient to point out that the field **Q** has "gaps" ($\sqrt{2}$, $\sqrt{3}$, $\sqrt{5}$, and π all are not in **Q**) and that **R** is without gaps—one can construct **R** from **Q** by, essentially, filling in the gaps (thus the four numbers just mentioned are in **R**). To put it another way, in terms of decimals, every number in **Q** can be expressed as a repeating decimal, whereas the field **R** can be thought of as the set of *all* decimals,

repeating and not. Roughly it is the filling in of the gaps of **Q** that enables us to establish a one-to-one correspondence between **R** and the set of points on a straight line.

Note that this last, loosely described, property distinguishes **R** from **Q** and from all other fields: the three properties uniquely characterize **R**.

Exercises

B.   **1.** Prove that the multiplicative identity in a field is unique.

2. Prove that in a field $a(-b) = -ab$. [*Hint:* show that $ab + a(-b) = 0$, and use Theorem 1.]

3. Prove the following parts of Theorem 3: 3, 4, 6, 8, 13, 16, 17, 20, 21.

4. One of the steps in the proof of Theorem 2 has a question mark where the reason should appear. What *is* the justification for the step?

5. Why are **N** and **Z** not fields? [*Hint:* do they satisfy all the axioms of Definition 1?]

6. True or false: $N \subset Z \subset Q$? Why?

7. Let F_2 denote the set $\{0, 1\}$ with addition and multiplication defined by

$$0 + 0 = 1 + 1 = 0 \qquad\qquad 0 \cdot 0 = 0 \cdot 1 = 1 \cdot 0 = 0$$
$$0 + 1 = 1 + 0 = 1 \qquad\qquad\qquad\quad 1 \cdot 1 = 1. \qquad\qquad [1]$$

Prove that F_2 is a field, i.e., that it satisfies all the axioms of Definition 1. [*Note:* if 0 stands for even and 1 stands for odd, the equations in [1] describe the behavior of even and odd numbers under addition and multiplication.]

8. Prove that in an ordered field

$$a < b \Leftrightarrow b - a > 0. \qquad\qquad\qquad [2]$$

[*Hint:* there are two things to prove; (a) $a < b \Rightarrow b - a > 0$ and (b) $b - a > 0 \Rightarrow a < b$; use some of the O axioms.]

9. Prove the following assertion:

$$\left.\begin{array}{c} a < b \\ c < d \end{array}\right\} \Rightarrow a + c < b + d. \qquad\qquad [3]$$

[*Hint:* use assertion [2] in Exercise B8.]

10. In assertion [3] in Exercise B9, take $c = 0$. This justifies the verbal rule "If the big side of an inequality is made bigger, the inequality is preserved." What rule results from taking $d = 0$?

11. Prove the following:

$$c < 0 \Rightarrow -c > 0. \qquad\qquad\qquad [4]$$

[*Hint:* try supposing $-c = 0$ and $-c < 0$; then use axiom O_1.]

12. Prove the following:

$$\left.\begin{array}{c} a < b \\ c < 0 \end{array}\right\} \Rightarrow ac > bc. \qquad\qquad [5]$$

[*Hint:* use [4] and [2].]

13. Prove that F_2 (see Exercise B7) is not ordered. [*Hint:* first assume $0 < 1$ and then use axiom O_3; next assume $1 < 0$ and use axiom O_3—in both cases arrive at a contradiction, with the help of O_2.]

14. In this exercise we give the skeleton of Euclid's proof that $\sqrt{2} \notin \mathbf{Q}$, i.e., that $\sqrt{2}$ is not expressible as the ratio of two integers. The exercise consists of providing the reasons for the implications. The argument is a contrapositive one. Thus we begin by assuming that there *do* exist integers p and q such that $p/q = \sqrt{2}$. We further assume that the fraction p/q is in lowest terms, i.e., that p and q have no common factors. Now let us see where these assumptions lead us.

$$\frac{p}{q} = \sqrt{2} \Rightarrow p^2 = 2q^2$$

$\Rightarrow p^2$ even   (why?)
$\Rightarrow p$ even   (why?)
$\Rightarrow p = 2r$ (why?)
$\Rightarrow p^2 = 4r^2$
$\Rightarrow 4r^2 = 2q^2$
$\Rightarrow q^2 = 2r^2$ (why?)
$\Rightarrow q^2$ even
$\Rightarrow q$ even   (why?)
$\Rightarrow$ a contradiction.   What?

Therefore $\sqrt{2} \notin \mathbf{Q}$.

1.3 Absolute Value and Inequalities

We conclude this chapter with several topics, related to numbers, that will be of use to us later.

1. Absolute Value

It may be convenient to insert here a reminder of a simple fact: if $a = -2$, then $-a = -(-2) = 2$. Thus a minus before a literal number does not necessarily mean that the number is negative. With this preliminary we go on to define a concept that will be of considerable importance to us.

DEFINITION 3.   *Let $a \in \mathbf{R}$. The* absolute value *of a, denoted by $|a|$, is defined as follows:*

if $a \geqslant 0$,   then $|a| = a$,
if $a < 0$,   then $|a| = -a$.

Notice that in every case $|a| \geqslant 0$, that $|a| = 0 \Leftrightarrow a = 0$, and that $a \neq 0 \Rightarrow |a| > 0$.

We shall exploit a geometric interpretation of absolute value in Chapter 2 and in subsequent chapters.

There are a few properties of absolute value, relating in part to the arithmetic operations, which it will be useful to have.

THEOREM 4. *The absolute value satisfies*

1. $-|a| \leqslant a \leqslant |a|$.
2. $|a + b| \leqslant |a| + |b|$.
3. $|ab| = |a| \cdot |b|$.
4. $\left|\dfrac{a}{b}\right| = \dfrac{|a|}{|b|}$, $\quad (b \neq 0)$.
5. $|-a| = |a|$.

PROOF. Part 1: either (a) $a \geqslant 0$ or (b) $a < 0$; thus by Definition 3, either

$$a = |a|, \quad \text{in which case } a \geqslant -|a| \text{ (i.e., } -|a| \leqslant a = |a|),$$

or

$$a = -|a|, \quad \text{in which case } a < |a| \text{ (i.e., } -|a| = a < |a|).$$

In any case assertion 1 holds.

Part 2: we use the result of part 1 of this theorem:

$$-|a| \leqslant a \leqslant |a|$$
$$-|b| \leqslant b \leqslant |b|.$$

Adding these inequalities, we have

$$-(|a| + |b|) \leqslant a + b \leqslant |a| + |b|. \qquad [6]$$

Now, from [6] we have

$$a + b \geqslant 0 \Rightarrow |a + b| = a + b \leqslant |a| + |b|,$$

whereas

$$a + b < 0 \Rightarrow |a + b| = -(a + b) \leqslant |a| + |b|.$$

Parts 3, 4, and 5 are reasonably obvious and we shall omit a formal proof. In any case, part 4 follows from part 3 and the observation that

$$\left|\frac{1}{b}\right| = \frac{1}{|b|}. \quad \blacksquare$$

2. Inequalities

It is frequently a matter of great importance to be able to solve an inequality that contains a letter representing an unspecified number. The result of solving will be a set of numbers, each of which makes the inequality statement valid when it is substituted throughout for the unknown. This set is called the *solution set*; it is understood that it will contain *all* the numbers that are solutions. We illustrate the process of solving inequalities with a few examples.

Example 1.   Solve for x:

$2x + 1 < 4 - x.$

If we add $x - 1$ to both sides (why can we do this?), we get

$3x < 3.$

Now multiplying both sides by $\frac{1}{3}$ (why is this possible?) gives

$x < 1.$

Strictly speaking, we are not finished. What we have done might be looked on as an exploratory process, the result of which suggests that $\{x \in \mathbf{R} \mid x < 1\}$ is the solution set. The correct completion of the process involves reversing the steps:

$x < 1 \Rightarrow 3x < 3 \Rightarrow 2x + 1 < 4 - x.$

A more sophisticated description of the two parts of this solution is that the first part, ending with $x < 1$, provides us with a *necessary condition* for elements to be in the solution set S. In symbols, this means

$S \subset \{x \in \mathbf{R} \mid x < 1\}.$

Then the second part, the reversal of the steps, amounts to showing that this necessary condition is in fact a *sufficient condition*, i.e., that

$\{x \in R \mid x < 1\} \subset S.$

Together, then, the two parts show that

$S = \{x \in \mathbf{R} \mid x < 1\}.$

Customarily, however, it is sufficient to do the first part and *then check that the steps used are reversible.*

Example 2.   We find the solution set S for

$x^2 < 4.$

We have

$x^2 < 4 \Rightarrow x^2 - 4 < 0 \Rightarrow (x + 2)(x - 2) < 0.$

Now (see Exercise B1) the product of two numbers is negative exactly when one of the numbers is positive and the other is negative. Thus, the last statement leads to either

$$\begin{cases} x + 2 < 0 \Rightarrow x < -2 \\ \quad \text{and} \\ x + 2 > 0 \Rightarrow x > 2, \end{cases}$$

conditions that are incompatible (why?), or

$$\left.\begin{cases} x + 2 > 0 \Rightarrow x > -2 \\ \quad\text{and} \\ x - 2 < 0 \Rightarrow x < 2 \end{cases}\right\} \Rightarrow -2 < x < 2.$$

Reversing the steps, then, gives

$$S = \{x \in \mathbf{R} \mid -2 < x < 2\}.$$

Example 3.   We find S for $x^2 > 9$. We have

$$x^2 > 9 \Rightarrow x^2 - 9 > 0 \Rightarrow (x + 3)(x - 3) > 0.$$

Now the product of two numbers is positive if either both are positive or both are negative. The first of these leads to

$$\left.\begin{cases} x + 3 > 0 \Rightarrow x > -3 \\ \quad\text{and} \qquad\qquad \text{and} \\ x - 3 > 0 \Rightarrow x > 3 \end{cases}\right\} \Rightarrow x > 3$$

(the last $\Rightarrow$ follows from the fact that $3 > -3$), whereas the second leads to

$$\left.\begin{cases} x + 3 < 0 \Rightarrow x < -3 \\ \quad\text{and} \qquad\qquad \text{and} \\ x - 3 < 0 \Rightarrow x < 3 \end{cases}\right\} \Rightarrow x < -3,$$

since $-3 < 3$. Thus (*you* reverse the steps)

$$S = \{x \in \mathbf{R} \mid x < -3\} \cup \{x \in \mathbf{R} \mid x > 3\}.$$

Example 4.   We use a technique like that used in Example 1 to find S for $x^2 + 6 < 5x$. We have

$$x^2 + 6 < 5x \Rightarrow x^2 - 5x + 6 < 0 \Rightarrow (x - 2)(x - 3) < 0.$$

One of the two alternatives for this last statement is

$$\left.\begin{cases} x - 2 < 0 \Rightarrow x < 2 \\ \quad\text{and} \qquad\qquad \text{and} \\ x - 3 > 0 \Rightarrow x > 3 \end{cases}\right\}.$$

But $x < 2$ and $2 < 3 \Rightarrow x < 3$, so these two conditions are incompatible. The other alternative is

$$\left.\begin{cases} x - 2 > 0 \Rightarrow x > 2 \\ \quad\text{and} \qquad\qquad \text{and} \\ x - 3 < 0 \Rightarrow x < 3 \end{cases}\right\} \Rightarrow 2 < x < 3.$$

Thus $S = \{x \mid 2 < x < 3\}$.

Exercises

A. Find the solution set S for each of the following:

   1. $3x - 2 < 10 - x$.

   2. $1 - x < 3x - 7$.

   3. $x^2 - 3x < 0$.

   4. $x^2 - 3x > 0$.

   5. $(x - 2)/(x + 4) > 0$. [*Hint:* both numerator and denominator must be positive or both must be negative.]

   6. $x^2 - 10 < 3x$.

   7. $x^2 + 9x > -18$.

   8. $x/(x - 1) < 0$.

   9. $(x - 1)(x - 2)(x - 3) > 0$.

   10. $x^2 + x + 1 > 0$. [*Hint:* $x^2 + x + 1 = (x^2 + x + \frac{1}{4}) + \frac{3}{4}$.]

   11. $2x^2 - 3 < x^2 - 5$.

   12. $(x + 3)/(x - 5) < 0$.

   13. $x^2 - x < 6$.

   14. $x^2 + 6x > -8$.

   15. $x^2 - x + 1 > 0$.

   16. $x^2 + 2x + 2 < 0$.

   17. $x^2 + 5x > -7$.

   18. $x^3 > 1$.

   19. $|x| < 2$. [*Hint:* $|x| < 2 \Leftrightarrow -2 < x < 2$.]

   20. $|x - 3| < 2$. [See hint for Exercise A19.]

   21. $|x + 4| < 5$.

   22. $|2x - 1| < 5$.

   23. $|4x + 3| < 11$.

   24. $|3x - 1| < 0$.

   25. $|x| > 2$. [*Hint:* $|x| > 2 \Leftrightarrow x > 2$ or $x < -2$.]

   26. $|x - 3| > 2$. [See hint for Exercise A25.]

   27. $|x + 4| \geqslant 5$.

   28. $|3x + 2| \geqslant 5$.

   29. $|2x - 5| > 7$.

   30. $|4x - 1| > -2$.

B.   **1.** Let $a, b \in \mathbf{R}$. Prove the following:

     (a) $ab > 0 \Leftrightarrow (a > 0$ and $b > 0)$ or $(a < 0$ and $b < 0)$.

     (b) $ab < 0 \Leftrightarrow (a > 0$ and $b < 0)$ or $(a < 0$ and $b > 0)$.

   2. Prove $|x - y| \geqslant ||x| - |y||$. [*Hint:* as a start, take $x - y = a$, $y = b$, and use part 2 of Theorem 4.]

2

Coordinate Systems, Functions, and Graphs

2.1 Introduction

In this chapter we begin our study of analytic geometry. The first step will be to set up a coordinate system. In the case of one-dimensional geometry this amounts to choosing a particular one-to-one correspondence between the points on a line and the numbers in **R**; in the case of two-dimensional geometry the correspondence will be between points of a plane (2-space) and *ordered pairs* of real numbers. Similarly, for three-dimensional geometry we shall (later) set up a one-to-one correspondence between points of 3-space and ordered triples of real numbers.

We next take some *geometric* concepts, such as length or distance and midpoint of a line, and express these *analytically*, i.e., in terms of numbers. Finally, to show that the road between geometry and analysis is a two-way path, we take the analytic concept of function and give it a geometric interpretation.

2.2 Coordinates on a Line and in a Plane

We set up a coordinate system on a straight line as follows: We first select, quite arbitrarily, a point called the *origin* and labeled O. Next we choose a direction from O, to be called the *positive direction*. Again this can be done

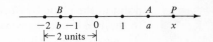

Figure 1

arbitrarily, but it is customary if the line is horizontal to choose the direction to the right—and if vertical, upward. The final choice to be made is a unit of distance; this determines the point on the line that corresponds to the number 1. See Figure 1. The rest is simple. Given a point P on the line, measure its distance x from O; if P lies to the right of O (in the positive direction), then P corresponds to x, whereas if P is to the left of O, then P corresponds to $-x$. Conversely, given a positive number a, it will correspond to the point A, which is a units to the right of O, whereas the negative number b corresponds to the point B, which is $-b$ units to the left of O. The number corresponding to a point is called its *coordinate*.

For a coordinate system in a plane (2-space) we use two perpendicular straight lines, one horizontal and one vertical. These lines are called, respectively, the *x-axis* and the *y-axis*; their point of intersection is the *origin*, labeled O. We set up a coordinate system on each line (in the manner just described) taking the positive direction to the right on the x-axis, upward on the y-axis. We shall always, unless otherwise specifically stated, use the same distance unit on each axis.

We now set up a correspondence between points and ordered pairs of real numbers as follows. Given a point P in the plane, draw lines through P parallel to the y- and x-axes, respectively. The first of these intersects the x-axis in a point (with coordinate) x and the second intersects the y-axis in a point (with coordinate) y. See Figure 2. The *coordinates* of P will be the ordered pair (x, y), the x-coordinate always being specified first. Conversely, given an order pair of real numbers, say (2, 1), one obtains the corresponding

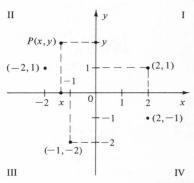

Figure 2

point in the plane by drawing through the point 2 on the *x*-axis a line parallel to the *y*-axis and drawing through the point 1 on the *y*-axis a line parallel to the *x*-axis. The desired point is the intersection of those two lines. In Figure 2 we show the points (corresponding to) (2, 1), (−2, 1), (−1, −2), and (2, −1). In the preceding sentence we enclosed the words "corresponding to" in parentheses, because in the future we shall generally omit them; thus we shall speak of the point (−4, 2), of the line $y = x + 1$, and of the circle $x^2 + y^2 = 4$, i.e., we shall use the analytic name for the geometric object.

The *x*-coordinate of a point is also called its *abscissa*, the *y*-coordinate its *ordinate*. Thus the point (−4, 2) has abscissa −4, ordinate 2.

Notice that the coordinate axes divide the plane into four sections or *quadrants*. It is customary to number these as shown in Figure 2. In quadrant I both coordinates are positive; in quadrant III both are negative; in quadrant II the abscissa is negative, the ordinate positive; in quadrant IV, vice versa.

The set of points in the plane is often referred to as *Euclidean 2-space* and may be denoted by the symbol E_2. The establishment of a coordinate system on a plane gives a one-to-one correspondence between E_2 and **R** × **R** or **R**², as we shall write it. In keeping with a remark made earlier we shall generally use **R**² to denote both the set of ordered pairs of real numbers and the set of points in the plane.

It is worth remarking that it is not essential that the two axes used in setting up a coordinate system be perpendicular, so long, of course, as they are not coincident. However, for most purposes it is simpler to use perpendicular axes and this is the common practice.

Exercises

A.   **1.** Draw coordinate axes and plot the following points:
  (a) (0, 0), (1, 1), (3, 3), (−2, −2), (π, π).
  (b) (2, 1), (3, 1), (−3, 1), (0, 1).
  (c) (−1, −4), (−1, −2), (−1, 0), (−1, 3), (−1, 4).
  (d) (−2, 2), (−1, 1), (1, −1), (3, −3).

  2. There is a feature common to the points in each part of Exercise A1. What is it?

  3. Describe (geometrically) the following sets of points:
  (a) $\{(x, y) \mid y = 0\}$.
  (b) $\{(x, y) \mid x = 0\}$.
  (c) $\{(x, y) \mid y = 2\}$.
  (d) $\{(x, y) \mid x = -1\}$.
  (e) $\{(x, y) \mid y = x\}$.

  4. For a fixed *c* the sets of points $\{(x, y) \mid x = c\}$ and $\{(x, y) \mid y = c\}$ are called *coordinate curves*. Draw some coordinate curves for the following values of *c*: 0, −1, 1, −2, 2. Describe them geometrically.

5. Sketch the following set of points: $\{(x, y) \mid 0 \leqslant x \leqslant 1, \, y = 0\} \cup$ $\{(x, y) \mid x = 1, \, 0 \leqslant y \leqslant 1\} \cup \{(x, y) \mid 0 \leqslant x \leqslant 1, \, y = 1\} \cup \{(x, y) \mid x = 0,$ $0 \leqslant y \leqslant 1\}$.

6. Sketch the points described by
  (a) $\{(x, y) \mid x \leqslant 1\}$.
  (b) $\{(x, y) \mid y > -1\}$.
  (c) $\{(x, y) \mid x \leqslant 1 \text{ and } y \leqslant 1\}$.

7. Describe analytically (i.e., as is done in Exercise A6) the points
  (a) In quadrant II.
  (b) Below the x-axis.
  (c) On and to the right of the y-axis.

8. Set up an oblique coordinate system, i.e., one with a horizontal axis and an upward axis not perpendicular to the horizontal axis. Plot the points $(3, 2), (-2, 1), (-2, -2), (3, -1)$.

9. For the coordinate system set up in Exercise A8 sketch the set of points described by
  (a) $\{(x, y) \mid x = 1\}$.
  (b) $\{(x, y) \mid y = 2\}$.
  (c) $\{(x, y) \mid x \leqslant 1 \text{ and } y \leqslant 2\}$.

B. Give an analytic description (i.e., an equation) of
  1. The x-axis.
  2. The y-axis.
  3. A horizontal line c units above (below) the x-axis. Assume $c > 0$.
  4. A vertical line c units to the right (left) of the y-axis.

2.3 Line Segments: Length, Direction, and Points of Division

Our aim in this section is to find analytic formulations for a few elementary concepts such as length (distance) and direction in 1-space and in the plane (2-space). As we shall be largely concerned with line segments, we begin with a formal definition.

DEFINITION 1. *The line segment $\overline{AB}$ determined by two distinct points A and B is the set of points between A and B, including A and B, on the line determined by A and B.*

Length (distance)

First we consider one-dimensional geometry. The following assertion is reasonably obvious, but we give a formal statement and proof.

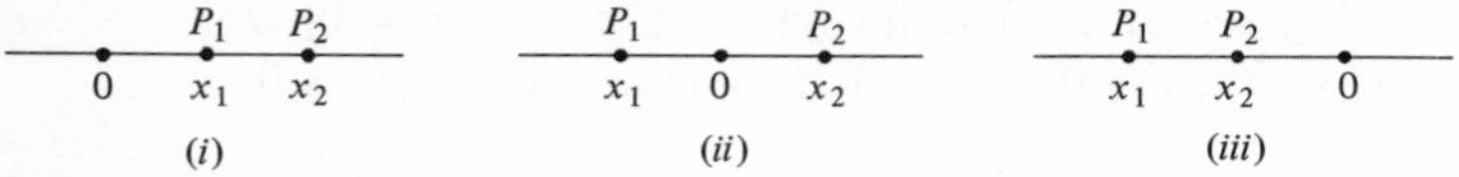

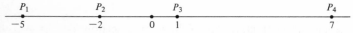

Figure 3

THEOREM 1. *On a straight line with a coordinate system the length $|P_1P_2|$ of the segment determined by $P_1(x_1)$ and $P_2(x_2)$ is*

$$|\overline{P_1P_2}| = |x_1 - x_2|. \qquad [1]$$

PROOF. 1. If one of the points is the origin and the other is $P(x)$, it follows directly from the method of establishing a coordinate system that

$$|\overline{OP}| = |x|.$$

2. For a more general assertion, we consider three cases: (*i*) $0 < x_1 < x_2$, (*ii*) $x_1 < 0 < x_2$, and (*iii*) $x_1 < x_2 < 0$ (see Figure 3).

(*i*) We have, using the result of part 1,

$$|x_1| + |\overline{P_1P_2}| = |x_2|,$$

or, since $x_2 > x_1 > 0$, $|\overline{P_1P_2}| = x_2 - x_1 = |x_2 - x_1|$.

(*ii*) Using part 1,

$$\begin{aligned}|\overline{P_1P_2}| &= |x_1| + |x_2| \\ &= x_2 - x_1 \\ &= |x_2 - x_1|,\end{aligned}$$

since $x_1 < 0 < x_2$.

(*iii*) In the same way as before,

$$|x_2| + |\overline{P_1P_2}| = |x_1|,$$

or

$$\begin{aligned}|\overline{P_1P_2}| &= |x_1| - |x_2| = -x_1 + x_2 \\ &= |x_2 - x_1|,\end{aligned}$$

since $x_1 < x_2 < 0 \Rightarrow |x_1| = -x_1$, $|x_2| = -x_2$, $|x_2 - x_1| = x_2 - x_1$.

3. Finally, since $|-a| = |a|$ (see part 5 of Theorem 1.4), $|x_1 - x_2| = |x_2 - x_1|$; thus the points can be in any relative position. ∎

Example 1. Given the points $P_1(-5)$, $P_2(-2)$, $P_3(1)$, and $P_4(7)$ on a line, we obtain the following lengths (see Figure 4):

$$
\begin{array}{ccccc}
P_1 & P_2 & & P_3 & P_4 \\
\bullet & \bullet & & \bullet & \bullet \\
\hline
-5 & -2 & 0 & 1 & 7
\end{array}
$$

Figure 4

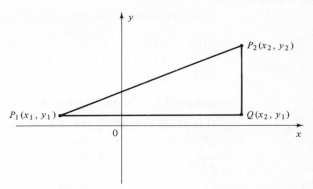

Figure 5

$$|\overline{P_1P_2}| = |-5 - (-2)| = |-5 + 2| = |-3| = 3$$
$$|\overline{P_1P_3}| = |-5 - 1| = |-6| = 6$$
$$|\overline{P_3P_4}| = |1 - 7| = |-6| = 6.$$

In the case of $\mathbf{R}^2$ we have the following result.

THEOREM 2.   *The length of the line segment determined by the two points* $P_1(x_1, y_1)$ *and* $P_2(x_2, y_2)$ *is given by*

$$|\overline{P_1P_2}| = \sqrt{(x_1 - x_2)^2 + (y_1 - y_2)^2}. \qquad [2]$$

PROOF.   For the proof we refer to Figure 5, make use of the Pythagorean Theorem (Appendix 2) and the facts (Theorem 1) that $|\overline{P_1Q}|^2 = (x_1 - x_2)^2$, $|\overline{QP_2}|^2 = (y_1 - y_2)^2$. ∎

Example 2.   Show that the triangle with vertices $A(6, 7)$, $B(-11, 0)$, and $C(1, -5)$ is isosceles. See Figure 6.

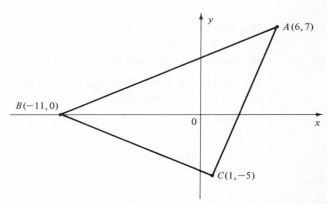

Figure 6

Using Theorem 2, we calculate the lengths of the sides:

$$|\overline{AB}| = \sqrt{(6 - (-11))^2 + 7^2} = \sqrt{289 + 49} = \sqrt{338}$$
$$|\overline{BC}| = \sqrt{(-11 - 1)^2 + (+5)^2} = \sqrt{144 + 25} = \sqrt{169} = 13$$
$$|\overline{CA}| = \sqrt{(1 - 6)^2 + (-5 - 7)^2} = \sqrt{25 + 144} = 13.$$

Since $|\overline{BC}| = |\overline{CA}|$ the triangle ABC is isosceles.

It is worth remarking that the geometric concept we have been referring to as "length of a line segment" is often described instead by the phrase "distance between two points," by which is meant, of course, the straight-line distance. Had we chosen to use the alternative term, we would then have given Equations [1] and [2] as definitions rather than theorems. It is interesting to consider that one could define distance between two points to mean something different from straight-line distance. For example, one such definition could be

$$d(P_1, P_2) = |x_1 - x_2| + |y_1 - y_2|. \tag{3}$$

Look at Figure 5 and consider what kind of distance (geometrically) Equation [3] gives. Notice, though, that if P_1 and P_2 are in the same horizontal line ($y_1 = y_2$) or same vertical line ($x_1 = x_2$), then [3] reduces to [1].

Slope (direction)

In $\mathbf{R}^1$ (one-dimensional geometry) the direction of a line segment—as we have been considering it—is without meaning. We could, of course, introduce the concept of *directed* line segment (we shall have quite a lot to say about this later) or, alternatively, of the direction from $P_1(x_1)$ to $P_2(x_2)$, and then we could observe that our method of setting up a coordinate system implies the following assertion:

$P_2(x_2)$ is in the positive direction from $P_1(x_1) \Leftrightarrow x_2 - x_1 > 0.$

In general, the number $x_2 - x_1$ is called the *directed distance* from P_1 to P_2. But we shall return to such matters later.

In $\mathbf{R}^2$ the direction of a line segment is described by a number called the *slope*, often denoted by the letter m.

DEFINITION 2.   *The slope m of the line segment determined by $P_1(x_1, y_1)$ and $P_2(x_2, y_2)$ is defined by*

$$m = \frac{y_2 - y_1}{x_2 - x_1}, \tag{4}$$

if $x_2 \neq x_1$. If $x_2 = x_1$ the slope of the line segment is not defined.

Since

$$\frac{y_1 - y_2}{x_1 - x_2} = \frac{y_2 - y_1}{x_2 - x_1},$$

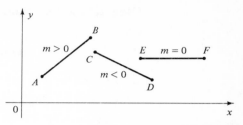

Figure 7

the formula for slope is nonpreferential—we can use either subscript for either point.

The slope of a line segment can be any real number. In general, the line segment "slopes uphill" $\Leftrightarrow m > 0$, slopes downhill $\Leftrightarrow m < 0$, and is horizontal $\Leftrightarrow m = 0$. See Figure 7.

Example 3. Find the slopes of the sides of the triangle ABC of Example 2 (Figure 6).

Using [4], we have

$$M_{AB} = \frac{7 - 0}{6 - (-11)} = \frac{7}{17}$$

$$M_{BC} = \frac{-5 - 0}{1 - (-11)} = \frac{-5}{12}$$

$$M_{CA} = \frac{7 - (-5)}{6 - 1} = \frac{12}{5}.$$

As we shall see in Chapter 3, the relation between the slopes M_{BC} and M_{CA} (their product equals -1) is exactly the condition for two lines to be perpendicular; thus triangle ABC is an isosceles right triangle.

Points of Subdivision

We conclude this section with a simple problem of dividing a line segment into two segments whose lengths bear a specified ratio to one another. We take $\mathbf{R}^1$ first and consider the segment $\overline{P_1P_2}$; our aim is to find the point P_0 such that $|\overline{P_1P_0}| = \lambda |\overline{P_1P_2}|$, where $0 < \lambda < 1$ (see Figure 8).

Figure 8

Using [1] and the condition involving lengths, we have

$$x_0 - x_1 = \lambda(x_2 - x_1)$$

or

$$x_0 = (1 - \lambda)x_1 + \lambda x_2.$$ [5]

Notice that if $\lambda = \frac{1}{2}$, the equation for x_0 becomes

$$x_0 = \tfrac{1}{2}(x_1 + x_2),$$ [6]

the *midpoint formula*.

The analogous result for $\mathbf{R}^2$ is easily obtained from [5] and the use of similar triangles. See Figure 9.

If P_0 is to divide $\overline{P_1P_2}$ such that

$$|\overline{P_1P_0}| = \lambda|\overline{P_1P_2}|,$$

then, since the triangles P_1MP_0, P_0NP_2, and P_1QP_2 are similar, M and N must divide, respectively, $\overline{P_1Q}$ and $\overline{QP_2}$ in the same ratio. Thus, using [5] twice,

$$\left\{ \begin{aligned} x_0 &= (1 - \lambda)x_1 + \lambda x_2 \\ y_0 &= (1 - \lambda)y_1 + \lambda y_2 \end{aligned} \right\} \qquad \text{where } 0 < \lambda < 1.$$ [7]

Setting $\lambda = \frac{1}{2}$, we have the midpoint formula in $\mathbf{R}^2$:

$$x_0 = \tfrac{1}{2}(x_1 + x_2), \quad y_0 = \tfrac{1}{2}(y_1 + y_2).$$ [8]

Example 4. Returning again to Example 2, Figure 6, we find the coordinates of the midpoints of AC and BC. For the midpoint D of AC we have

$$x_D = \tfrac{7}{2}, \quad y_D = 1;$$

for the midpoint E of BC, we find

$$x_E = -5, \quad y_E = -\tfrac{5}{2}.$$

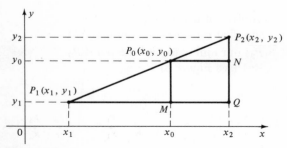

Figure 9

Example 5.   Find the point $P_0(x_0, y_0)$ that divides side $\overline{AB}$ of the triangle of Example 2 such that $|\overline{AP_0}| = 2|\overline{P_0B}|$.

A word of caution here: the given condition implies that $\lambda = \frac{2}{3}$ ($|\overline{P_0B}| = \frac{1}{2}|\overline{AP_0}| \Rightarrow |\overline{AP_0}| = \frac{2}{3}|\overline{AB}|$). Thus, from [7],

$$x_0 = \frac{1}{3}(6) + \frac{2}{3}(11) = \frac{-16}{3}$$

$$y_0 = \frac{1}{3}(7) + \frac{2}{3}(0) = \frac{7}{3}.$$

Exercises

A. **1.** Given the triangle with vertices $A(6, 2)$, $B(-1, 1)$, and $C(3, -2)$, find
   (a) The length of each side.
   (b) The slope of each side.
   (c) The midpoint of each side.
   (d) The point two thirds of the distance between A and the midpoint of $\overline{BC}$.

2. Given the quadrilateral with vertices $A(7, 2)$, $B(-3, 5)$, $C(-2, -3)$, and $D(5, -2)$.
   (a) Find the length of each side.
   (b) Find the slope of each side.
   (c) Find the midpoint of each side.
   (d) Let the midpoint of $\overline{AB}$ be K, that of BC be L, etc. Find slopes of the segments $\overline{KL}$, $\overline{LM}$, $\overline{MN}$, and $\overline{NK}$.
   (e) Does the result of (d) suggest anything about the quadrilateral $KLMN$?
   (f) Is $KLMN$ a rhombus? Why?

3. Given the pentagon with vertices $A(6, 0)$, $B(4, 4)$, $C(-2, 2)$, $D(-4, -4)$, and $E(4, -6)$.
   (a) Find the length of each side.
   (b) Find the slope of each side.
   (c) Find the midpoint of each side.
   (d) Let the midpoint of AB be S, that of BC be T, etc. Find the slopes of the segments $\overline{ST}$, $\overline{TU}$, $\overline{UV}$, $\overline{VW}$, and $\overline{WS}$.
   (e) Is there any discernible regularity to the pentagon $STUVW$?

4. Find the relation satisfied by the points (x, y), which are equidistant from A and B. As a rough check, find the midpoint of AB and show that it satisfies the relation.
   (a) $A(-1, 3)$, $B(4, -7)$.
   (b) $A(-2, -5)$, $B(3, -2)$.
   (c) $A(-4, 2)$, $B(4, 2)$.
   (d) $A(-4, 2)$, $B(-4, -4)$.

5. Find the relation satisfied by the points (x, y) whose distance from A is twice that from B. Is there a rough check similar to that in Exercise A4?

(a) $A(3, 3)$, $B(-3, 6)$.

(b) $A(4, 1)$, $B(-4, -3)$.

(c) $A(0, 6)$, $B(-3, -3)$.

(d) $A(8, 4)$, $B(2, 1)$.

C. **1.** Prove that the quadrilateral whose vertices are the midpoints of the sides of an arbitrary quadrilateral is a parallelogram. [*Hint:* take one vertex of the arbitrary quadrilateral at the origin and one on the positive x-axis.]

2. Strictly speaking, Exercise C1 is premature. Why?

3. This refers to Exercise C1. Can you find a condition, say on the coordinates of the vertices of the given quadrilateral, that will guarantee that the midpoint parallelogram is a rhombus?

4. If, instead of an arbitrary quadrilateral, one begins with an arbitrary triangle, forming a new one by using the midpoints of the sides, is there any regularity in the new one?

5. Same as Exercise C4, only with a pentagon, rather than a triangle.

6. In this exercise we outline a derivation of Equation [8] for the midpoint of the segment $\overline{P_1 P_2}$ that does not draw on results from synthetic geometry. See Figure 9.

(a) First use the fact that the desired point $P_0(x_0, y_0)$ must be equidistant from P_1 and P_2, i.e., $|\overline{P_1 P_0}| = |\overline{P_0 P_1}|$. Write the analytic equation that describes this and call it [*].

(b) Next, since P_0 is on the segment $\overline{P_1 P_2}$, one can use it to calculate the slope m of $\overline{P_1 P_2}$. Specifically,

$m_{\overline{P_1 P_0}} = m_{\overline{P_0 P_2}} = m$.

Set up the equation $m_{\overline{P_1 P_0}} = m_{\overline{P_0 P_2}}$ in terms of the coordinates.

(c) Multiply the equation found in (b) by $(x_2 - x_0)/(y_0 - y_1)$, obtaining an equation which has x's in one member and y's in the other. Let the common value be t.

(d) From the equations in (c) we can find

$$x_2 - x_0 = t(x_0 - x_1), \quad y_2 - y_0 = t(y_0 - y_1). \qquad [**]$$

(e) Substitute the expressions in [**] into Equation [*]. This should give

$$[(x_0 - x_1)^2 + (y_0 - y_1)^2][1 - t^2] = 0. \qquad [***]$$

(f) Produce arguments to show that one must conclude from [***] that $t = 1$.

(g) Use $t = 1$ in [**] to obtain Equations [8].

7. Definition 2 for the slope m of segment $\overline{P_1 P_2}$ is sometimes described as the ratio of the *rise* $(y_2 - y_1)$ to the *run* $(x_2 - x_1)$. An alternative definition is the ratio of rise to length, i.e.,

$$m' = \frac{y_2 - y_1}{|P_1 P_2|}.$$

One advantage of m' is that it is defined for a vertical segment. Are there other advantages? Are there disadvantages?

2.4 Functions

In this section we shift our point of view and begin by introducing an abstract concept, that of function, and, for some special kinds of functions, looking at their geometric interpretation.

DEFINITION 3.   *A function f consists of a set X, a set Y, and a rule which makes correspond to every element $x \in X$ exactly one element $y \in Y$.*

The element y that corresponds to x is often written as $y = f(x)$; we call $f(x)$ the *image* of x. The set X is called the *domain* of f; the set $\{y \in Y \mid y = f(x), x \in X\}$ is called the *range* of f. Occasionally we may use $f[X]$ for the range. The range is a subset of Y, possibly proper. We shall refer to Y as the *range set*. The notation $f: X \to Y$ is often convenient; it can be verbalized as "f maps X into Y."

As defined above, the concept of function is a very general one: X and Y can be arbitrary sets and the rule of correspondence can be given in any way whatsoever. For example, X could be a set of people in a room, Y could be $\mathbf{R}$, and, for $x \in X, f(x)$ could equal the age of x to the nearest year. Or, as another example, $X = \{x, y, z\}$, $Y = \{a, b\}$, and $f(x) = a, f(y) = b, f(z) = a$. In this example $f[X] = Y$, whereas in the first example $f[X]$ would be a relatively "small" subset of the range set Y.

The second example also illustrates the fact that it is perfectly proper for an element of Y to serve as the image of different elements of X (for an extreme example of this let $X = Y = \mathbf{R}$ and for every $x \in \mathbf{R}$ let $f(x) = 2$; this is a *constant* function, where $f[X]$ is a singleton). What is not legitimate is to have two distinct elements of Y serve as the image of a single x.

Our immediate concern, however, will not be with functions of such a general nature. We shall, in fact, in this section be interested in functions for which X and Y are both subsets of $\mathbf{R}$ and the rule is given by a formula or set of formulas. We give some illustrations.

Example 6.

1. $f(x) = x$.
2. $f(x) = -x$.
3. $f(x) = \begin{cases} x, & \text{if } x \geqslant 0 \\ -x, & \text{if } x < 0 \end{cases}$,
4. $f(x) = x^2 + 1$.
5. $f(x) = \begin{cases} x, & x \leqslant 0 \\ 0, & 0 < x < 2 \\ (x-2)^2, & 2 \leqslant x \end{cases}$,

6. $f(x) = \sqrt{x + 1}$.

7. $f(x) = \dfrac{x^2}{x^2 - 1}$.

Strictly speaking, we have been derelict in giving only the formulas to define the functions in Example 6, because Definition 3 specifies that one must prescribe the domain. For the most part we shall adopt the following procedure: if the function f is defined by a formula and if its domain and range are understood to be subsets of **R**, then the domain X is the maximum subset of **R** admissible under the formula. Thus, in Example 6, for formulas 1–5 every $x \in \mathbf{R}$ is admissible, so for these functions $X = \mathbf{R}$. For formula 6, we must have $x + 1 \geqslant 0$, i.e., $X = \{x \in \mathbf{R} \mid x \geqslant -1\}$. For formula 7, x cannot equal ± 1, but all other values of **R** are admissible, so $X = \mathbf{R} - \{-1, 1\}$. Of course, this policy still permits us to define a function in the following way:

$$f: X \to \mathbf{R}, \quad X = \{x \mid -1 < x < 1\}, \quad f(x) = 1 - x^2. \tag{9}$$

The formula that appears at the end of [9] allows every $x \in \mathbf{R}$ to be used, but the function f defined by [9] clearly specifies the domain X to be a proper subset of **R**.

Our geometric purposes begin to become clear when we introduce the following concept.

DEFINITION 4.   *The* graph *of a function* $f: X \to Y$ *is the subset of* $X \times Y$ *defined by*

$$G = \{(x, y) \mid y = f(x), x \in X\}.$$

As we did in defining a function, we have given a general definition of the graph. But, as explained above, we shall be working with functions that have $X, Y \subset \mathbf{R}$. For such functions $G \subset \mathbf{R} \times \mathbf{R} = \mathbf{R}^2$, and we are in position to do some analytic geometry.

[We remark that the standard definition of a function $f: X \to Y$ is as follows: f is a subset of $X \times Y$ with the property that no two distinct ordered pairs have the same first element. Thus this definition is essentially the same as that of the graph given in Definition 4.]

Example 7.   We turn our attention to illustrating the graphs of the functions defined in Example 6.

1. $[f(x) = x]$.

Here,

$$G = \{(x, y) \mid y = x\} = \{(x, x) \mid x \in \mathbf{R}\}.$$

Clearly pairs such as $(-3, -3), (-2, -2), (0, 0), (1, 1), (2, 2), (\tfrac{1}{2}, \tfrac{1}{2}), \ldots$ are

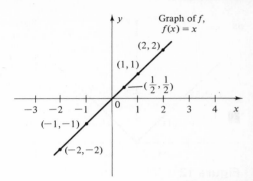

Figure 10

in G, as are the points between these, so the graph of this f is as shown in Figure 10.

    2. $[f(x) = -x]$.

In this case

    $G = \{(x, y) \mid y = -x\} = \{(x, -x) \mid x \in \mathbf{R}\}.$

A few elements of G are $(-2, 2)$, $(-1, 1)$, $(0, 0)$, $(1, -1)$, $(2, -2)$, and $(\frac{1}{2}, -\frac{1}{2})$. Clearly the points of G lie in quadrants II and IV, and the graph is as shown in Figure 11.

    3. $\left[f(x) = \begin{cases} x, & x \geqslant 0 \\ -x, & x < 0 \end{cases} \right]$.

The function f defined here is the absolute value function, i.e., we could write $f(x) = |x|$. The graph is

    $G = \{(x, -x) \mid x < 0\} \cup \{(x, x) \mid x \geqslant 0\}.$

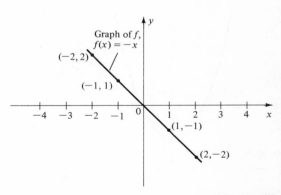

Figure 11

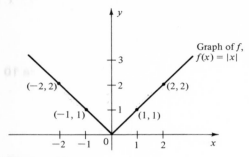

Figure 12

Thus *G* consists of parts of the lines that appear in Figures 10 and 11—to be specific, the parts in quadrants I and II. See Figure 12.

    4. $[f(x) = x^2 + 1]$.

The graph is

$$G = \{(x, y) \mid y = x^2 + 1\} = \{(x, x^2 + 1) \mid x \in \mathbf{R}\}.$$

The following observations follow easily from the formula for *f*:

(a) When $x = 0$, $y = 1$.
(b) $y \geqslant 1$ for all *x*.
(c) Since $(-x)^2 = x^2$, we note that $f(-x) = f(x)$ and, except for $(0, 1)$, the points of *G* occur in pairs, each point of a pair having the same ordinate; *example*: $(-1, 2)$ and $(1, 2)$. This characteristic is known as symmetry with respect to the *y*-axis. See the B exercises.
(d) As $|x|$ increases, *y* increases.

The graph is shown in Figure 13.

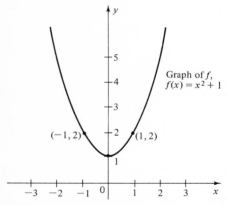

Figure 13

5. $\left[f(x) = \begin{cases} x^2, & x \leqslant 0 \\ 0, & 0 < x \leqslant 2 \\ (x-2)^2, & 2 < x \end{cases} \right].$

In this case G is the union of three sets:

$$G = G_1 \cup G_2 \cup G_3,$$

where

$G_1 = \{(x, y) \mid y = x^2, x < 0\}$
$G_2 = \{(x, 0) \mid 0 < x < 2\}$
$G_3 = \{(x, y) \mid y = (x-2)^2, 2 \leqslant x\}.$

It is reasonably easy to see that G_1 consists of the left half of the curve in Figure 13, but lowered one unit. Next, G_2 is the portion of the x-axis between $x = 0$ and $x = 2$. Finally, we assert—and ask the reader to assure himself that it is so—that G_3 consists of the right half of the curve in Figure 13, but lowered one unit and shifted two units to the right (a knight's move). Thus the graph of f is as shown in Figure 14.

6. $[f(x) = \sqrt{x + 1}].$

Here we have

$$G = \{(x, y) \mid y = \sqrt{x + 1}, x \geqslant -1\}.$$

We can make the following observations about G:

(a) $x = -1 \Rightarrow y = 0$ (x-intercept).
(b) $x = 0 \Rightarrow y = 1$ (y-intercept).
(c) $x > -1 \Rightarrow y > 0.$
(d) $x \rightarrow \infty \Rightarrow y \rightarrow \infty.$

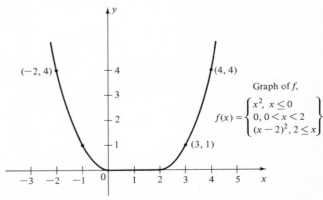

Graph of f,

$$f(x) = \begin{cases} x^2, & x \leq 0 \\ 0, & 0 < x < 2 \\ (x-2)^2, & 2 \leq x \end{cases}$$

Figure 14

We have introduced a new notation here: $x \to \infty$ means "x is getting big beyond all bounds, positively." Since, for $b > 1$, $\sqrt{b}$ increases more slowly than does b, we know that y will increase—beyond bounds—more slowly than x. We can, if we wish, calculate a few specific points on G: $(1, \sqrt{2})$, $(3, 2)$, $(8, 3)$, etc. Thus the graph of G is as shown in Figure 15.

As we shall see later (Chapter 5), this graph is again the left side of the curve in Figure 13 with its position in the plane altered.

Notice the behaviour of the curve (as drawn) in the vicinity of the point $(-1, 0)$. Nothing in our analysis shows that the curve is perpendicular to the x-axis at $(-1, 0)$. However this is so, as can be shown by means of calculus.

We shall defer the discussion and graph of the function in 7 of Example 6 to the next section.

Our purpose in the preceding examples was to suggest how to extract geometric information from the formula that defines the function. The fact is that our approach in this section has been rather haphazard. It is possible to systematize these techniques and we shall do this in Section 2.5.

We conclude this section by describing a few types of functions which are important.

DEFINITION 5.   *A* polynomial function *is one that is defined by a formula*

$$f(x) = a_0 x^n + a_1 x^{n-1} + \cdots + a_{n-1} x + a_n,$$

where n is a non-negative integer and $a_0, a_1, \ldots, a_n \in \mathbf{R}$.

For example, the functions 1, 2, and 4 of Example 6 are polynomial functions. The domain for a polynomial function is $\mathbf{R}$. Why? The range may be a proper subset of $\mathbf{R}$ (e.g., $f(x) = 1$ or $f(x) = x^2$).

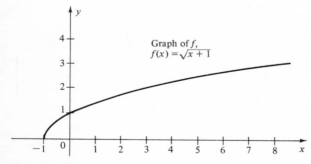

Graph of f,
$f(x) = \sqrt{x + 1}$

Figure 15

DEFINITION 6. *A rational function is one that is defined by a formula*

$$f(x) = \frac{p(x)}{q(x)} = \frac{a_0 x^n + \cdots + a_{n-1} x + a_n}{b_0 x^m + \cdots + b_{m-1} x + b_m},$$

i.e., a rational function is the ratio of two polynomial functions.

The function in 7 of Example 6 is a rational function. The domain of a rational function is the set

$$X = \{x \mid q(x) \neq 0\}.$$

No useful general statement can be made about the range.

Exercises

A. **1.** For the functions defined by the following formulas determine the domain and range. [*Hints:* for the domain use the principle given just after Example 6; for the range the procedure illustrated in the partial solution of (a) may be helpful.]

(a) $f(x) = x^2 + x$.

[To find $f[X]$, the range, set $y = x^2 + x$ and solve for x, using the quadratic formula: $x^2 + x - y = 0$,

$$x = \frac{-1 \pm \sqrt{1 + 4y}}{2}.$$

Thus, y must satisfy $1 + 4y \geqslant 0$, or $y \geqslant -\frac{1}{4}$. This gives

$$f[X] = \{y \mid y \geqslant -\tfrac{1}{4}\}.]$$

(b) $f(x) = \dfrac{1}{x}$.

(c) $f(x) = \dfrac{x}{x^2 + 1}$.

(d) $f(x) = \sqrt{x - 2}$.

(e) $f(x) = \sqrt{1 - x^2}$.

(f) $f(x) = \dfrac{x}{x - 1}$.

(g) $f(x) = x^3$.

(h) $f(x) = x^4 - x^2 = x^2(x^2 - 1)$.

(i) $f(x) = 4$.

(j) $f(x) = 2x + 1$.

(k) $f(x) = \sqrt{x^2 - 1}$.

2. Sketch the graph of each of the functions in Exercise A1.

3. Let $f(x) = ax + b$. Sketch the graph of f for the following pairs of values of a and b.

(a) $a = b = 1$.

(b) $a = 2, b = 1$.

     (c) $a = 3, b = 1$.
     (d) $a = 6, b = 1$.
     (e) $a = -1, b = 1$.
     (f) $a = -2, b = 1$.
     (g) $a = 0, b = 1$.
     (h) $a = b = 0$.
     (i) $a = 3, b = -3$.

4. Let $f(x) = x^2 - 2x + c$. Sketch the graph of f for each of the following values of c.

     (a) 0.
     (b) 1.
     (c) -1.
     (d) 4.

5. In each of the following equations replace y by $f(x)$ and determine if the equation defines a function:

     (a) $x - y^2 = 0$.

SOLUTION: Letting $y = f(x)$, we have

$$x - [f(x)]^2 = 0,$$

or

$$[f(x)]^2 = x,$$

or

$$f(x) = \pm \sqrt{x},$$

not a function, since to each positive value of x there correspond two values for $f(x)$.]

     (b) $3x - 2y + 7 = 0$.
     (c) $x^2 + y^2 = 4$.
     (d) $y + 3 = 0$.
     (e) $x^2 - y^2 = 4$.
     (f) $x - y^3 = 1$.

B. In this set of exercises we discuss the concept of symmetry, already briefly encountered, and obtain some useful theorems about symmetry.

First we introduce a new symbol. If S_1 and S_2 are statements, we shall use $S_1 \Leftrightarrow S_2$ to mean that S_2 is the definition of S_1. From a logical point of view, to say $S_1 \Leftrightarrow S_2$ means that S_1 and S_2 are equivalent, so that we *could* use $S_1 \Leftrightarrow S_2$, but we prefer to distinguish the case where the equivalence is due to definition ($\Leftrightarrow$) from that where it is the assertion of a theorem ($\Leftrightarrow$).

1. We begin with a definition.

DEFINITION 7.   *The points P_1 and P_2 are symmetric with respect to the line $l \Leftrightarrow l$ is the perpendicular bisector of $\overline{P_1 P_2}$.*

Let l be the y-axis. Which of the following pairs of points are symmetric with respect to l?

    (a) $(2, 3)$ and $(-2, 3)$.
    (b) $(3, 1)$ and $(-3, 2)$.
    (c) $(3, 1)$ and $(-2, 1)$.
    (d) (x_0, y_0) and $(-x_0, y_0)$.

2. Another definition.

DEFINITION 8. *A set S in the plane is symmetric with respect to the line $l \Leftrightarrow$ for every point $P \in S$ there exists a point $Q \in S$ such that P and Q are symmetric with respect to l.*

    NOTE: The essential part is that Q be an element of S.

Let l be the y-axis. Which of the following sets are symmetric with respect to l?

    (a) $S = \{(x, y) \mid x = 0\}$.
    (b) $S =$ quadrants I and II.
    (c) $S =$ quadrants I and IV.
    (d) $S = \{(x, y) \mid y = x\}$.
    (e) $S = \{(x, y) \mid x^2 + y^2 \leqslant 1\}$.
    (f) $S =$ graph of f, where $f(x) = x^2 - 1$.
    (g) $S = x$-axis.
    (h) $S =$ graph of f, where $f(x) = |x|$.

3. Next concept.

DEFINITION 9. *A function $f: X \to \mathbf{R}$ is even $\Leftrightarrow$ (i) $x \in X \Rightarrow -x \in X$ (i.e., X is symmetric with respect to the origin) and (ii) for every $x \in X, f(-x) = f(x)$.*

Which of the following functions are even?

    (a) $f(x) = 3x^2 + 5$.
    (b) $f(x) = 2x^2 + 4x + 6$.
    (c) $f(x) = |x|$.
    (d) $f(x) = \sin x$.
    (e) $f(x) = \cos x$.
    (f) $f(x) = \begin{cases} x^4, & -1 \leqslant x < 0 \\ x^2, & 0 \leqslant x \leqslant 1 \end{cases}$.
    (g) $f(x) = x^4 - 3x^2 - 31$.

4. Prove the following assertion.

THEOREM 3. *If a function $f: X \to \mathbf{R}$ is even, then the graph G of f is symmetric with respect to the y-axis.*

5. Another new concept.

DEFINITION 10.   *The points P_1 and P_2 are symmetric with respect to a point $P_0 \Leftrightarrow P_0$ is the midpoint of $\overline{P_1P_2}$.*

Prove that (x_1, y_1) and (x_2, y_2) are symmetric with respect to the origin $\Leftrightarrow x_2 = -x_1$ and $y_2 = -y_1$.

6. Here we go again.

DEFINITION 11.   *A set S in the plane is symmetric with respect to a point $P_0 \Leftrightarrow \cdots$.*

As your exercise, complete the definition. If necessary, refer to Definition 8.

7. The final one.

DEFINITION 12.   *A function $f\colon X \to \mathbf{R}$ is odd $\Leftrightarrow$ (i) X is symmetric with respect to the origin and (ii) for every $x \in X$, $f(-x) = -f(x)$.*

Which of the following functions are odd?
  (a) $f(x) = 3$.
  (b) $f(x) = x^3 + x$.
  (c) $f(x) = \cos x$.
  (d) $f(x) = 5x^5 + 3x^3 + x - 1$.
  (e) $f(x) = \tan x$.
  (f) $f(x) = x$.

8. Prove the following assertion.

THEOREM 4.   *If a function $f\colon X \to \mathbf{R}$ is odd, then the graph G of f is symmetric with respect to the origin.*

9. We are finished, for now, with symmetry, but we are not finished with definitions. In this exercise we discuss a way of combining functions.

DEFINITION 13.   *Let $f\colon X_f \to \mathbf{R}$ and $g\colon X_g \to \mathbf{R}$. By the* composition *of f and g we mean the function $f \circ g$ defined by*

$$(f \circ g)(x) = f(g(x)).$$

For example, let f and g be defined by the formulas $f(x) = x^2 + 1$ and $g(x) = 1/x$. Then

$$(f \circ g)(x) = f(g(x)) = f\left(\frac{1}{x}\right) = \left(\frac{1}{x}\right)^2 + 1 = \frac{1}{x^2} + 1 = \frac{1 + x^2}{x^2},$$

and

$$(g \circ f)(x) = g(f(x)) = g(x^2 + 1) = \frac{1}{x^2 + 1}.$$

Find the formula for $f \circ g$ and for $g \circ f$ for each of the following pairs.
  (a) $f(x) = \sqrt{x}, g(x) = x^2$.
  (b) $f(x) = x^2 + 1, g(x) = \sqrt{x - 1}$.

(c) $f(x) = \sin x$, $g(x) = \dfrac{x}{x^2 + 1}$.

(d) $f(x) = \dfrac{1}{x}$, $g(x) = \dfrac{1}{x}$.

(e) $f(x) = -x^2 - 7$, $g(x) = \sqrt{x^2 + 4}$.

(f) $f(x) = \dfrac{x^2 - 1}{x^2 + 1}$, $g(x) = \dfrac{x^2 + 1}{x^2 - 1}$.

10. See the preceding exercise. Let f_1, f_2, f_3, and f_4 be functions with a common domain X that is symmetric with respect to the origin. Suppose f_1 and f_3 are odd and f_2 and f_4 are even functions. Which of the following are odd and which are even?

(a) $f_1 \circ f_2$.

(b) $f_1 \circ f_3$.

(c) $f_2 \circ f_4$.

(d) $f_2 \circ f_3$.

2.5 Some Techniques of Curve Sketching

The problem of extracting geometric information from the formula for, or properties of, a function can be a difficult one. Moreover, some of the most powerful tools make use of calculus and will not be taken up here. Even so, a few elementary techniques will often yield enough information so that one can make at least an intelligent guess at the nature of the graph of a function.

We list a few properties that should be investigated; the order is not essential, but we do urge that the student develop a systematic approach, so that available information is not overlooked.

Throughout we shall be considering the geometric properties of the graph G of a function $f: X \to \mathbf{R}$, where $X \subset \mathbf{R}$.

1. Intercepts

The points (if any) where the curve (graph) crosses the coordinate axes are called the *intercepts*. If $0 \in X$, the y-intercept is the point $(0, y_0)$, where $y_0 = f(0)$. The graph of a function can, of course, have at most one y-intercept.

The x-intercept(s) will be points $(x_0, 0)$, where $f(x_0) = 0$. A number x_0 such that $f(x_0) = 0$ is called a *zero* of f. The number of zeros can be zero, finite, or infinite; examples: $f(x) = x^2 + 1, f(x) = x^4 - x^2 = x^2(x + 1)$ $(x - 1)$, and $f(x) = \sin x$.

Example 8. Let $f(x) = x^2 - 5x + 4$. Then $f(0) = 4$, so the y-intercept is $(0, 4)$. To investigate x-intercepts we factor the polynomial,

$f(x) = (x - 1)(x - 4)$, making it obvious that f has two zeros 1 and 4, and the curve has two x-intercepts $(1, 0)$ and $(4, 0)$.

2. Extent (Domain and Range of f)

The domain and range of f determine the *extent* of the curve. For example, if f is defined by $f(x) = \sqrt{1 - x^2}$, it is clear that the domain is $X = \{x \mid -1 \leqslant x \leqslant 1\}$ and it is also easy to see that the corresponding values of f must be $f[X] = \{y \mid 0 \leqslant y \leqslant 1\}$. Thus, the graph of this function lies entirely in the rectangle one unit high based on the segment from $(-1, 0)$ to $(1, 0)$.

We have already remarked that there might be difficulties in finding the range. If these appear to be too great, this piece of information can be dispensed with.

Example 8 (continuation).   The function f, where $f(x) = x^2 - 5x + 4$, has, as do all polynomials, $X = \mathbf{R}$. To find the range of f we let $y = f(x)$ and use the quadratic formula:

$$y = x^2 - 5x + 4,$$

or

$$x^2 - 5x + 4 - y = 0.$$

Solving, we get

$$x = \frac{5 \pm \sqrt{9 + 4y}}{2}. \tag{10}$$

Since every admissible value of y must give real x, we must have $9 + 4y \geqslant 0$, or $y \geqslant (-9)/4$. (Notice that when $y = (-9)/4$, $x = \frac{5}{2}$.) Thus the graph of f lies in the half-plane on and above the horizontal line $\frac{9}{4}$ units below the x-axis.

Example 9.   The device just used, letting $y = f(x)$ and solving for x, can be misleading. Consider the function defined by $f(x) = \sqrt{x + 1}$. The nature of this formula makes it obvious that $X = \{x \mid x \geqslant -1\}$, and that $f[X] = \{y \mid y \geqslant 0\}$. (Why?) But using the technique previously demonstrated, we would have

$$y = \sqrt{x + 1},$$

or

$$y^2 = x + 1,$$

or

$$x = y^2 - 1.$$

From this it would appear that $f[X] = \mathbf{R}$. (Why?) See Figure 15.

3. Symmetry

Symmetry of a set of points with respect to a line or point has already been introduced in the B exercises following Section 4. Such symmetry, when it exists, can be useful in curve sketching in that it essentially reduces the work involved by a factor of two. For, if we know that a curve is symmetric with respect to the y-axis, then knowledge of its "behavior" in quadrants I and IV, along with the symmetry, enables one to describe its behavior completely.

We recall, from Theorems 3 and 4, that

1. f even (i.e., $f(-x) = f(x)$) $\Rightarrow \begin{cases} \text{the graph of } f \text{ is symmetric} \\ \text{with respect to the } y\text{-axis} \end{cases}$,

and

2. f odd (i.e., $f(-x) = -f(x)$) $\Rightarrow \begin{cases} \text{the graph of } f \text{ is symmetric} \\ \text{with respect to the origin} \end{cases}$.

These types of symmetry are the easiest to detect but we shall mention one or two others later. (Why, in discussing graphs of functions, is there no need to include symmetry with respect to the x-axis?)

Example 10.   Let $f(x) = \sqrt{1 - x^2}$. Then, as we have already pointed out, $X = \{x \mid -1 \leqslant x \leqslant 1\}$ is symmetric with respect to the origin and $f(-x) = f(x)$, so the graph of f is symmetric with respect to the y-axis. As the functional values must be non-negative, we need study the behavior of the curve only in quadrant I. Clearly as x increases from 0 to 1, $f(x)$ decreases from 1 to 0, so the graph of f must resemble the curve in Figure 16.

By means of the length formula, it is easy to determine that the curve is in fact a semicircle.

Example 11.   Let f be defined by $f(x) = x + (1/x)$. It is easy to see that $X = \mathbf{R} - \{0\}$. By the technique already described one can find that $f[X] = \{y \mid y^2 \geqslant 4\} = \{y \mid y \leqslant -2\} \cup \{y \mid y \geqslant 2\}$. Moreover, f is odd, so the graph is symmetric with respect to the origin. Clearly (why?) the graph must lie in quadrants I and III, and the symmetry permits us to focus attention on the first quadrant. We shall return to this example later. See Figure 21.

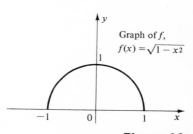

Graph of f,
$f(x) = \sqrt{1 - x^2}$

Figure 16

Example 8 (continuation).   The function f defined by $f(x) = x^2 - 5x + 4$ is neither even nor odd, so there is symmetry neither to the y-axis nor to the origin. However, Equation [10] *suggests* a kind of symmetry: a given y-value, other than $y = (-9)/4$, corresponds to two x-values, equally spaced about $x = \frac{5}{2}$. We now obtain this result by a different approach. We have

$$f(x) = x^2 - 5x + 4,$$

or, completing the square,

$$f(x) = (x^2 - 5x + \tfrac{25}{4}) + 4 - \tfrac{25}{4}$$
$$= (x - \tfrac{5}{2})^2 - \tfrac{9}{4}.$$

If we set $x - \frac{5}{2} = x'$, and let $g(x') = x'^2 - \frac{9}{4}$, then we see that $f(x) = g(x')$, where g is an even function in terms of x'. By Theorem 5, which we shall state in a moment, and which we shall help you prove in the exercises that follow, the graph of f is symmetric with respect to the vertical line $x = \frac{5}{2}$. See Figure 17.

It is easily seen that this is the same curve as in Figure 13 but that it occupies a different position in the plane.

We now give the assertion alluded to previously.

THEOREM 5.   *Suppose the formula for a function f can be written as*

$$f(x) = g(x - k)$$
$$= g(x'),$$

where $x' = x - k$. Suppose further that g is even in terms of x'. Then the graph of f is symmetric with respect to the vertical line $x = k$.

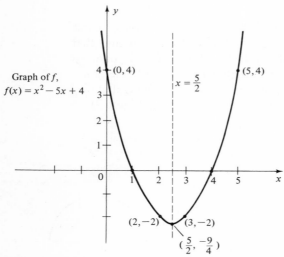

Graph of f,
$f(x) = x^2 - 5x + 4$

Figure 17

(Proof is outlined in Exercise B1.)

The reader should realize that symmetry need not be present in a curve (see Figure 15), but that one should always look for it.

4. Changes of Sign in Ordinate

Occasionally the form of the formula for a function may make it easy to determine when, i.e., for what x-values, y is positive, and when y is negative. Such information enables one to specify regions of the plane where the curve must lie (or, alternatively, regions where the curve cannot lie).

Example 8 (continuation).   If we write the formula for f as $f(x) = x^2 - 5x + 4 = (x - 1)(x - 4)$, we find that

$$x < 1 \Rightarrow \quad f(x) > 0$$
$$1 < x < 4 \Rightarrow f(x) < 0$$
$$4 < x \Rightarrow \quad f(x) > 0.$$

Thus, we know the curve cannot lie in the shaded regions shown in Figure 18. See also Figure 17.

Example 12.   Consider the function f defined by $f(x) = x^3 - 4x^2 = x^2(x - 4)$. We see that the zeros of f are 0 and 4. Thus we consider three x-regions:

$$x < 0 \Rightarrow \quad f(x) < 0$$
$$0 < x < 4 \Rightarrow f(x) < 0$$
$$4 < x \Rightarrow \quad f(x) > 0.$$

(Notice that f does not change sign at 0. Why?) We know then that the graph cannot occupy the regions shaded in Figure 19.

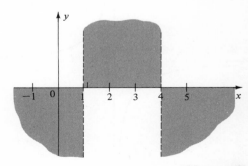

Figure 18

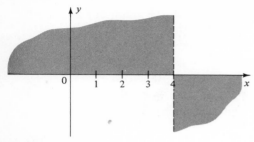

Figure 19

5. Asymptotes

We begin the discussion of asymptotes by considering an especially simple illustration.

Example 13. Let f be defined by $f(x) = 1/x$. The graph of f is the set $G = \{(x, y) \mid y = 1/x, x \neq 0\}$. It is immediately seen that neither x nor y can equal zero (and zero is the only inadmissible value). This tells us that the curve has no intercepts and that $X = \mathbf{R} - \{0\} = f[X]$. Also, f is odd, and G, symmetric with respect to 0, lies entirely in quadrants I and III. But our real interest in this function is due to the following assertions:

1. $x \to \infty \Rightarrow y \to 0^+$.
2. $x \to -\infty \Rightarrow y \to 0^-$.
3. $x \to 0^+ \Rightarrow y \to \infty$.
4. $x \to 0^- \Rightarrow y \to -\infty$.

The symbol $x \to 0^+$ means "x is close to zero, but bigger than zero"; similarly, $x \to 0^-$ means "x is close to zero, but less than zero." Like meanings apply to $x \to a^+$ and $x \to a^-$.

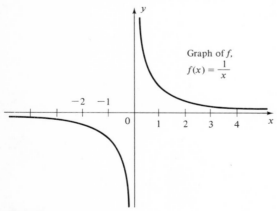

Graph of f,
$$f(x) = \frac{1}{x}$$

Figure 20

From this brief, but adequate, analysis we can sketch the graph of f as in Figure 20.

We return to statements 1 and 2. They say that the x-axis ($y = 0$) is a *horizontal asymptote* of the curve, in the sense that as a point P on the curve gets arbitrarily far from the origin ($|\overline{OP}| \to \infty$) in the direction of the x-axis, the perpendicular distance between P and the x-axis gets arbitrarily small ($y \to 0$). Similarly, assertions 3 and 4 say that the y-axis is a *vertical asymptote*.

An asymptote need be neither horizontal nor vertical. For the general definition we let $d(P, l)$ denote the perpendicular distance between a point P and a line l.

DEFINITION 14.   *A line l is an* asymptote *of a curve $\Leftrightarrow$ if P is a point on the curve, then as $|\overline{OP}| \to \infty$ in the direction of l, $d(P, l) \to 0$.*

Example 14.   Let f be defined by $f(x) = x + (1/x)$. We quickly note that $X = \mathbf{R} - \{0\}$, that f is odd, and that the graph of f, symmetric with respect to the origin, lies in quadrants I and III. We also see that

1. $x \to \infty \Rightarrow f(x) \to x$ or $f(x) - x$ tends to 0,   since $1/x \to 0$.
2. $x \to 0^+ \Rightarrow f(x) \to \infty$.

Statement 1 tells us that the line $y = x$ is an asymptote and statement 2 tells us that $x = 0$ (y-axis) is an asymptote, both in quadrant I. (As a vertical line is not the graph of a function, the investigation of vertical asymptotes is handled a little differently from that for nonvertical asymptotes. This accounts for the difference in form between statements 1 and 2.) The symmetry

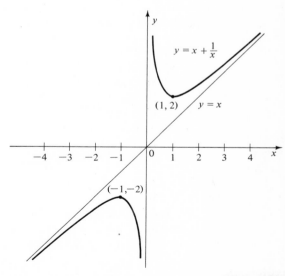

Figure 21

then gives these same lines as asymptotes in quadrant III. The curve is shown in Figure 21.

A rigorously correct formulation of the definition of an asymptote to a curve requires the concept of limit, which we have largely sidestepped in Definition 14. As a result, theorems giving sufficient conditions for a line to be an asymptote would require the use of limits for their proofs. Since we do not intend to discuss limits here, we give only one such theorem (without proof), which describes horizontal and vertical asymptotes of a rational function.

THEOREM 6. *Let the rational function f be defined by*

$$f(x) = \frac{a_0 x^m + a_1 x^{m-1} + \cdots + a_{m-1}x + a_m}{b_0 x^n + b_1 x^{n-1} + \cdots + b_{n-1}x + b_n} = \frac{p(x)}{q(x)},$$ [11]

where the polynomials p and q have no common zeros. Then the following are true:

1. *$m < n \Rightarrow y = 0$ (x-axis) is a horizontal asymptote.*
2. *$m = n \Rightarrow y = a_0/b_0$ is a horizontal asymptote.*
3. *$x = r$ is a vertical asymptote for every zero r (there can be at most n) of the polynomial q.*

Note that a rational function can have asymptotes that are neither horizontal nor vertical (Example 14).

We now turn to the graph of function 7 of Example 6 in Section 2.4.

7. $\left[f(x) = \dfrac{x^2}{x^2 - 1} \right].$

We have the following analysis:

1. Intercepts: $(0, 0)$.
2. Domain: $X = \mathbf{R} - \{1, -1\}$.
   Range: $f[X] = \{y \mid y < 0\} \cup \{y \mid y > 1\}$ (exercise for student).
3. Symmetry with respect to y-axis (f even).
4. $x^2 > 1 \Rightarrow f(x) > 0$; $x^2 < 1 \Rightarrow f(x) < 0.$
5. Asymptotes: $y = 1$ (statement 1 of Theorem 6)
   $\left. \begin{array}{l} x = -1 \\ x = 1 \end{array} \right\}$ (statement 3 of Theorem 6).

The graph of f is now easily sketched, using the above analysis, as shown in Figure 22.

We end this section on a slightly sour note: the systematic analysis we have described *can* produce very little helpful information. Consider, for example, the function f defined by

$$f(x) = \frac{x^4 - 5x^3 - 7x^2 + x + 6}{x^2 + 1}.$$

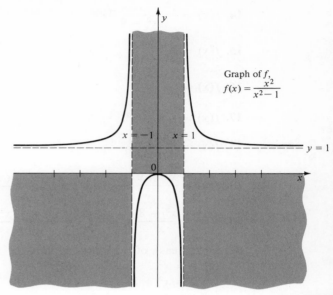

Graph of f,
$$f(x) = \frac{x^2}{x^2 - 1}$$

Figure 22

All that we learn from our procedure is that $X = \mathbf{R}$ and that the y-intercept is at $(0, 6)$.

Exercises

A. In numbers 1–20 analyze and sketch the graphs of the functions defined by the given formulas.

 1. $f(x) = x^2 + x - 6$.
 2. $f(x) = x^2 - x - 20$.
 3. $f(x) = x^3 + x^2 - 6x$.
 4. $f(x) = x^3 - x^2 - 20x$.
 5. $f(x) = x^3 - x$.
 6. $f(x) = x^2 - x^3$.
 7. $f(x) = \sqrt{x - 4}$.
 8. $f(x) = \sqrt[3]{x + 1}$.
 9. $f(x) = \sqrt[3]{x - 8}$.
10. $f(x) = \sqrt{x^2 - 4}$.
11. $f(x) = \dfrac{x}{x - 1}$.
12. $f(x) = \dfrac{x - 1}{x}$.
13. $f(x) = \dfrac{x^2 - 9}{x^2 - 3x + 2}$.

14. $f(x) = \dfrac{x^2 - 3x + 2}{x^2 - 9}.$

15. $f(x) = \dfrac{1}{x^2 - 1}.$

16. $f(x) = \dfrac{x}{x^2 + 1}.$

17. $f(x) = \sqrt{9 - x^2}.$

18. $f(x) = \dfrac{1}{\sqrt{9 - x^2}}.$

19. $f(x) = \dfrac{x^3 + x - 2}{x^2} = x + \dfrac{x - 2}{x^2} = \dfrac{(x - 1)(x^2 + x + 2)}{x^2}.$

20. $f(x) = \dfrac{x^3 - 8}{x^2} = x - \dfrac{8}{x^2} = \dfrac{(x - 2)(x^2 + 2x + 4)}{x^2}.$

21. Sketch each of the following curves:
   (a) $y = x^2.$
   (b) $y = x^2 + 2.$
   (c) $y = x^2 - 3.$

22. Sketch each of the following curves:
   (a) $y = x^2.$
   (b) $y = x^2 + x.$
   (c) $y = x^2 - 4x.$
   (d) $y = x^2 + 6x.$

23. Sketch each of the following curves:
   (a) $y = x^2.$
   (b) $y = 2x^2.$
   (c) $y = -\frac{1}{2}x^2.$

24. Sketch each of the following curves:
   (a) $y = x^4.$
   (b) $y = 2x^4.$
   (c) $y = -2x^4.$
   (d) $y = -\frac{1}{2}x^4.$

25. Determine the range of the function f defined by

$$f(x) = \dfrac{x^2}{x^2 - 1}.$$

B. **1.** Prove Theorem 5. The hypotheses are
   (i) The formula for a function f can be written as

   $$f(x) = g(x - k) = g(x'),$$

   where $x' = x - k.$
   (ii) The function g is even in terms of $x'.$

The conclusion is that the graph of f is symmetric with respect to the vertical line $x = k$.

    (a) What must be proven? See Definitions 7 and 8 in Exercises B1 and B2, respectively, after Section 4. Make a sketch, similar to that in Figure 23.

    (b) If the point x_2 on the x-axis (see Figure 23) is such that $x_1 - k = k - x_2$, show that $x_2 = 2k - x_1$. What if the positions of x_1 and x_2 are interchanged?

    (c) Verify that what must be proven is the following: For each x_1 in the domain of f, $f(2k - x_1) = f(x_1)$.

    (d) Prove the assertion in (c). [*Hint:* by the hypothesis,

$$f(2k - x_1) = g(2k - x_1 - k)$$
$$= g(k - x_1) = g(-(x_1 - k))$$
$$= g(-x_1') = \cdots.]$$

    (e) What happens if $k = 0$?

    2. Let f be the general polynomial of degree 2, i.e.,

$$f(x) = ax^2 + bx + c, \qquad a \neq 0.$$

Complete the square, as done with Example 8, immediately following Example 11, and use Theorem 5 to show that the graph of f is always symmetric to the vertical line $x = (-b)/(2a)$.

    3. Look at Exercises A21, A22, and A23. What is the effect of changing each of the coefficients a, b, and c in the formula for the function of Exercise B2?

C.   **1.** This exercise refers to the comment made after the statement of Theorem 6 and to Example 14.

    Let f be the rational function [Equation 11] of Theorem 6. Give conditions on m and n and the coefficients a_1 and b_1 so that the graph of f will have $y = x$ as an asymptote.

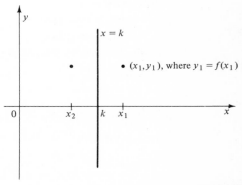

Figure 23

3

The Straight Line

3.1 Slope of a Line

We have already made use of lines in setting up a coordinate system in the plane. Moreover, we have encountered horizontal and vertical lines as the coordinate curves ($y = c$ and $x = c$) of a rectangular coordinate system; see Exercises A3 and B1–4 of Section 2.2. As we remarked in Chapter 1, we shall take *straight line* as an undefined term, but the essential geometric property of a straight line is this: it is a *curve* of *constant direction*. We utilize this property in the following definition.

DEFINITION 1. *The* slope *of a nonvertical straight line is the slope of any segment on that line (see Definition 2.2). The slope of a vertical line is not defined.*

A simple but occasionally useful property of the slope of a line is contained in the following assertion.

THEOREM 1. *The slope m of a line measures the change in y (the ordinate) which corresponds to an increase of one unit in x (the abscissa).*

PROOF. We consider the segment on the line determined by the two points $P_1(x_1, y_1)$ and $P_2(x_1 + 1, y_2)$. See Figure 1. Using P_1 and P_2 to calculate the slope, we have

$$m = \frac{y_2 - y_1}{(x_1 + 1) - x_1} = y_2 - y_1,$$

which is the change in the ordinate. ∎

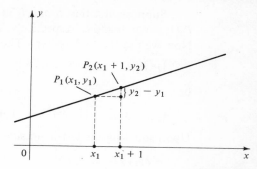

Figure 1

We now define two lines to be *parallel* to mean that they have the same direction. From this definition the following is an immediate consequence.

THEOREM 2. *Two lines l_1 and l_2 with slopes m_1 and m_2, respectively, are parallel $\Leftrightarrow m_1 = m_2$. Two vertical lines are parallel.*

We can also obtain a relation between the slopes of perpendicular lines.

THEOREM 3. *Two lines l_1 and l_2 with slopes m_1 and m_2, respectively, are perpendicular $\Leftrightarrow m_1m_2 + 1 = 0$. In symbols,*

$$l_1 \perp l_2 \Leftrightarrow m_1m_2 + 1 = 0.$$

PROOF. Because of Theorem 2 we may consider lines through the origin (see Figure 2).

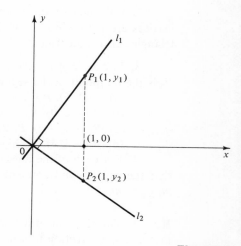

Figure 2

Suppose first that l_1 and l_2 are perpendicular. Take points $P_1(1, y_1)$ and $P_2(1, y_2)$ on l_1 and l_2, respectively. Then, by Theorem 1, $m_1 = y_1$ and $m_2 = y_2$. Now we use the Pythagorean Theorem on the right triangle OP_1P_2:

$$|P_1P_2|^2 = |OP_1|^2 + |OP_2|^2,$$

or

$$(y_1 - y_2)^2 = (1 + y_1^2) + (1 + y_2^2).$$

Upon squaring the left-hand side and simplifying, we get

$$-2y_1y_2 = 2,$$

or

$$m_1m_2 + 1 = 0,$$

since $y_1 = m_1$ and $y_2 = m_2$.

To prove the other half of the theorem, we can start with $m_1m_2 + 1 = 0$, reverse the steps, and use, finally, the converse of the Pythagorean Theorem, thus obtaining that triangle OP_1P_2 is a right triangle. ∎

Exercises

A.   **1.** Prove by two methods that each of the triangles with vertices A, B, and C is a right triangle. Which is the right angle?
> (a) $A(-2, 1)$, $B(5, 4)$, $C(8, -3)$. Can you say anything about the other angles?
> (b) $A(10, 11)$, $B(-3, 0)$, $C(-5, 5)$.
> (c) $A(-5, -11)$, $B(4, 1)$, $C(7, -5)$.
> (d) $A(-3, -1)$, $B(6, -1)$, $C(6, 5)$.

2. For each of the triangles in Exercise A1 find the triangle whose vertices are the midpoints of the sides of triangle ABC. Are these midpoint triangles also right triangles?

3. For each of the pairs of points P_1 and P_2 find a point P_3 such that P_2 is the midpoint of the segment $\overline{P_1P_3}$.
> (a) $P_1(3, 5)$, $P_2(7, 2)$.
> (b) $P_1(-2, 0)$, $P_2(0, 6)$.
> (c) $P_1(-4, -6)$, $P_2(2, 3)$.
> (d) $P_1(-3, 4)$, $P_2(3, -4)$.

4. For each of the lines determined by P_1 and P_2 in Exercise A3 verify that the slope is independent of the pair of points picked (e.g., show that $m_{P_1P_2} = m_{P_1P_3}$).

B.   **1.** The slope m of a line can be defined in the following manner. We first assign a direction to a line. If the line is horizontal its positive direction is from left to right (exactly as for the x-axis); if a line is not horizontal its

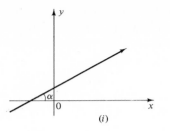 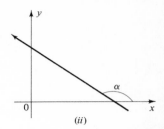

(i)   *(ii)*

Figure 3

positive direction is the upward one (analogous to that for the y-axis). The positive direction is indicated by the arrow in Figure 3.

DEFINITION 2. *The angle of inclination, α, of a nonhorizontal line is the angle between the positive directions of the x-axis and the line. The angle of inclination of a horizontal line is $\alpha = 0°$.*

Notice that Definition 2 requires that the angle of inclination must satisfy $0° \leqslant \alpha < 180°$.

DEFINITION 3. *The slope m of a line is $m = \tan \alpha$, where α is the angle of inclination of the line.*

(a) Why can we not have $\alpha = 180°$?
(b) Does Definition 3 assign a slope to a vertical line?
(c) Verify that Definitions 1 and 3 are consistent, i.e., that for an arbitrary line in the plane the slope as given by Definition 3 agrees with that of Definition 1. [*Hint:* use some elementary geometry.]
(d) Use Definition 3 and some trigonometry to prove Theorem 3. [*Hint:* if $l_1 \perp l_2$, what is the relation between α_1 and α_2?]

2. In this exercise we return to the subject of symmetry considered in the B exercises after Section 2.4 and used in Section 2.5.

As we know, the equation $y = x$ describes the line that bisects quadrants I and III.

(a) Prove the following assertion.

THEOREM 4. *Two points $P_1(x_1, y_1)$ and $P_2(x_2, y_2)$ are symmetric with respect to the lines $y = x \Leftrightarrow \begin{Bmatrix} x_2 = y_1 \\ y_2 = x_1 \end{Bmatrix}$.*

We give a few hints. See Figure 4.

    (i) There are two assertions to prove, symbolically, $\Rightarrow$ and $\Leftarrow$.
    (ii) For $\Rightarrow$ we assume (hypothesis) that P_1 and P_2 are symmetric with respect to $y = x$. We must show $x_2 = y_1$ and $y_2 = x_1$.

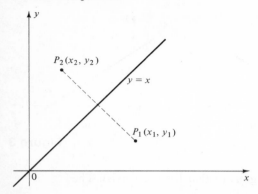

Figure 4

(iii) By Definition 2.7 we know from the hypothesis that $y = x$ is the perpendicular bisector of $\overline{P_1 P_2}$.

(iv) What is the slope of $y = x$? What must be the slope of $\overline{P_1 P_2}$ for perpendicularity? Write this condition as an equation with x_2 and y_2 on the left-hand side.

(v) The "bisector" part of the hypothesis says that the mid-point of $\overline{P_1 P_2}$ must lie on $y = x$. This gives another equation involving x_2 and y_2 in terms of x_1 and y_1.

(vi) Solve the equations from (iv) and (v) simultaneously. You should get $x_2 = y_1$ and $y_2 = x_1$.

(vii) The $\Leftarrow$ half is easy. If P_2 has coordinates (y_1, x_1), show that $y = x$ is the perpendicular bisector of $\overline{P_1 P_2}$.

(b) Prove the following assertion.

THEOREM 5. *A set S of points in the plane is symmetric with respect to $y = x \Leftrightarrow (x, y) \in S \Rightarrow (y, x) \in S$.*

Hint: Use Definition 2.3 and Theorem 4 of part (a) of this exercise.

(c) Which of the following functions have graphs symmetric with respect to $y = x$?

(i) $f(x) = x$.

(ii) $f(x) = x + 1$.

(iii) $f(x) = \dfrac{1}{x}$.

(iv) $f(x) = \dfrac{-1}{x}$.

(v) $f(x) = \dfrac{c}{x}$.

(vi) $f(x) = x^3$.

(vii) $f(x) = -x$.

C. **1.** Consider the triangle OAB, where $A(a, 0)$, $B(b, c)$. Show by two different methods that the triangle has a right angle at $B \Leftrightarrow b^2 + c^2 = ab$.

2. Same initial setup as in Exercise C1. Find a necessary and sufficient condition on a, b, and c so that triangle OAB has equal angles at

(a) O and A.

(b) O and B.

(c) O and A with a right angle at B.

3. See Exercise B2.

(a) Find all functions f of the form $f(x) = ax + b$ whose graphs are symmetric with respect to $y = x$. [*Hint:* by Theorem 5, if $y = f(x)$, the function must satisfy $x = f(y)$. Substituting the first of these into the second gives $x = f(f(x))$, i.e., f must satisfy $(f \circ f)(x) = x$.]

(b) Same as part (a) for f of the form $f(x) = ax^2 + bx + c$.

(c) Make a guess, based on the result of part (b), about which polynomial functions p satisfy $(p \circ p)(x) = x$.

(d) Same as part (a) for functions of the form

$$f(x) = \frac{ax + b}{cx + d}.$$

3.2 Equations of a Line

We have already seen that horizontal and vertical lines can be described by equations of the type $y = b$ and $x = c$, respectively, and that the line which bisects quadrants I and III is described by $y = x$. In this section we find the equation of an arbitrary line in the plane, expressing it in various forms, depending on the given information.

As we have indicated, we consider a straight line as a curve of constant direction, and we have defined two lines to be parallel if they have the same direction. Consequently, if we specify a direction, say $m = \frac{1}{2}$, we are specifying a set (frequently called in this connection a *family*) of parallel lines. To determine a unique member of this family we need to impose a further condition, e.g., that the line go through the point $P_1(-2, 1)$. See Figure 5.

Suppose now that $P(x, y)$ is any other point on the line through P_1 with slope $m = \frac{1}{2}$. We can use Definition 1 (for the slope) to obtain a condition which x and y must satisfy:

$$\frac{y - 1}{x - (-2)} = \frac{1}{2},$$

or

$$y - 1 = \frac{1}{2}(x + 2), \qquad\qquad [1]$$

which can also be written as $y = \frac{1}{2}x + 2$.

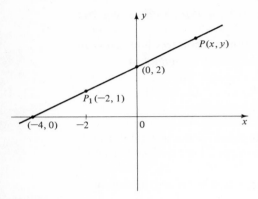

Figure 5

Conversely, note that the coordinates of $P_1(-2, 1)$ satisfy (1), and that if (x, y) is any other pair that satisfies [1], one can divide by $x + 2$ to obtain the statement that the slope of the line determined by $P_1(-2, 1)$ and $P(x, y)$ is $\frac{1}{2}$. In other words, Equation [1] is both necessary and sufficient that a point (x, y) lie on the line through P_1 with $m = \frac{1}{2}$.

It is a simple step to generalize the preceding example and assert that $P(x, y)$ is on the line through $P_1(x_1, y_1)$ with slope m if and only if x and y satisfy

$$y - y_1 = m(x - x_1). \tag{2}$$

Equation [2] is called the *point-slope form* of the equation for the straight line.

If P_1 is the point $(0, b)$, the y-intercept of the line, then [2] takes the form

$$y - b = mx,$$

or

$$y = mx + b. \tag{3}$$

This is called the *slope-intercept form* of the equation for the straight line.

Of course the line could be determined by specifying two points on the line, say $P_1(x_1, y_1)$ and $P_2(x_2, y_2)$, where $x_1 \neq x_2$. One can use this information to calculate the slope:

$$m = \frac{y_2 - y_1}{x_2 - x_1}.$$

Now Equation [2] is applicable:

$$y - y_1 = \frac{y_2 - y_1}{x_2 - x_1}(x - x_1). \tag{4}$$

This is called the *two-point form* of the equation for the straight line. We shall mention two other forms in later exercises.

The preceding discussion, dealing with lines with slope, of necessity does not apply to vertical lines, for the definition of slope requires of the two points that the abscissas be different. If we consider the line through two points with the same abscissas, say $P_1(3, -1)$ and $P_2(3, 5)$, we see that the line is vertical and that a point $P(x, y)$ is on this line $\Leftrightarrow x = 3$. Thus the equation $x = 3$ can be used as an exact and unambiguous description of the line (there is no restriction or requirement imposed on the ordinate y).

More generally, a vertical line with x-intercept a can be described by the equation $x = a$.

A formal description of the preceding discussion is the following assertion.

THEOREM 6. *A set of points in the plane is a straight line $\Leftrightarrow$ the co-ordinates (x, y) of points in the set satisfy the equation*

$$Ax + By + C = 0, \tag{5}$$

where A and B are not both zero.

PROOF. For the $\Rightarrow$ part of the proof we consider first a line with slope. Then the slope-intercept form $y = mx + b$ can be used to describe the line; but this equation can be written as

$$mx - y + b = 0,$$

which is in the form of [5] with $A = m$, $B = -1 \neq 0$, and $C = b$. If the line is vertical, its description is $x = a$, which can be written as

$$x - a = 0,$$

which is in the form of [5] with $A = 1 \neq 0$, $B = 0$, and $C = -a$.

For the $\Leftarrow$ part of the proof we consider a set of points which satisfy [5]. Suppose first that $B \neq 0$; then we can rewrite [5] as

$$y = \left(-\frac{A}{B}\right)x + \left(-\frac{C}{B}\right). \tag{6}$$

But this shows that the set of points is the line with slope $m = -(A/B)$ and y-intercept $b = -(C/B)$. Second, if $B = 0$, then we must have that $A \neq 0$, and Equation [5] can be written as

$$x = -\frac{C}{A}; \tag{7}$$

this shows that the set of points is the vertical line that intersects the x-axis at $-(C/A)$. ∎

Because of Theorem 6 the equation $Ax + By + C = 0$ is called the *linear equation* in x and v.

It is worthwhile to point out the geometric contribution made by the coefficients A, B, and C of Equation [5]. As Equation [6] shows, when $B \neq 0$, A and B determine the *direction* of the line and B and C its *position*. When $B = 0$ we turn to Equation [7] to observe that the line is vertical (thus B alone determines this direction) and that A and C determine its position. Consider, for example,

$$3x + 4y - 7 = 0.$$

This can be written as

$$y = -\tfrac{3}{4}x + \tfrac{7}{4},$$

from which we see that the equation corresponds to the line with slope $m = -\tfrac{3}{4}$ and y-intercept $b = \tfrac{7}{4}$. Conversely, if we consider any line with slope $m = -\tfrac{3}{4}$, we can write its equation as $y = -\tfrac{3}{4}x + b$, which can be written in the form of Equation [5] as

$$3x + 4y - 4b = 0,$$

showing how the direction and the values of A and B are interrelated.

Example 1.   Find the equation of the line through $P_1(3, -2)$ perpendicular to the line $4x + 2y - 1 = 0$.

We can write the equation of the given line as

$$y = -2x + \tfrac{1}{2}$$

to see that its slope is $m_1 = -2$. Thus the slope of the desired line is $m = \tfrac{1}{2}$. Using the point-slope form, we have the equation

$$y + 2 = \tfrac{1}{2}(x - 3),$$

or

$$y = \tfrac{1}{2}x - \tfrac{7}{2},$$

or

$$x - 2y - 7 = 0.$$

See Figure 6.

Example 2.   Find the point of intersection of the two lines of Example 1.

If $P_0(x_0, y_0)$ is the required point, then using the two slope-intercept forms in Example 1, we see that x_0 and y_0 must satisfy

$$y_0 = -2x_0 + \tfrac{1}{2}$$

and

$$y_0 = \tfrac{1}{2}x_0 - \tfrac{7}{2}.$$

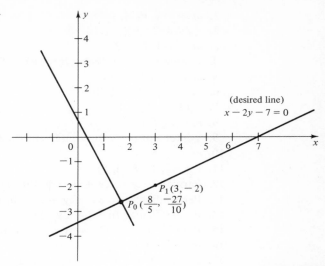

Figure 6

We can equate these values of y_0 and solve for x_0:

$$-2x_0 + \tfrac{1}{2} = \tfrac{1}{2}x_0 - \tfrac{7}{2}$$

or

$$-\tfrac{5}{2}x_0 = -\tfrac{8}{2},$$

so $x_0 = \tfrac{8}{5}$. Substituting this value into either of the slope-intercept forms gives $y_0 = -\tfrac{27}{10}$. Thus the point of intersection is $(\tfrac{8}{5}, -\tfrac{27}{10})$. See Figure 6.

    Example 3.   Explain why the system of equations

$$\left\{\begin{matrix} 2x + 3y = 4 \\ 6x + 9y = 10 \end{matrix}\right\}$$

has no solution.

    From the geometric point of view the first equation represents a line with slope $m_1 = -\tfrac{2}{3}$ and the second is a line with slope $m_2 = -\tfrac{6}{9} = -\tfrac{2}{3}$. Thus the two lines have the same direction and are either coincident (share all points) or do not intersect (share no points). The y-intercept of the first line is $b_1 = -\tfrac{4}{3}$, whereas that of the second is $b_2 = -\tfrac{10}{9} \neq b_1$. The two lines consequently are distinct and have *no* points in common:

$$\{(x, y) \mid 2x + 3y = 4\} \cap \{(x, y) \mid 6x + 9y = 10\} = \varnothing.$$

Exercises

A.   In each of Exercises 1–16 find the equation of the line determined by the given conditions. We agree that P_1 and P_2 are on the line, m is the slope, and b is the y-intercept.

1. $m = -\frac{1}{3}, P_1(4, -1)$.
2. $P_1(-4, 2), P_2(-1, 0)$.
3. $m = -1, b = 2$.
4. x-intercept $(3, 0)$, y-intercept $(0, -5)$.
5. $m = \frac{2}{3}, P_1(-2, 3)$.
6. $m = -\frac{3}{2}, P_1(-2, 3)$.
7. $P_1(2, 1), P_2(2, 8)$.
8. $m = 0, P_1(-2, -3)$.
9. x-intercept $(-5, 0)$, y-intercept $(0, 2)$.
10. $m = \frac{1}{2}, b = -1$.
11. $P_1(-2, 4), P_2(3, 5)$.
12. Parallel to $x - 2y + 3 = 0$, through $(4, -7)$.
13. Perpendicular to $x - 2y + 3 = 0$, through $(-3, 1)$.
14. Perpendicular to $3x + 2y - 6 = 0$, through $(1, 8)$.
15. Parallel to $3x + 2y - 6 = 0$, through $(-4, -3)$.
16. $m = 20, P_1(1, 0)$.
17. (a) Draw the graph of $Ax + 2y + 3 = 0$ for a few values of A. What do all graphs obtained in this way have in common?
    (b) Same as part (a), only for $4x + By + 3 = 0$.
    (c) Same as part (a), only for $4x + 2y + C = 0$.
18. Find the line with slope $m = -1$ that goes through the point of intersection of $3x - y - 1 = 0$ and $2x - 5y + 8 = 0$.
19. Find the line with slope $m = -2$ that goes through the point of intersection of $2x + 3y = 0$ and $2x - y - 8 = 0$.
20. Describe geometrically the set of points $\{(x, y) \mid y < -2x + 3\}$.
21. Describe geometrically the set of points $\{(x, y) \mid y \geq x + 1\}$.
22. Describe geometrically the set of points $\{(x, y) \mid 2x - y + 4 > 0\}$.
23. Describe analytically the set of points which lie above the line $y = x - 1$.
24. Describe analytically the set of points which lie on and below the line $4x + 2y - 3 = 0$.
25. Graph the equation $|x - y| = 2$. [*Hint:* $|x - y| = 2 \Leftrightarrow x - y = \pm 2$.
26. Graph the equation $|x| + |y| = 2$. [*Hint:* consider four cases: (i) $x \geq 0, y \geq 0$; (ii) $x \geq 0, y < 0$, etc.
27. Graph the equation $|x| - |y| = 2$.
28. Graph the inequality $|x - y| < 2$.

B.   1. Suppose $ab \neq 0$. If a line has x-intercept $(a, 0)$ and y-intercept $(0, b)$, show that its equation can be written in the *intercept form*:

$$\frac{x}{a} + \frac{y}{b} = 1.$$ [8]

2. Consider two lines $l_1 : A_1 x + B_1 y + C_1 = 0$, and $l_2 : A_2 x + B_2 y + C_2$. Show that

$$l_1 \perp l_2 \Leftrightarrow A_1 A_2 + B_1 B_2 = 0. \tag{9}$$

3. (a) Exercise A18 can be done by the following technique. Find the value of t such that

$$3x - y - 1 + t(2x - 5y + 8) = 0 \tag{10}$$

represents a line with slope $m = -1$. Then substitute this value of t into Equation [10]. Check that the result agrees with that found earlier.

(b) Explain why the method described in part (a) works. [*Hint:* Equation [10] represents a family of lines. Is there a common feature, a family characteristic?]

4. (a) Do Exercise A19 by the following variation of the method suggested in the preceding exercise. Find the value of k_1 in terms of k_2 such that

$$k_1(2x + 3y) + k_2(2x - y - 8) = 0$$

represents a line with slope $m = -2$. Substituting in the equation of the family will give the desired line.

(b) Why does the method work?

(c) Is there any advantage over the method described in Exercise B3? [*Hint:* try to use the earlier method on Exercise A19 but with $m = 2$.]

5. Each of the equations below describes a family of lines. In each case describe the family characteristic. Also in each case say whether the equation includes all lines with this common feature.

(a) $y = mx + 2$.

(b) $y = 2x + b$.

(c) $\dfrac{x}{-2} + \dfrac{y}{b} = 1$.

(d) $y = \dfrac{b}{2}(x + 2)$.

C.   **1.** In this exercise we derive the *normal* form for the equation of a straight line.

(a) Consider first a line l which does *not* go through the origin. Draw the line segment from the origin perpendicular to l intersecting l at P_0 (see Figure 7). Let $p > 0$ be the length of this normal segment and let ω (omega) be the angle between the positive x-axis and this normal segment where $0 \leqslant \omega \leqslant 360°$.

(i) Show that the coordinates of P_0 are $(p \cos \omega, p \sin \omega)$.

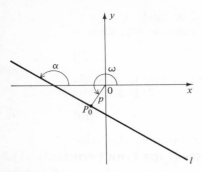

Figure 7

(ii) Show that in all possible cases
$$\tan \alpha = -\cot \omega = \frac{-\cos \omega}{\sin \omega}.$$

(iii) Use the point-slope form to obtain the equation of *l*. Show that it can be put in the form

$$(\cos \omega)x + (\sin \omega)y - p = 0. \tag{11}$$

Equation [11] is called the *normal* (meaning perpendicular) *form* for the equation of a straight line.

(iv) Show that Equation [11] is applicable even when *l* is vertical.

(b) If *l* goes through the origin we agree that $0 \leqslant \omega \leqslant 180°$. Show that [11] holds with $p = 0$. Note in particular that in this case the coefficient of *y* will be $\geqslant 0$.

(c) Given a line with equation $Ax + By + C = 0$, where A and B are not both zero, explain how to convert the equation to the normal form. [*Hints:* if $C \neq 0$, use the fact that $p > 0$; if $C = 0$, use the last sentence of part (b).]

2. Given a line *l* and a point $P_1(x_1, y_1)$ not on *l*. Use the normal form (see Exercise C1) to obtain the following formula for the *directed* perpendicular distance d from P_1 to *l*:
$$d = (\cos \omega)x_1 + (\sin \omega)y_1 - p,$$
where the normal form of *l* is $(\cos \omega)x + (\sin \omega)y - p = 0$. [*Hint:* consider the normal form of the line l_1 through P_1 parallel to *l*. For l_1 the normal distance $p_1 = p + d$.] Explain the sign of d.

3. See part (c) of Exercise C1. Express each of the following lines in the normal form. Identify $\cos \omega$, $\sin \omega$, and p.

(a) $3x - 4y + 10 = 0$. [*Answer:* $-\frac{3}{5}x + \frac{4}{5}y - 2 = 0$; $\cos \omega = -\frac{3}{5}$ $\sin \omega = \frac{4}{5}, p = 2.$]

(b) $5x + 12y - 26 = 0$.

(c) $x + y + 1 = 0.$
(d) $3x - 4y = 0.$ [*Answer:* $-\frac{3}{5}x + \frac{4}{5}y = 0$; $\cos \omega = -\frac{3}{5}$, $\sin \omega = \frac{4}{5}$, $p = 0.$]
(e) $x + 2y = 0.$
(f) $4x + 3y + 15 = 0.$

4. See Exercise C2. Find the distance between $P_1(1, -2)$ and each of the lines in Exercise C3.

3.3 The Straight Line (continued). Translation of Coordinates

In this section we consider several additional topics related to straight lines.

Angle Between Two Lines

Given two lines l_1 and l_2, we may need to find the angle θ between them. First of all, if one of the lines, l_2, say, is either horizontal or vertical, the problem is trivial (see Figure 8)—*a fortiori* if one is vertical and the other horizontal.

Thus we assume l_1 and l_2 have (nonzero) slopes m_1 and m_2, respectively. In terms of angle of inclination, $m_1 = \tan \alpha_1$, and $m_2 = \tan \alpha_2$ (cf. Definition 3). Thus from a standard trigonometric identity, we have (see Figure 9)

$$\tan \theta = \tan(\alpha_2 - \alpha_1) = \frac{\tan \alpha_2 - \tan \alpha_1}{1 + \tan \alpha_2 \tan \alpha_1},$$

or

$$\tan \theta = \frac{m_2 - m_1}{1 + m_1 m_2}. \qquad [12]$$

There was, to be sure, an element of sloppiness in the preceding discussion: two intersecting lines create two pairs of vertical angles, and, unless the lines are perpendicular, the angles in different pairs are not equal.

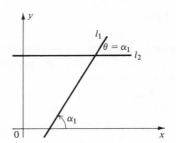
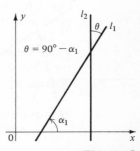

Figure 8

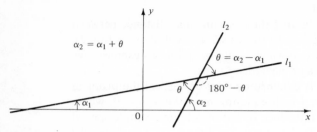

Figure 9

However, the two different angles are supplementary, one being acute and the other obtuse. If we call one of the angles θ, then the other is $180° - \theta$. Since

$$\tan(180° - \theta) = -\tan \theta, \qquad [13]$$

we can use the equation in [12] in the following way: if the number on the right is positive, it is the tangent of the acute angle; if negative, the obtuse angle.

Example 4. Find the tangent of the acute angle between the lines $l_1 : 2x + 3y - 6 = 0$, and $l_2 : 4x - y + 2 = 0$. See Figure 10.

We calculate that $m_1 = -\frac{2}{3}$, $m_2 = 4$, and, using [12],

$$\tan \theta = \frac{4 + \frac{2}{3}}{1 + 4(-\frac{2}{3})} = \frac{12 + 2}{3 - 8} = -\frac{14}{5}.$$

Thus we have found the tangent of the obtuse angle. For the acute angle $\theta_1 = 180° - \theta$, we have, by [13], $\tan \theta_1 = \frac{14}{5} = 2.8$. Of course, if the lines were numbered oppositely, Equation [12] would then give $\tan \theta = \frac{14}{5}$, the desired result.

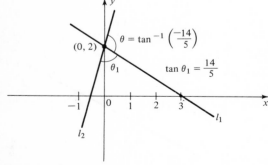

Figure 10

Distance from a Line to a Point

We next consider the problem of finding the perpendicular distance between a line and a point not on the line (see Exercises C2 and C4 after Section 2). The problem is a straightforward one which could be left as an exercise; we discuss it as a means of introducing a new idea or two.

We first note that if the line is either horizontal or vertical the problem is trivial. Thus we consider a line l with equation $ax + by + c = 0$, where $ab \neq 0$. The first "new" idea we introduce is that of solving a simple special case, namely, where the point P_1 is the origin. See Figure 11. The slope of l is $m_l = (-a)/b$, so the slope of the line perpendicular to l is $m = b/a$. Thus the equation of the line through $P_1(=O)$ perpendicular to l is $y = (b/a)x$. We use this value of y in the equation for l in order to find the point P_0 of intersection:

$$ax_0 + b\left(\frac{b}{a}x_0\right) + c = 0,$$

or

$$(a^2 + b^2)x_0 + ac = 0,$$

whence

$$x_0 = \frac{-ac}{a^2 + b^2}, \quad y_0 = \frac{-bc}{a^2 + b^2}. \tag{14}$$

It is now a simple matter to find $d = |\overline{OP_0}|$:

$$d = |\overline{OP_0}| = \sqrt{x_0^2 + y_0^2} = \sqrt{\frac{a^2c^2 + b^2c^2}{(a^2 + b^2)^2}} = \frac{|c|}{\sqrt{a^2 + b^2}}. \tag{15}$$

What if the point P_1 is not at the origin? Then the result in [15] is of no use to us. But is it? A coordinate system is a device introduced to facilitate our study of geometric problems. If the one we have at the moment is not as useful as it might be, why not change it? In the present instance we use the following simple procedure: If the point $P_1(x_1, y_1)$ is not at the origin, we

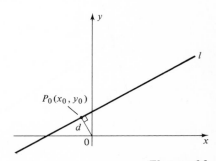

Figure 11

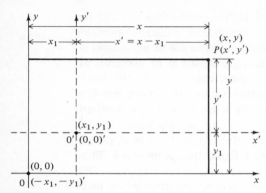

Figure 12

set up temporarily a new coordinate system with origin O' at P_1 and with axes (x' and y') parallel, respectively, to the original x and y axes. When this is done each point in the plane will have two sets of coordinates, old (x, y) and new (x', y'), the relation between them easily expressed as (see Figure 12)

$$\begin{cases} x = x' + x_1 \\ y = y' + y_1 \end{cases}, \qquad \begin{cases} x' = x - x_1 \\ y' = y - y_1 \end{cases}. \tag{16}$$

This type of coordinate change is called a *translation*.

To return to our distance problem, we can now make use of [15] as follows. We shift to the new coordinate system with origin at $P_1(x_1, y_1)$. In this system the equation of l can be found by using the first equation in [16]:

$$ax + by + c = 0$$

becomes

$$a(x' + x_1) + b(y' + y_1) + c = 0,$$

or

$$ax' + by' + (ax_1 + by_1 + c) = 0,$$

or

$$ax' + by' + c' = 0, \tag{17}$$

where $c' = ax_1 + by_1 + c$.

Using [15], but in terms of the new coordinate system, we have

$$d = \frac{|c'|}{\sqrt{a^2 + b^2}},$$

or

$$d = \frac{|ax_1 + by_1 + c|}{\sqrt{a^2 + b^2}}. \tag{18}$$

Notice that (18) is in terms of the original data: the coefficients of l and the coordinates of P_1.

It is worth pointing out about [17] that the coefficients of x' and y' remain unchanged—they are *invariant* under a translation of coordinates. As we have already mentioned, the role of these coefficients in the linear equation is to determine the slope or direction of the line; since the new axes are parallel to the old, the description of the direction of a line will remain unchanged.

Example 5.   We find the distance d from the point $P_1(4, 2)$ to the line $l: 4x - 3y + 15 = 0$. See Figure 13.

Although we could use [18] directly we illustrate the translation technique in the solution. Since $x = x' + 4$, $y = y' + 2$, the new equation of l becomes

$$4(x' + 4) - 3(y' + 2) + 15 = 0,$$

or

$$4x' - 3y' + 25 = 0.$$

Equation [15] then gives us

$$d = \frac{|25|}{\sqrt{4^2 + 3^2}} = \frac{25}{5} = 5.$$

Example 6.   We consider the same line l as in Example 5 and try to determine the set S of all points whose distance from l is 5. Clearly $S \neq \varnothing$, since $(4, 2) \in S$ as we have seen. The only difficulty is a minor notational one:

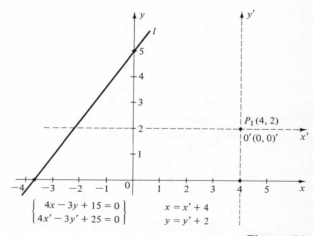

$$\left\{ \begin{array}{l} 4x - 3y + 15 = 0 \\ 4x' - 3y' + 25 = 0 \end{array} \right\} \qquad \begin{array}{l} x = x' + 4 \\ y = y' + 2 \end{array}$$

Figure 13

we now let (x, y) represent an element of S rather than a point on l. Then, according to [18] and the definition of S, we must have

$$\frac{|4x - 3y + 15|}{5} = 5,$$

or

$$|4x - 3y + 15| = 25.$$

Now $|k| = 25 \Leftrightarrow k = 25$ or $k = -25$. Since we are looking for *all* points $(x, y) \in S$ we have

$$4x - 3y + 15 = 25,$$

or

$$4x - 3y + 15 = -25.$$

Thus $S = S_1 \cup S_2$, where

$$S_1 = \{(x, y) \mid 4x - 3y - 10 = 0\}$$
$$S_2 = \{(x, y) \mid 4x - 3y + 40 = 0\};$$

i.e., S consists of two lines, both parallel to l, a result easily predictable from the original statement of the problem.

Exercises

A. In Exercises 1–10 find the tangent of the smaller angle determined by the pairs of lines given.

    1. $x - 2y + 3 = 0, 4x - 5y + 7 = 0$.
    2. $2x - 3y + 8 = 0, 5x + y + 6 = 0$.
    3. $6x + 7y + 5 = 0, x + y - 1 = 0$.
    4. $3x + 2y = 0, 2x - 5y + 1 = 0$.
    5. $3x - 5 = 0, 2x + y - 5 = 0$.
    6. $10x + 7y - 8 = 0, 2y + 3 = 0$.
    7. $3x - 4y + 5 = 0, 4x + 3y + 8 = 0$.
    8. $5x - 6y + 8 = 0, 2x + 3 = 0$.
    9. $x + y - 1 = 0, 2x + 2y + 5 = 0$.
    10. $2x + 3y - 1 = 0, 3x - 2y + 4 = 0$.

    11–20. Find the distance between $P_1(1, 2)$ and the first of the two lines given in each of Exercises A1–10.

    21. Find the lengths of the altitudes of the triangle ABC, where $A(6, 0)$, $B(3, 7)$, and $C(-4, 2)$.

    22. Same as Exercise A21 except $A(0, -5)$, $B(7, 2)$, and $C(4, 6)$.

    23. Find the set S of points which are three units distant from $5x + 12y - 8 = 0$. Describe S geometrically.

    24. Find the set S of points which are four units distant from $24x - 7y + 5 = 0$. Describe S geometrically.

B.   **1.** The derivation of [18] was obtained with the assumption that $ab \neq 0$. Show that [18] gives a valid result if either a or b—exclusive or—equals zero.
      2. Is [18] valid if P_1 is on the line l? Why?

C.   **1.** We refer to Example 6.
      (a) Is the following a correct analytical description of the set S:

$$(4x - 3y - 10)(4x - 3y + 40) = 0 ?$$

      Why?
      (b) Multiply out the left-hand side of the equation in (a) and notice that it is in the form of a second-degree polynomial in x and y:

$$Ax^2 + Bxy + Cy^2 + Dx + Ey + F,$$

      where at least one of A, B, or C is different from zero.
    2. Obtain [18] directly, i.e., without using a translation of coordinates.
    3. Verify that [18] agrees with the result obtained in Exercise C2 after Section 3.2.

3.4 Linear Inequalities in Two Variables

Suppose we consider the expression $ax + by + c$, where a, b, and c are fixed and a and b are not both zero. Given a pair of numbers (x, y) we know by Definition 1.2 that exactly one of the following holds:

1. $ax + by + c = 0$
2. $ax + by + c > 0$ *(law of the trichotomy)*.
3. $ax + by + c < 0$

We know that the points (x, y) that satisfy formula 1 lie on the line l: $ax + by + c = 0$. Common sense or intuition suggests that formula 2 describes the set of points which lie on one side of l and that formula 3 describes those points on the other side of l. This description is correct, as we now show.
    Suppose, to be specific, $b > 0$. Then

$$ax + by + c > 0 \Leftrightarrow by > -ax - c \Leftrightarrow y > \frac{-a}{b}x - \frac{c}{b} \qquad [19]$$

and

$$ax + by + c < 0 \Leftrightarrow by < -ax - c \Leftrightarrow y < \frac{-a}{b}x - \frac{c}{b}. \qquad [20]$$

If (x_0, y_0) is an arbitrary point on l, then

$$y_0 = -\frac{a}{b}x_0 - \frac{c}{b}.$$

If (x_0, y_1) is a point *above* l on $x = x_0$, then

$$y_1 > y_0 = \frac{-a}{b}x_0 - \frac{c}{b}.$$

Similarly, if (x_0, y_2) is a point on $x = x_0$ *below* l, then

$$y_2 < y_0 = \frac{-a}{b}x_0 - \frac{c}{b}.$$

Since (x_0, y_0) was an arbitrary point on l and (x_0, y_1) and (x_0, y_2) were arbitrary points on $x = x_0$ above and below l, respectively, we have shown the first part of the following assertion to be valid. The remaining parts are proven in a similar fashion.

THEOREM 7. *Let $ax + by + c = 0$ describe the line l. Then*

1. *If $b > 0$,*
   $\{(x, y) \mid ax + by + c > 0\}$ *is the set of points above l,*
   $\{(x, y) \mid ax + by + c < 0\}$ *is the set of points below l.*
2. *If $a > 0$,*
   $\{(x, y) \mid ax + by + c > 0\}$ *is the set of points to the right of l,*
   $\{(x, y) \mid ax + by + c < 0\}$ *is the set of points to the left of l.*
3. *If $b < 0$, interchange "above" and "below" in statement 1; and if $a < 0$, interchange "right" and "left" in statement 2.*

In practice one need not remember the particular details of Theorem 7. The crucial facts are that any point not on l lies on one side or the other of l (surprise!) and that all points on one side satisfy one kind of inequality, all points on the other side satisfy the other kind.

Example 7. Solve the inequality $3x - 4y + 4 > 0$.

We sketch the line $l\colon 3x - 4y + 2 = 0$, as in Figure 14. It is an easy matter to check that $(0, 0)$ satisfies the given inequality; since the origin lies below l, the solution set S for the inequality is the set of all points below l.

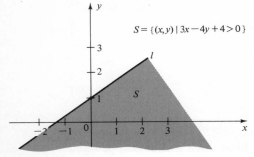

$$S = \{(x,y) \mid 3x - 4y + 4 > 0\}$$

Figure 14

(Of course statement 2 of Theorem 7 is immediately applicable, enabling one to describe S as the set of points to the right of l.)

DEFINITION 4.   1. *The set of points satisfying either*

$$\{(x, y) \mid ax + by + c > 0\} \quad \text{or} \quad \{(x, y) \mid ax + by + c < 0\}$$

is called an open half-plane.

2. *The set of points satisfying either*

$$\{(x, y) \mid ax + by + c \geqslant 0\} \quad \text{or} \quad \{(x, y) \mid ax + by + c \leqslant 0\}$$

is called a closed half-plane.

The distinction between an open and a closed half-plane is that the latter includes the line $l\colon ax + by + c = 0$, whereas the former does not. The line l is the *boundary* of the half-plane. In Euclidean space a set is closed if it includes its boundary and is open if its complement is closed. Unlike doors, sets need be neither open nor closed (example: the first quadrant including the positive x-axis, excluding the y-axis); moreover, they might be both open and closed (example: $\mathbf{R}^2$; see Exercise C4).

Sometimes one is interested in the solution of a system of (simultaneous) inequalities. We give several illustrations.

Example 8.   Find the solution set S for the system

$$\begin{cases} 2x + 3y - 6 < 0 \\ 4x - y + 2 < 0 \end{cases}.$$

We know that each inequality represents a half-plane; our work involves finding *which* half-plane for each one and then determining the intersection. We note that $(0, 0)$ satisfies the first inequality and does not satisfy the second. If we designate by l_1 and l_2, respectively, the lines $2x + 3y - 6 = 0$ and $4x - y + 2 = 0$, then the first inequality determines the half-plane containing the origin, and the second the half-plane that does not contain the origin (see Figure 15). (Since the coefficient of x is positive in each inequality one could use statement 2 of Theorem 7 to say that in each case the half-plane is the one to the left of the line.)

Example 9.   We find the solution set S for the system

$$\begin{cases} 5x - 9y + 11 > 0 \\ 2x + 7y + 15 > 0 \\ 7x - 2y - 27 \leqslant 0 \end{cases}.$$

The basic ideas are the same as in Example 8: each of the inequalities determines a half-plane. However, we now have three such, two open and one closed. Letting l_1, l_2, and l_3 be the lines obtained by replacing each

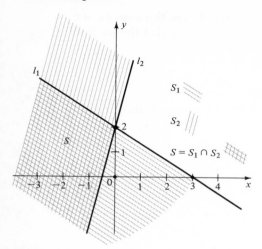

Figure 15

inequality by an equal sign, we first find the points of intersection of the lines. These are easily calculated to be

$$P_1(l_2, l_3) = (3, -3)$$
$$P_2(l_3, l_1) = (5, 4)$$
$$P_3(l_1, l_2) = (-4, -1).$$

See Figure 16.

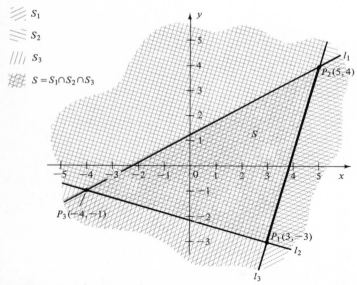

Figure 16

Once again the origin is a convenient "test point"; in this case we see that $(0, 0)$ satisfies each of the inequalities. It follows easily that the set S is the interior of the triangle $P_1 P_2 P_3$ plus the segment $\overline{P_1 P_2}$.

Exercises

A. In Exercises 1–14 find the solution set S for the system of inequalities.

1. $\begin{cases} 3x + 5y - 15 > 0 \\ x - y + 3 > 0 \end{cases}$.

2. $\begin{cases} 3x + 5y - 15 \geqslant 0 \\ x - y + 3 \leqslant 0 \end{cases}$.

3. $\begin{cases} x + y - 1 < 0 \\ x + y + 3 > 0 \end{cases}$.

4. $\begin{cases} x + y - 1 < 0 \\ x + y + 3 \leqslant 0 \end{cases}$.

5. $\begin{cases} x - 2y - 4 < 0 \\ x - 4 \leqslant 0 \end{cases}$.

6. $\begin{cases} x - 2y - 4 > 0 \\ y + 2 \geqslant 0 \end{cases}$.

7. $\begin{cases} 3x + 5y - 15 < 0 \\ x - y + 3 > 0 \\ y + 2 > 0 \end{cases}$ (see Exercise A1).

8. $\begin{cases} 3x + 5y - 15 < 0 \\ x - y + 3 > 0 \\ y + 2 \leqslant 0 \end{cases}$ (see Exercise A7).

9. $\begin{cases} 5x - 9y + 11 < 0 \\ 2x + 7y + 15 < 0 \\ 7x - 2y - 27 < 0 \end{cases}$ (see Example 9).

10. $\begin{cases} 5x - 9y + 11 < 0 \\ 2x + 7y + 15 < 0 \\ 7x - 2y - 27 > 0 \end{cases}$ (see Example 9).

11. $\begin{cases} x + 2y - 4 \leqslant 0 \\ 2x + 4y + 11 \geqslant 0 \\ x - y - 4 \leqslant 0 \end{cases}$.

12. $\begin{cases} x + 2y - 4 > 0 \\ 2x + 4y + 11 < 0 \\ x - y - 4 > 0 \end{cases}$ (see Exercise A11).

13. $\begin{cases} x + 2y - 4 > 0 \\ 2x + 4y + 11 > 0 \\ x - y - 4 > 0 \end{cases}$ (see Exercise A12).

14. $\begin{cases} x + 2y - 4 < 0 \\ 2x + 4y + 11 < 0 \\ x - y - 4 < 0 \end{cases}$ (see Exercise A13).

15. This refers to Example 9. The three lines l_1, l_2, and l_3 divide the plane into seven regions, exclusive of the lines themselves. Set up systems of inequalities to describe each of these regions. See, besides Example 9, Exercises A9 and 10. Cf. also Exercise C1.

16. See Exercises A7 and 8. Set up systems of inequalities to describe all the regions of the plane, exclusive of the lines, determined by the three lines.

C. **1.** (a) Abstractly, how many systems of inequalities can be written using two distinct linear expressions of the type $ax + by + c$? Consider only the strict inequalities such as < or > 0, i.e., do not consider those such as ⩽ or ⩾.

(b) Same as (a) only involving three distinct expressions. The word *distinct* is meant to imply that the lines obtained by using = 0 are distinct ($x + y + 1$ and $2x + 2y + 2$ are not distinct).

(c) Same as (b) only involving n distinct expressions.

(d) According to Exercise A15, only seven systems are used to describe the plane for the set of lines of Example 9. Which one is not used? Why?

2. See Exercise C1.

(a) Into how many regions can two distinct lines divide the plane? Exclude, as regions, the lines themselves. Consider all possibilities.

(b) Same as (a) only for three distinct lines.

(c) Same as (a) only for four distinct lines.

3. Review the discussion preceding the statement of Theorem 7.
Does it (the discussion) in fact give a complete proof of assertion 1 of that theorem?

4. See the discussion following Definition 4.

(a) Prove that $\mathbf{R}^2$ is closed. [*Hint:* if it were not, there would have to be a boundary point that is not in $\mathbf{R}^2$.]

(b) Prove that the null set ∅ is closed. See the hint for part (a).

(c) Prove that both $\mathbf{R}^2$ and ∅ are both open and closed. [*Hint:* what is the complement of $\mathbf{R}^2$? Use parts (a) and (b).]

(d) Something is lacking in the discussion following Definition 4 and in this exercise. What?

(e) Can you give a definition of *boundary* or of *boundary point* of a set S?

3.5 Convex Sets

A half-plane, defined in Section 3.4, is an example of a *convex set*, which we now consider.

DEFINITION 5.   *A set S of at least two points in $\mathbf{R}^2$ is convex $\Leftrightarrow$ if P_1 and P_2 are distinct points in S, then the entire segment $\overline{P_1P_2}$ lies in S. If S is either empty or a singleton, then S is convex.*

In Figure 17 S_1 is convex and S_2 and S_3 are not. Why?

We now prove the (geometrically obvious) assertion made earlier about half-planes.

THEOREM 8.   *A half-plane is convex.*

PROOF.   We consider an open half-plane $S = \{(x, y) \mid ax + by + c > 0\}$. The proofs for the other open half-plane and for the closed half-planes are similar and will not be given.

Suppose $P_1(x_1, y_1)$ and $P_2(x_2, y_2)$ are in S. Then

$$ax_1 + by_1 + c > 0 \qquad\qquad\qquad [21]$$

$$ax_2 + by_2 + c > 0. \qquad\qquad\qquad [22]$$

If $P_0(x_0, y_0)$ is on the line segment $\overline{P_1P_2}$, then by Equation [2.7]

$$\begin{cases} x_0 = (1 - \lambda)x_1 + \lambda x_2 \\ y_0 + (1 - \lambda)y_1 + \lambda y_2 \end{cases}, \qquad 0 < \lambda < 1. \qquad [23]$$

We show that $ax_0 + by_0 + c > 0$. In fact, using [23],

$$\begin{aligned} ax_0 + by_0 + c &= a[(1 - \lambda)x_1 + \lambda x_2] + b[(1 - \lambda)y_1 + \lambda y_2] + c \\ &= (1 - \lambda)(ax_1 + by_1) + \lambda(ax_2 + by_2) + (1 - \lambda + \lambda)c \\ &= (1 - \lambda)(ax_1 + by_1 + c) + \lambda(ax_2 + by_2 + c) \\ &> 0 \end{aligned}$$

because of [21] and [22] and the conditions on λ in [23]. Thus an arbitrary point of $\overline{P_1P_2}$ is also in S. ∎

Figure 17

The next two assertions begin to relate the material of this section with that of Section 3.4.

THEOREM 9.   *The intersection of two convex sets is convex. In symbols,*

$$S_1, S_2 \text{ convex} \Rightarrow S_1 \cap S_2 \text{ convex.}$$

PROOF.   First, if $S_1 \cap S_2$ consists of either 1 or 0 points, then $S_1 \cap S_2$ is convex by Definition 5.

Suppose next that $S_1 \cap S_2$ contains two distinct points P_1 and P_2. By the definition of intersection, both P_1 and P_2 are in both S_1 and S_2. Since S_1 and S_2 are, by hypothesis, convex, the segment $\overline{P_1 P_2}$ lies in both S_1 and S_2, i.e., $\overline{P_1 P_2} \subset S_1 \cap S_2$, and $S_1 \cap S_2$ is convex.

In symbols the proof can be expressed succinctly as follows:

$$P_1, P_2 \in S_1 \cap S_2 \Rightarrow \begin{cases} P_1, P_2 \in S_1 \Rightarrow \overline{P_1 P_2} \subset S_1 \\ \text{and} \qquad\qquad \text{and} \\ P_1, P_2 \in S_2 \Rightarrow \overline{P_1 P_2} \subset S_2 \end{cases} \Rightarrow \overline{P_1 P_2} \subset S_1 \cap S_2. \quad \blacksquare$$

With only a little more work—actually only a little more writing—we can prove (but we shall not) the following assertion.

THEOREM 10.   *For every $n \in \mathbf{N}$, if the sets $S_1, \ldots, S_n$ are convex, then the intersection $S_1 \cap S_2 \cap \cdots \cap S_n$ is convex.*

Two remarks are in order. The first is to the effect that the assertion of Theorem 10 in fact applies to an arbitrary collection (not necessarily finite) of convex sets. The proof is not hard, but Theorem 10 is all we shall need here. The second is to the effect that the proof of Theorem 9 (and Theorem 10) does not in any way use the fact that we are dealing with convex sets in the plane $\mathbf{R}^2$: in other words, the result applies to convex sets in general, in $\mathbf{R}^3$, say, or $\mathbf{R}^n$, for $n > 3$, if you please.

It follows now from Theorems 8 and 10 that any of the regions of the plane determined by systems of inequalities such as considered in Examples 8 and 9 and in the A exercises at the end of Section 3.4 will be convex.

We now state and then solve a problem which at first glance may seem unduly difficult. The solution we give illustrates an important fact: many difficult tasks are rendered relatively easy by having and using the right kind of tools.

Example 10.   Let $L(x, y) = L(P) = 6x - 4y + 11$. Find the maximum and minimum values assumed by L when $P(x, y)$ is restricted to the set S of Example 9; i.e., S is the set of points (x, y) satisfying the system

$$\begin{cases} 5x - 9y + 11 > 0 \\ 2x + 7y + 15 > 0 \\ 7x - 2y - 27 \leqslant 0 \end{cases}$$

(see Figure 16).

The tool that makes this problem a very easy one is Theorem 11, stated below, which says that if S is a polygon such as we have here (in this case a triangle) which is convex and if L is a linear function such as described in the example, then L takes on its minimum and maximum values at the vertices of S. Thus, all we need do is evaluate L at P_1, P_2, and P_3:

$$L(P_1) = L(3, -3) = 18 + 12 + 11 = 41$$
$$L(P_2) = L(5, 4) = 30 - 16 + 11 = 25$$
$$L(P_3) = L(-4, -1) = -24 + 4 + 11 = -9.$$

It follows that $P \in S \Rightarrow -9 \leqslant L(P) \leqslant 41$. Notice that, as defined, S includes P_1 and P_2 but not P_3. Since the maximum for L occurs at P_1 and the minimum at P_3, we can assert that L does have a maximum (41) on S, but we cannot be certain that L assumes its minimum value of -9 at a point of S.

The precise assertion used in the preceding example is as follows.

THEOREM 11. *Let S be a closed polygon with vertices P_1, P_2, $\ldots$, P_n, i.e., the boundary of S is the union of the line segments $\overline{P_1 P_2}$, $\overline{P_2 P_3}$, $\ldots$, $\overline{P_{n-1} P_n}$, and $\overline{P_n P_1}$. Suppose also that S is convex. Let L be the linear function $L(x, y) = L(P) = ax + by + c$. Then L takes on its maximum and minimum values at vertices of S, i.e., there are specific vertices, say P_j and P_k, such that for all $P \in S$,*

$$L(P_j) \leqslant L(P) \leqslant L(P_k).$$

The proof of this theorem is outlined in the B Exercises at the end of this section.

In applications of the theorem the set S is usually defined by a system of inequalities such as

$$a_i x + b_i y + c_i \geqslant 0, \quad i = 1, \ldots, n. \tag{24}$$

Notice that not every such system will, however, define a polygon; see the A Exercises after Section 3.4. Notice also that an inequality such as $a_1 x + b_1 y + c_1 \leqslant 0$ can be written in the form of [24] by multiplying by -1:

$$(-a_1)x + (-b_1)y + (-c_1) \geqslant 0.$$

The meaningful applications of this type of problem belong to a branch of mathematics known as linear programming and usually involve maximizing or minimizing a linear function L of many variables, such as

$$L(x_1, \ldots, x_m) = a_1 x_1 + a_2 x_2 + \cdots + a_m x_m$$

subject to a set of n conditions expressed as inequalities like those in [24] only in the m variables $x_1, \ldots, x_m$. Thus, instead of working in $\mathbf{R}^2$, we would be working in $\mathbf{R}^m$, where m is likely to be very much larger than 2. The corresponding version of Theorem 11 is still valid, however.

Example 11. We find the maximum and minimum values of the function L defined by $L(x, y) = 7x - 5y + 10$ subject to the restrictions

$$\left\{\begin{array}{r} x - 6y + 24 \geqslant 0 \\ 4x - 5y + 20 \geqslant 0 \\ 3x + 2y + 15 \geqslant 0 \\ -x + 12y + 33 \geqslant 0 \\ -7x - 3y + 57 \geqslant 0 \end{array}\right\}. \qquad [25]$$

The system of inequalities defines a convex (why?) pentagon S, as shown in Figure 18. The first step (left as an exercise) is to find the vertices of the pentagon.

These are as shown in Figure 18. All that remains to be done is to evaluate L at each of the vertices:

$L(P_1) = L(6, 5) = 7(6) - 5(5) + 10 = 27$
$L(P_2) = L(0, 4) = 7(0) - 5(4) + 10 = -10$
$L(P_3) = L(-5, 0) = 7(-5) - 5(0) + 10 = -25$
$L(P_4) = L(-3, -3) = 7(-3) - 5(-3) + 10 = 4$
$L(P_5) = L(9, -2) = 7(9) - 5(-2) + 10 = 83.$

Thus L has a minimum of -25 at $(-5, 0)$, a maximum of 83 at $(9, -2)$, and for all $P \in S$ we know that

$$-25 \leqslant L(P) \leqslant 83.$$

Exercises

A. **1.** Verify that the inequalities [25] of Example 11 do determine the vertices $P_1, \ldots, P_5$ as shown in Figure 18.

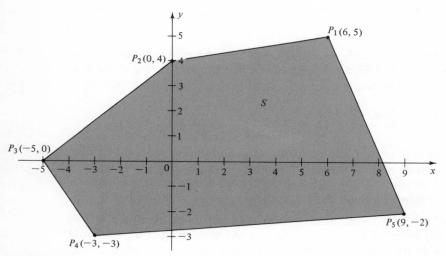

Figure 18

2. This exercise also refers to Example 11. Verify that the inequalities [25] determine the region S shown in Figure 18.

In Exercises 3–8 find the maximum and minimum values of the function L subject to the given conditions.

3.
$$L(x, y) = 3x + 7y - 2, \qquad \left\{ \begin{array}{r} 4x - 9y + 16 \geqslant 0 \\ 3x + 4y + 12 \geqslant 0 \\ -7x + 5y + 15 \geqslant 0 \end{array} \right\}.$$

4.
$$L(x, y) = 4x - y, \qquad \left\{ \begin{array}{r} y \geqslant 0 \\ -x \geqslant -1 \\ -y \geqslant -1 \\ x \geqslant 0 \end{array} \right\}.$$

5.
$$L(x, y) = x + y, \qquad \left\{ \begin{array}{r} x \geqslant 0 \\ -x + y + 1 \geqslant 0 \\ -y \geqslant -1 \\ x - y \geqslant 0 \end{array} \right\}.$$

6.
$$L(x, y) = 2x - 3y + 4, \qquad \left\{ \begin{array}{r} x + y - 3 \geqslant 0 \\ -7x + 4y + 21 \geqslant 0 \\ 4x - 7y + 21 \geqslant 0 \end{array} \right\}.$$

7. (a)
$$L(x, y) = 5x + 3y, \qquad \left\{ \begin{array}{r} -x - y + 1 \geqslant 0 \\ x - y + 1 \geqslant 0 \\ x + y + 1 \geqslant 0 \\ -x + y + 1 \geqslant 0 \end{array} \right\}.$$

(b) $L(x, y) = 3x + 5y$, same conditions as in (a).
(c) $L(x, y) = -5x + 3y$, same conditions as in (a).
(d) $L(x, y) = -5x - 3y$, same conditions as in (a).
(e) $L(x, y) = ax + by$, same conditions as in (a).

8.
$$L(x, y) = 4x - 6y + 11, \qquad \left\{ \begin{array}{r} -x + 1 \geqslant 0 \\ -y + 1 \geqslant 0 \\ x + 1 \geqslant 0 \\ x + y + 1 \geqslant 0 \\ -x + y + 1 \geqslant 0 \end{array} \right\}.$$

9. Which of the following classes of figures are invariably convex? In each case by *figure* we mean the given boundary and its interior points.

(a) Triangle.
(b) Parallelogram.
(c) Rectangle.
(d) Quadrilateral.

(e) Regular pentagon.

(f) Pentagon.

(g) Circle.

10. If any of the classes of figures in Exercise A9 is not invariably convex, give (i.e., draw) a counterexample, i.e., a figure of the class that is not convex.

B. **1.** Prove that $L(x, y) = ax + by + c$ has a maximum and a minimum on a set S exactly when $L_0(x, y) = ax + by$ has, respectively, a maximum and a minimum on S.

2. As a start toward proving Theorem 11, prove the following assertion.

THEOREM 12. *The maximum and minimum values of a linear function L defined by* $L(P) = L(x, y) = ax + by + c$, *when* $P(x, y)$ *is restricted to a line segment* $\overline{P_1 P_2}$, *occur at the endpoints of the segment.*

Hints: Suppose P_1 and P_2 have coordinates (x_1, y_1) and (x_2, y_2), respectively, and suppose—this is simply a matter of labeling—that $L(P_1) = m$, $L(P_2) = M$, and $m \leqslant M$. Let $P_0(x_0, y_0)$ be an arbitrary point of $\overline{P_1 P_2}$. You must show $m \leqslant L(P_0) \leqslant M$.

(a) Use Equations [2.7] to express x_0 and y_0 in terms of x_1, x_2, y_1, and y_2. See the proof of Theorem 8.

(b) Use the result of (a) to write $L(P_0)$ as

$$L(P_0) = (1 - \lambda)m + \lambda M.$$

(c) Use the equation in (b), the conditions on λ, and the relation between m and M to show that

$$m \leqslant L(P_0) \leqslant M.$$

3. Prove Theorem 11.

Hints: Consider $L(P_1), \ldots, L(P_n)$. Let j and k be two indices such that for all $i = 1, 2, \ldots, n$,

$$L(P_j) \leqslant L(P_i) \leqslant L(P_k);$$

i.e., $L(P_j) = m$ is the minimum value of L on the vertices and $L(P_k) = M$ is the maximum value of L on the vertices.

(a) Show that if P_0 is a point on the boundary, then

$$m \leqslant L(P_0) \leqslant M.$$

(b) Next let P_0 be a point on the interior of S. Draw the segment $\overline{P_1 P_0}$ and extend it until it intersects the boundary of S at a point B, say. Must this segment extended intersect the boundary of S? Why? Could it intersect the boundary in more than one point? Why?

(c) Use Theorem 12 to show that $L(P_0)$ must lie between $L(P_1)$ and $L(B)$.

(d) Use Theorem 12 again to show

$$m \leqslant L(P_0) \leqslant M.$$

(e) Could it happen that $B = P_i$ for some i? If so, must any of the steps of the proof be changed?

C.   **1.** Let L be the linear function defined by $L(x, y) = L(P) = ax + by$ (see Exercise B1). Consider the segment $\overline{P_1 P_2}$ determined by two distinct points $P_1(x_1, y_1)$ and $P_2(x_2, y_2)$. Let $L(P_1) = m$, $L(P_2) = M$, where $m \leqslant M$. Let $P_0(x_0, y_0)$ be a point of $\overline{P_1 P_2}$ distinct from P_1 and P_2. Show that

$$\left.\begin{array}{c} L(P_0) = m \\ \text{or} \\ L(P_0) = M \end{array}\right\} \Leftrightarrow m = M.$$

    Hints.   Use Theorem 12 (in Exercise B2). The proof of the implication $\Leftarrow$ is truly trivial.

    2. See Exercise C1. The linear function L is $L(P) = L(x, y) = ax + by$, where a and b are not both zero. The points $P_1(x_1, y_1)$ and $P_2(x_2, y_2)$ are distinct. Under what conditions on x_1, x_2, y_1, y_2, a, and b will $L(P_1) = L(P_2)$?

4

The Circle

In this chapter we make a brief study of circles. There may be some basis for considering straight lines and circles together, for one could define a straight line as a set of points equidirectional from a given point, and a circle as a set of points equidistant from a given point. However, we have taken *straight line* as an undefined term.

Thus, we shall for the first time be defining a curve by a geometric property and using this definition to obtain its analytic representation. In Chapter 5 we shall continue this program.

4.1 Definition and Equations

We begin with the standard definition of a circle.

DEFINITION 1. *A circle is the set of all points in the plane that are a fixed distance from a given point. More particularly, if the given point (the center) is C and the fixed distance (the radius) is a, then the circle $\mathscr{C}$ determined by C and a is the set*

$$\mathscr{C} = \{P \mid |\overline{CP}| = a\}.$$

When a coordinate system has been established in the plane, the following assertion is an immediate consequence of Definition 1 and Theorem 2.2.

THEOREM 1.   *The equation of a circle with center $C(h, k)$ and radius a is*

$$(x - h)^2 + (y - k)^2 = a^2.$$ [1]

PROOF.   Let $P(x, y)$ be a point on the circle. Then, using Theorem 2.2, we have

$$\sqrt{(x - h)^2 + (y - k)^2} = a;$$

upon squaring both sides we get [1]. Conversely, it is obvious that if a point $P(x, y)$ satisfies [1], then its distance from (h, k) is a. ∎

An important special case of [1] occurs when the center of the circle is at the origin, i.e., $(h, k) = (0, 0)$. We then have the equation

$$x^2 + y^2 = a^2.$$ [2]

A further special case arises by letting $a = 1$. We then have what is usually called *the unit circle*:

$$x^2 + y^2 = 1.$$ [3]

It may be worth pointing out that it is always possible to represent a circle by Equation [3]: it is only necessary to set up the coordinate system with the origin at the center of the circle and with the unit of distance equal to the radius of the circle. However, other considerations may enter in which render such choices inadvisable or inconvenient. Along the same lines, though, it may be convenient to introduce a translation of coordinates, such as was done in Section 3.3, in this case letting

$$\begin{aligned} x' &= x - h \\ y' &= y - k. \end{aligned}$$ [4]

Then, as is readily seen, Equation [1] becomes

$$x'^2 + y'^2 = a^2.$$ [5]

Example 1.   A circle $\mathscr{C}$ has center at $C(2, 1)$ and radius $a = 3$. By Theorem 1 its equation is

$$(x - 2)^2 + (y - 1)^2 = 9.$$

If the origin is translated to $(2, 1)$, the new axes remaining parallel, respectively, to the original, so that $x' = x - 2$, $y' = y - 1$, then the equation of the circle is

$$x'^2 + y'^2 = 9.$$

See Figure 1.

If we rewrite Equation [1], we can put it in the form

$$x^2 + y^2 - 2hx - 2ky + (h^2 + k^2 - a^2) = 0,$$ [6]

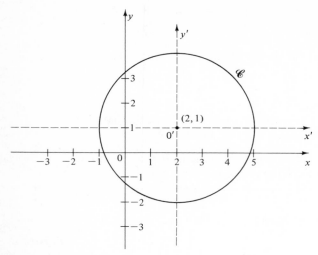

Figure 1

an equation of the second degree in x and y. The most general such equation is

$$Ax^2 + Bxy + Cy^2 + Dx + Ey + F = 0, \qquad [7]$$

where at least one of A, B, and C is different from zero. We shall study other special cases of [7] in Chapter 5. For the present we note that necessary conditions for an equation such as [7] to represent a circle are

$$B = 0 \quad \text{and} \quad A = C \neq 0. \qquad [8]$$

Given such an equation, we can obtain the geometric features of the circle by completing the squares in x and y.

Example 2. We consider

$$2x^2 + 2y^2 + 4x - 7y + 2 = 0, \qquad [9]$$

where $B = 0$ and $A = C = 2$. We divide by 2 and regroup to obtain

$$(x^2 + 2x \qquad) + (y^2 - \tfrac{7}{2}y \qquad) = -1.$$

We now add 1 and $\tfrac{49}{16}$, respectively, to the parenthetical expressions and to the right-hand side:

$$(x^2 + 2x + 1) + (y^2 - \tfrac{7}{2}y + \tfrac{49}{16}) = -1 + 1 + \tfrac{49}{16},$$

or

$$(x + 1)^2 + (y - \tfrac{7}{4})^2 = (\tfrac{7}{4})^2,$$

indicating that the circle has center at $(-1, \tfrac{7}{4})$ and radius $a = \tfrac{7}{4}$. See Figure 2.

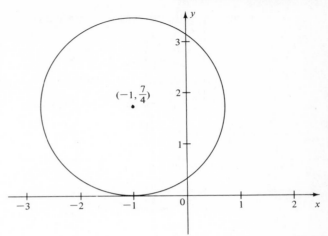

Figure 2

It is important to realize that an equation such as [9] need not represent a circle. Suppose we change the constant term 2 in [9] to 10:

$$2x^2 + 2y^2 + 4x - 7y + 10 = 0, \qquad [10]$$

or, dividing by 2,

$$x^2 + 2x + y^2 - \tfrac{7}{2}y + 5 = 0,$$

or, completing the square,

$$x^2 + 2x + 1 + y^2 - \tfrac{7}{2}y + \tfrac{49}{16} = -5 + 1 + \tfrac{49}{16},$$

or

$$(x + 1)^2 + (y - \frac{7}{4})^2 = \frac{-15}{16}.$$

As the left-hand side must be non-negative for all (x, y) and the right-hand side is negative, the equation in [10] represents the null set.

There is still a third possibility (we are again dealing with the Law of the Trichotomy for an ordered field): suppose the constant term in [9] had been $\tfrac{65}{8}$. Then completing the squares as before would give

$$(x + 1)^2 + (y - \tfrac{7}{4})^2 = 0,$$

an equation that determines the single point $(-1, \tfrac{7}{4})$, sometimes called a *point circle.*

The general situation is as follows. Since the coefficients of x^2 and y^2 must be equal and nonzero, we may as well assume we have divided through by this number and consider an equation such as

$$x^2 + y^2 + Dx + Ey + F = 0. \qquad [11]$$

Completing the squares in x and y gives

$$\left(x + \frac{D}{2}\right)^2 + \left(y + \frac{E}{2}\right)^2 = \frac{D^2 + E^2 - 4F}{4}.$$

Thus, given an equation such as [11], we can say that

1. $D^2 + E^2 - 4F > 0 \Rightarrow$ [11] represents a circle with center at

$$\left(-\frac{D}{2}, -\frac{E}{2}\right)$$

and radius

$$a = \tfrac{1}{2}\sqrt{D^2 + E^2 - 4F}.$$

2. $D^2 + E^2 - 4F = 0 \Rightarrow$ [11] represents the point

$$\left(-\frac{D}{2}, -\frac{E}{2}\right).$$

3. $D^2 + E^2 - 4F < 0 \Rightarrow$ [11] represents the null set.

For any specific problem it may be better to proceed as in Example 2 rather than try to remember the general statements just given.

Notice that each of Equations [1] and [11] involves three constants. The implication of this observation is that it takes three conditions (e.g., three points on the circle) to determine the circle. [However, the "counting" of the conditions might be confusing: clearly, the coordinates of the center determine two of the three constants in [1]; thus, the center is "worth" two points on the circle. We shall not pursue this. See Example 4.]

Example 3. Find the equation of the circle that goes through the points $(1, 3)$, $(-8, 0)$, and $(0, 6)$.

We use [11] and substitute in the coordinates of the given points; for $(1, 3)$ we get

$$1 + 9 + D + 3E + F = 0.$$

Similarly, for $(-8, 0)$ and $(0, 6)$. The system of three equations in the three unknowns D, E, and F can be written as

$$\left\{\begin{array}{rcl} D + 3E + F &=& -10 \\ 6E + F &=& -36 \\ -8D + F &=& -64 \end{array}\right\}.$$

The solution is easily found to be $D = 8$, $E = -6$, and $F = 0$; thus an equation for the circle is

$$x^2 + y^2 + 8x - 6y = 0.$$

(What is the geometric significance of the fact that $F = 0$?)

By completing the squares in the usual way we get the more informative equation

$$(x + 4)^2 + (y - 3)^2 = 25,$$

showing the center to be at $(-4, 3)$ and the radius to be 5 (see Figure 3).

Example 4. Find the equation of the circle that goes through the points $(1, 2)$ and $(3, 4)$ and has radius $a = 2$.

Because the value of the radius is given, we use Equation [1], substituting in the given information:

$$\begin{cases} (1 - h)^2 + (2 - k)^2 = 4 \\ (3 - h)^2 + (4 - k)^2 = 4 \end{cases}.$$

Squaring, simplifying, and then subtracting the second of these from the first gives

$$h + k = 5. \tag{12}$$

Using $k = 5 - h$ in either of the above equations, we find

$$h^2 - 4h + 3 = 0,$$

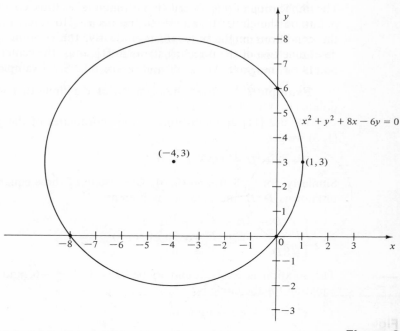

Figure 3

which produces two values of $h: h_1 = 1$, $h_2 = 3$. The corresponding values of k [from [12]] are $k_1 = 4$, $k_2 = 2$. Thus the problem has two solutions:

$$(x - 1)^3 + (y - 4)^2 = 4$$

and

$$(x - 3)^2 + (y - 2)^2 = 4.$$

See Figure 4. Notice that Equation [12] is the equation (in h and k) of the line on which the two centers lie.

Exercises

A. In each of Exercises 1–16 find the equation(s) of the circles defined by the given conditions. If the center and/or radius are not explicitly given, find them. Make a sketch.

1. $C(0, -2)$, $a = 2$.
2. $C(4, -3)$, $a = 3$.
3. $C(-3, -4)$, $a = 5$.
4. $C(-4, 7)$, $a = 8$.
5. Through $(1, -3)$, $(2, -2)$, and $(-2, 6)$.
6. Through $(-1, 1)$, $(1, 0)$, and $(-3, -3)$.
7. Ends of a diameter at $(-4, -2)$ and $(2, 8)$.
8. Ends of a diameter at $(4, 3)$ and $(-2, 9)$.
9. Through $(-6, 7)$ and $(1, 8)$; radius $a = 5$.
10. Through $(0, 0)$ and $(16, 0)$; radius $a = 10$.
11. Through $(1, 11)$, $(-16, 4)$, and $(-9, 11)$.
12. Through $(3, 0)$ and $(0, 0)$; radius $a = \frac{5}{2}$.
13. Through $(1, 1)$, $(2, 8)$, and $(8, 0)$.
14. Through $(-3, 2)$, $(1, -6)$, and $(5, -14)$.

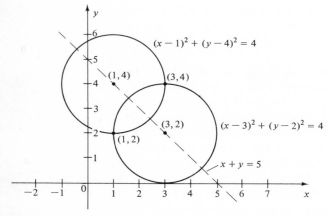

Figure 4

15. Ends of a diameter at $(1, 7)$ and $(7, 1)$.

16. Through $(1, 0)$, $(0, 1)$, and $(1, 1)$.

17. Is there a circle through $(-\frac{1}{2}, \sqrt{3}/2)$, $(-1, 1)$, $(-2, 0)$, and $(-\frac{3}{2}, -(\sqrt{3}/2))$? If so, find its equation.

18. Is there a circle through $(3, 0)$, $(2, 2)$, $(-4, 1)$, and $(-3, -2)$? If so, find its equation.

In each of Exercises 19–26 find the center and radius of the given circle.

19. $x^2 + y^2 - 4x + 2y - 3 = 0$.

20. $x^2 + y^2 + 6y = 0$.

21. $x^2 + y^2 - 4x + 6y + 13 = 0$.

22. $x^2 + y^2 + 4x + 8y - 8 = 0$.

23. $3x^2 + 3y^2 - 6x + 3y - 4 = 0$.

24. $2x^2 + 2y^2 + 5x - 4y + 8 = 0$.

25. $x^2 + y^2 - 2y = 0$.

26. $x^2 + y^2 + 6x = 0$.

C. In this set of exercises we define and discuss tangents to a circle. In general, a tangent to a curve should be studied by using the techniques of calculus, but the special nature of the circle permits us to bypass the use of limits required for most other curves.

We begin with a definition. It should be noted that the formulation we give does not generalize to other curves.

DEFINITION 2. *A tangent to a circle is a straight line that intersects the circle at exactly one point, called the point of tangency.*

1. Prove the following assertion.

THEOREM 2. *At each point (x_0, y_0) of the circle $x^2 + y^2 = a^2$ there is exactly one tangent line whose equation is*

$$x_0 x + y_0 y = a^2. \qquad [13]$$

We shall give a series of hints, which you may skip if you wish.

    (a) Assume first that $P_0(x_0, y_0)$ is on the circle and that $y_0 \neq 0$.

        (i) Write the equation of the line through (x_0, y_0) with slope m.

        (ii) Solve for y and substitute into the equation of the circle.

        (iii) Write the result from (ii) as a quadratic equation in x; use, if possible, the fact that (x_0, y_0) is on the circle.

        (iv) Recall from algebra the fact that the quadratic equation $ax^2 + bx + c = 0$ has two equal roots $\Leftrightarrow b^2 - 4ac = 0$. The definition of tangent line to a circle implies that the quadratic equation of (iii) should have two equal roots. Convince yourself of this.

(v) Set up the equation $b^2 - 4ac = 0$ as an equation in m and solve for m. You should find that $m = -x_0/y_0$.

(vi) Use the result of (v) in the result of (i) to obtain [13].

(b) Why did we have to assume in (a) that $y_0 \neq 0$?

(c) Show that even if $y_0 = 0$, Equation [13] still applies.

(d) Have you in fact demonstrated the uniqueness, the "exactly one" part of the statement of Theorem 2?

2. Prove the following generalization of Theorem 2.

THEOREM 3.   *At each point (x_0, y_0) of the circle $(x - h)^2 + (y - k)^2 = a^2$ there is exactly one tangent line whose equation is*

$$(x_0 - h)(x - h) + (y_0 - k)(y - k) = a^2. \qquad [14]$$

Hint: Use a translation of coordinates (Section 3.3) and apply Theorem 2.

3. Prove the following assertion.

THEOREM 4.   *The tangent line at any point P_0 on a circle is perpendicular to the radius drawn from the center to P_0.*

4. Prove the following assertion.

THEOREM 5.   *Let $P_1(x_1, y_1)$ be a point outside the circle $\mathscr{C}: (x - h)^2 + (y - k)^2 = a^2$. Draw a line through P_1 tangent to $\mathscr{C}$. Let d be the length of the segment from P_1 to the point of tangency. Show that*

$$d^2 = (x_1 - h)^2 + (y_1 - k)^2 - a^2. \qquad [15]$$

Hint: Use Theorem 4.

5. Prove the following.

THEOREM 6.   *Let $P_1(x_1, y_1)$ be a point outside the circle $\mathscr{C}: x^2 + y^2 + Dx + Ey + F = 0$. Draw a line through P_1 tangent to $\mathscr{C}$. Let d be the length of the segment from P_1 to the point of tangency. Show that*

$$d^2 = x_1^2 + y_1^2 + Dx_1 + Ey_1 + F. \qquad [16]$$

6. Consider the circle $\mathscr{C}: x^2 + y^2 = 25$, the point $P_0(4, 3)$ and the point $P_1(8, 7)$.

(a) Find the equation of the tangent line to $\mathscr{C}$ at P_0.

(b) Find the length of the segment of the tangent line drawn from P_1 to a point of tangency on $\mathscr{C}$.

(c) How many tangent lines can be drawn from P_1 to $\mathscr{C}$?

(d) Find the equation(s) of the line(s) of part (c). **Hint:**   The distance from the origin to such a line must equal 5. Why? See Section 3.3.

7. See Exercise C6(d). If you really want to show off, prove the following.

Let $\mathscr{C}$ be the circle $x^2 + y^2 = a^2$ and let $P_1(x_1, y_1)$ be a point external to $\mathscr{C}$. The equations of the tangent lines from P_1 to $\mathscr{C}$ are

$$(x_1 y_1 \pm ad)x - (x_1^2 - a^2)y - a(ay_1 \pm dx_1) = 0, \tag{17}$$

where

$$d^2 = x_1^2 + y_1^2 - a^2.$$

Show also that [17] reduces to [13] if P_1 is taken on $\mathscr{C}$, i.e., if $d = 0$. Is [17] correct if $x_1 = \pm a$?

    8. Prove that the set $S = \{(x,y) | x^2 + y^2 \le a^2\}$ is convex.

    Hint: Use: i) Equations [2.7],

                         ii) $2uv \le u^2 + v^2$, all $u, v \in \mathbf{R}$.

4.2 Radical Axis. Families of Circles

In this section we shall discuss several further topics related to circles.

Radical Axis

Suppose we have two distinct circles $\mathscr{C}_1$ and $\mathscr{C}_2$ and we want to find their points of intersection (if any). When put in analytic terms this geometric problem becomes a routine (although possibly messy) problem in algebra. For if the equations of $\mathscr{C}_1$ and $\mathscr{C}_2$ are

$$\left.\begin{array}{l} \mathscr{C}_1 : x^2 + y^2 + D_1 x + E_1 y + F_1 = 0 \\ \mathscr{C}_2 : x^2 + y^2 + D_2 x + E_2 y + F_2 = 0 \end{array}\right\}, \tag{18}$$

then all we need do is find the (simultaneous) solution of this system.

    Before continuing with the general case, we look at a particular case.

    Example 5.   We seek the points of intersection (if any) of the circles $\mathscr{C}_1$ and $\mathscr{C}_2$, where

$$\begin{array}{l} \mathscr{C}_1 : x^2 + y^2 - 4x - 2y + 1 = 0 \\ \mathscr{C}_2 : x^2 + y^2 - 6x + 4y + 4 = 0. \end{array} \tag{19}$$

    The first obvious step is to subtract the second equation from the first; this gives

$$2x - 6y - 3 = 0, \tag{20}$$

a straight line. The geometric significance of [20] is that any points common to $\mathscr{C}_1$ and $\mathscr{C}_2$ must also lie on this line. It is a straightforward process to find points of intersection of this line and either $\mathscr{C}_1$ or $\mathscr{C}_2$. One way is to solve [20] for x in terms of y, substitute into the equation for $\mathscr{C}_1$, find the two (real) values of y, and then use [20] again to find the corresponding values of x. This procedure (or an equivalent one) will produce as points of intersection

$$P_1\left(\frac{9}{4} + \frac{3\sqrt{135}}{20}, \frac{1}{4} + \frac{\sqrt{135}}{20}\right) \approx (3.99, 0.83)$$

and

$$P_2\left(\frac{9}{4} - \frac{3\sqrt{135}}{20}, \frac{1}{4} - \frac{\sqrt{135}}{20}\right) \approx (0.51, -0.33)$$

(see Figure 5).

The fact is that we are less interested in the points of intersection than in the relation between the line [20] and the line through C_1 and C_2, the centers of the circles: they appear, in Figure 5, to be perpendicular. They are, as is easily checked: from [20] we calculate the slope of the line to be $m_l = \frac{1}{3}$; the slope of $\overline{C_1C_2}$ is $m_c = -3$. Thus $m_l m_c + 1 = 0$, and the two lines are perpendicular.

The observations made in the particular case of Example 5 hold true in general. Given two distinct circles, such as [18], if we subtract the one equation from the other we get

$$(D_1 - D_2)x + (E_1 - E_2)y + (F_1 - F_2) = 0. \qquad [21]$$

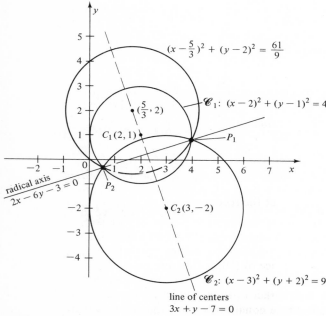

Figure 5

The line determined by this equation is called the *radical axis* of the two circles. (Equation [21] will fail to determine a line if and only if $D_1 = D_2$ and $E_1 = E_2$; in this case, since the circles are assumed to be distinct, $F_1 \neq F_2$ and the circles are concentric.) Clearly, as in Example 5, if $\mathscr{C}_1$ and $\mathscr{C}_2$ have points in common, these points will also lie on the radical axis. Moreover, whether or not the circles intersect, the radical axis is always perpendicular to the line of centers, as we now show. The slope of the line [21] is

$$m_{\mathrm{RA}} = \frac{-(D_1 - D_2)}{E_1 - E_2}.$$

Since the centers of $\mathscr{C}_1$ and $\mathscr{C}_2$ are at

$$C_1\left(\frac{-D_1}{2}, \frac{-E_1}{2}\right) \quad \text{and} \quad C_2\left(\frac{-D_2}{2}, \frac{-E_2}{2}\right),$$

the slope of the line of centers is easily calculated to be

$$m_{C_1 C_2} = \frac{E_1 - E_2}{D_1 - D_2},$$

Thus the slopes, if they exist, are negative reciprocals. If either one fails to exist, the other one is zero. In any case the lines are perpendicular.

We give a formal summary of this discussion.

THEOREM 7.   *If two circles such as described in* [18] *are distinct and nonconcentric, then the radical axis* [21] *contains any points of intersection of the circles and is perpendicular to the line joining the centers of the circles.*

Families of Circles

The radical axis of two circles $\mathscr{C}_1$ and $\mathscr{C}_2$ can also be obtained as a special case of the following equation:

$$x^2 + y^2 + D_1 x + E_1 y + F_1 + k(x^2 + y^2 + D_2 x + E_2 y + F_2) = 0.$$
$$[22]$$

In general, for a specific value of k, Equation [22] represents a circle. Moreover, it is clear that if a point is on both $\mathscr{C}_1$ and $\mathscr{C}_2$, its coordinates will satisfy [22]. Another way of describing this is to say that [22] represents a family of circles, all members of the family going through the points of intersection (if any) of $\mathscr{C}_1$ and $\mathscr{C}_2$. (See Exercise B3 after Section 3.2.) However, for the particular value $k = -1$, Equation [22] becomes precisely [21], the radical axis.

Example 6.   This is a continuation of Example 5. We find the equation of the circle that goes through the points of intersection of the circles [19] and that also goes through the origin.

Although the points of intersection of the circles $\mathscr{C}_1$ and $\mathscr{C}_2$ were found in Example 5 we ignore that result and use instead the equation corresponding to [22]:

$$x^2 + y^2 - 4x - 2y + 1 + k(x^2 + y^2 - 6x + 4y + 4) = 0, \qquad [23]$$

or

$$(1 + k)x^2 + (1 + k)y^2 - (4 + 6k)x - (2 - 4k)y + (1 + 4k) = 0.$$

A circle from this family will go through $(0, 0)$ if and only if the constant term $1 + 4k = 0$. Thus, $k = -\frac{1}{4}$, and the desired member of the family is

$$x^2 + y^2 - \tfrac{10}{3}x - 4y = 0,$$

or (See Figure 5.)

$$(x - \tfrac{5}{3})^2 + (y - 2)^2 = \tfrac{61}{9}.$$

One can, of course, write other types of equations of families of circles, depending in part on the family characteristic. For example,

$$(x - 2)^2 + (y - 1)^2 = a^2 \qquad [24]$$

represents the family of concentric circles with center at $(2, 1)$. The equation $x^2 + y^2 + 2x + Ey + F = 0$ represents the family of all circles whose centers are on $x + 1 = 0$. And $(x - h)^2 + y^2 = h^2$ is the family of circles with centers at $(h, 0)$ on the x-axis and radius equal to h; hence all are tangent to the y-axis at the origin (see Figure 6).

Exercises

A. **1.** Find the equations of the radical axis and the line of centers for each pair of circles.

(a) $x^2 + y^2 + 3x - 8y + 16 = 0$, $x^2 + y^2 - 4x - 2y + 1 = 0$.
(b) $x^2 + y^2 - 6x - 2y - 6 = 0$, $2x^2 + 2y^2 + 4x - 5y + 2 = 0$.
(c) $x^2 + y^2 = 4$, $x^2 + y^2 - 2x = 0$.
(d) $3x^2 + 3y^2 + 6x - 8y = 0$, $x^2 + y^2 + 8x + 6y - 11 = 0$.

In Exercises 2–6 say what geometric characteristic every member of the given family has.

2. $x^2 + y^2 + Ey = 0$.
3. $x^2 + y^2 + Dx - 2y + 1 = 0$. Is there a point common to every member of the family?
4. $(x - h)^2 + (y - 1)^2 = a^2$.
5. $x^2 + y^2 + Dx + Ey = 0$.
6. $k_1(x^2 + y^2 + D_1x + E_1y + F_1) + k_2(x^2 + y^2 + D_2x + E_2y + F_2) = 0$.

7. Write the equation for the family of circles through the intersection of the two circles in Exercise A1(c).

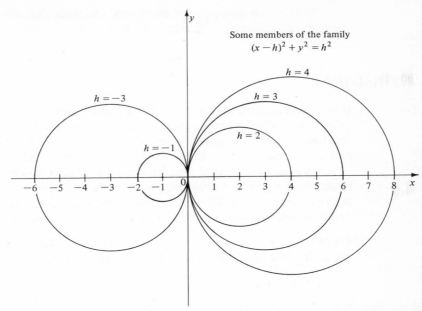

Some members of the family
$(x - h)^2 + y^2 = h^2$

$h = 4$

$h = -3$

$h = 3$

$h = 2$

$h = -1$

Figure 6

8. Let $\mathscr{C}_1$ and $\mathscr{C}_2$ be the circles in Exercise A1(b). Find the equation of the circle through $(-2, -3)$ and the common points of $\mathscr{C}_1$ and $\mathscr{C}_2$.

9. Write the equation for the family of circles through the points of intersection of the two circles in Exercise A1(d). Show that the center of every circle in the family lies on the line of centers of the two given circles.

10. Write an equation for the family of circles through $(2, 1)$.

11. Write an equation for the family of circles that have centers on the x-axis and go through $(5, -1)$.

12. Write an equation for the family of circles whose centers lie on $x + y = 1$.

13. Write an equation for the family of circles that are tangent externally to $x^2 + y^2 = 1$.

14. Same as Exercise A13, only tangent internally.

15. Write an equation for the family of circles that are tangent to the y-axis.

16. Write an equation for the family of circles that are tangent to the line $x = 1$.

C.   **1.** Show that every circle of the family described by Equation [22] has its center on the line of centers of $\mathscr{C}_1$ and $\mathscr{C}_2$; in other words, the family [22] has the same line of centers as well as the same radical axis.

2. Write an equation for the family of circles that are all tangent to the line $Ax + By + C = 0$, where $A^2 + B^2 \neq 0$.

4.3 Relations

It may already have been noticed that a circle is not the graph of a function (why is this so?). The same is true of vertical lines (again, why?). As we shall see, there are many important curves which are not the graphs of functions, and a few remarks about the concepts involved are in order.

A circle, or a vertical line, or the set of points inside a circle are all examples of a graph of a *relation* (or, from the usual point of view, these *are* the relations). As we did with functions, we shall give a general definition and then indicate the kind of restrictions of it in which we shall be interested.

DEFINITION 3.   *Given two sets X and Y, a* relation *on X to Y is a subset R of the cartesian product $X \times Y$. The subset of X,*

$$\{x \mid (x, y) \in R\},$$

is the domain *of the relation, and the subset of Y,*

$$\{y \mid x, y) \in R\},$$

is the range *of the relation.*

It will be observed from the alternate definition of a function, given in brackets just after Definition 2.4, that a function is a special (why special?) kind of relation. In other words, every function is a relation, but not vice versa.

For our immediate purposes the two sets X and Y will each be, of course, the set **R** of real numbers, and a relation will usually be defined for us by an equation or an inequality involving x and y. Examples:

$$R_1 = \{(x, y) \mid x^2 + y^2 = a^2\}$$
$$R_2 = \{(x, y) \mid x^2 + y^2 \leqslant a^2\}$$
$$R_3 = \{(x, y) \mid x - 1 = 0\}$$
$$R_4 = \{(x, y) \mid x^2 - y^2 = 0\}$$
$$R_5 = \{(x, y) \mid x + y = 1\}$$
$$R_6 = \{(x, y) \mid y = f(x), \text{ where } f \text{ is a function}\}.$$

Notice from the form of these examples that we do not have to speak of the graph of a relation: the relation *is* the graph—it is, after all, by Definition 3, a subset of $\mathbf{R}^2$. This is simply consistent with our practice of identifying the geometric object and its analytic description, e.g., the circle $x^2 + y^2 = 4$.

In Section 2.5 we discussed a systematic procedure for obtaining geometric information from the formula defining a function. In particular, we mentioned five types of information that should be investigated:

1. Intercepts.
2. Domain and range of f.
3. Symmetry.
4. Changes of sign in the ordinate.
5. Asymptotes.

Since the previous discussion was oriented toward working with the formula for a function, we mention modifications which apply when working with relations, specifically as regards intercepts and symmetry.

INTERCEPTS.   For the x-intercept, put $y = 0$ and solve for x. Similarly, for the y-intercept, put $x = 0$ and solve for y.

SYMMETRY.   Let R denote the relation. Then the various tests for symmetry can be formulated as follows. With respect to:

x-axis: $(x, y) \in R \Rightarrow (x, -y) \in R.$

(Verbally: is the equation or inequality still satisfied if y is replaced by $-y$?)

y-axis: $(x, y) \in R \Rightarrow (-x, y) \in R.$

(Verbally: is the equation or inequality still satisfied if x is replaced by $-x$?)

origin: $(x, y) \in R \Rightarrow (-x, -y) \in R.$

(Verbally: you formulate it.)

y = x: $(x, y) \in R \Rightarrow (y, x) \in R.$

(Verbally: exercise for student.)

Notice that symmetry with respect to both x- and y-axes implies symmetry with respect to the origin.

It should also be pointed out that in some cases formulas that define relations which are not functions can sometimes be decomposed into formulas for several functions. As a simple example, consider the equation of a circle with center at the origin:

$$x^2 + y^2 = a^2,$$

By solving for y we can write

$$f_1(x) = \sqrt{a^2 - x^2} \quad \text{and} \quad f_2(x) = -\sqrt{a^2 - x^2},$$

defining functions f_1 and f_2 whose graphs are the upper and lower semicircles, respectively. The graph of the original relation is the union of the graphs of the functions. However, such a procedure may be rather difficult for algebraic reasons.

Example 7.   We consider the relation defined by

$$x + xy^2 + y^2 - 1 = 0. \qquad [25]$$

INTERCEPTS.

$y = 0 \Rightarrow x = 1; \quad (1, 0)$.
$x = 0 \Rightarrow y^2 = 1; \quad (0, 1), (0, -1)$.

EXTENT.   We first solve for y^2, finding

$$y^2 = \frac{1 - x}{1 + x}. \qquad [26]$$

Then $y^2 > 0 \Rightarrow (1 - x)/(1 + x) > 0 \Rightarrow -1 < x < 1$. Thus the curve lies entirely in the vertical strip between $x = -1$ and $x = 1$.

SYMMETRY.   With respect to x-axis. Why?

ASYMPTOTES.   The only asymptote is $x = -1$. Why?

Notice that we can decompose [26] into the formulas for two functions:

$$f_1(x) = \sqrt{\frac{1 - x}{1 + x}} \quad \text{and} \quad f_2(x) = -\sqrt{\frac{1 - x}{1 + x}}.$$

If we consider the behavior of f_1 as x decreases from 1 to -1, we see that under the radical the numerator increases from 0 to 2 whereas the denominator decreases from 2 to 0. The curve (determined by) [25] is shown in Figure 7. That it does indeed behave as shown near the point $(1, 0)$ is most easily found by the techniques of calculus.

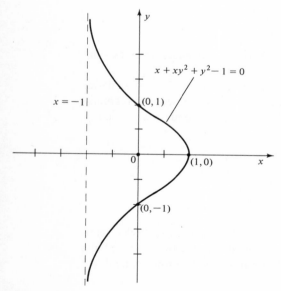

Figure 7

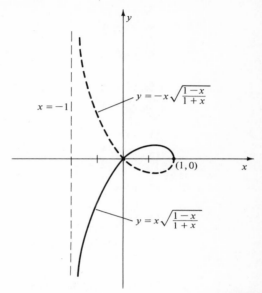

Figure 8

Example 8.   A relation somewhat more interesting than that just considered is

$$x^3 - x^2 + xy^2 + y^2 = 0. \tag{27}$$

Solving for y, we get

$$y^2 = x^2 \frac{1 - x}{1 + x}. \tag{28}$$

The analysis is similar to that of Example 7, except that the only intercepts are at $(1, 0)$ and $(0, 0)$. Again the expression can be decomposed into two functions:

$$f_1(x) = x\sqrt{\frac{1 - x}{1 + x}} \quad \text{and} \quad f_2(x) = -x\sqrt{\frac{1 - x}{1 + x}}$$

The graph of f_1 is shown solid in Figure 8, and that of f_2 is dashed. The union of the two, the graph of [27], is called the *strophoid*.

As remarked earlier, analyses such as these are seriously hampered by the lack of the techniques provided by calculus. For this reason we do not pursue them.

Exercises

A.   In Exercises 1–16 make a geometric analysis and a sketch.

    1. $x^2 - y^2 = 0$.
    2. $x - y^2 = 0$.

3. $x - y^2 = 1.$
4. $x^2 - y^2 = 1.$
5. $x - y^3 = 0.$
6. $x^2y^2 + y^2 - x = 0.$
7. $x^2 + y^2 \geqslant 4.$
8. $x^2 - 5x + 6 - y = 0.$
9. $x^3 - y^2 = 0.$
10. $y^2 - y - 6 - x = 0.$
11. $xy^2 - 2y^2 - x = 0.$
12. $y^2 = \dfrac{4 - x}{2 + x}.$
13. $y^2 = \dfrac{2 + x}{4 - x}.$
14. $y^2 = \dfrac{4x}{4 - x^2}.$
15. $x^2 + x^2y^2 - 4 = 0.$
16. $x^4 + y^4 - 1 = 0.$

C.   **1.** Which of the relations in the A exercises are also functions?

2. In Example 7, in going from Equation [25] to [26], there was a division by $1 + x$. This can be done provided $1 + x \neq 0$. Does this step change the graph? Why?

The Conic Section Curves

5

In this chapter we shall study three curves that belong together from several points of view, as we shall see. These are the *parabola*, *ellipse*, and *hyperbola*; generically they are called the *conic section curves*, or conic sections. The reason for this term is that these curves can be obtained by cutting, or sectioning, a cone with a plane in various ways. We shall return to this point later. The fact is that the circle occurs as a special case of the ellipse and so could be studied along with the conic section curves, but because of the very special nature of the circle we have considered it separately.

Our approach will be to define each curve by a geometric property, obtain an analytic representation (an equation) for the curve, and then study the properties of the curve by means of the equation. In Chapter 6 we shall give a single definition that encompasses all three of these curves.

5.1 The Parabola

The definition of a parabola involves distances from a point and a line.

DEFINITION 1.   *Given a fixed point F, the* focus, *and a fixed line l, the* directrix, *a parabola is the set of points P that are equidistant from F and l. In symbols, a point P is on the parabola determined by F and l $\Leftrightarrow$*

$$|\overline{PF}| = d(P, l).$$

[1]

Recall that for P a point and l a line the symbol $d(P, l)$ means perpendicular distance between P and l.

We now convert this definition into an equation. This, of course, requires choosing a coordinate system. To do this in the most efficient manner we draw on the well-known authorial omniscience and choose the x-axis through the focus and perpendicular to the directrix with the origin midway between the focus and directrix. This means we can describe the focus and directrix by $F(p, 0)$ and $x = -p$, respectively. See Figure 1, where p has been chosen as positive; it can be negative.

Using the condition of Equation [1], we now have for $P(x, y)$

$$\sqrt{(x - p)^2 + y^2} = |x + p|^2, \tag{2}$$

or, squaring both sides,

$$x^2 - 2px + p^2 + y^2 = x^2 + 2px + p^2,$$

or, upon simplifying,

$$y^2 = 4px. \tag{3}$$

Conversely, it is easy to see that if a point $P(x, y)$ satisfies [3], one can reverse the steps to obtain [2], showing that, in fact, P is on the parabola determined by F and l.

Equation [3] is one of the standard forms for a parabola. As already noted, p can be negative, which means that the focus and the directrix would have their positions with respect to the y-axis interchanged. For example, the equation $y^2 = -4x$ represents a parabola with focus $F(-1, 0)$ and directrix $l: x = 1$.

In a similar vein, we note that we could have taken the focus F on the y-axis at $F(0, p)$, where again p could be either positive or negative, and the

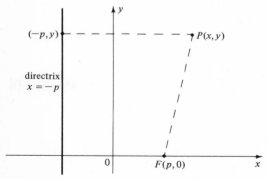

Figure 1

directrix perpendicular to the y-axis, i.e., $l: y = -p$. This interchange of the roles of x- and y-axes would obviously produce the equation

$$x^2 = 4py. \tag{4}$$

We give a formal summary of this discussion.

THEOREM 1.   *A point $P(x, y)$ is on the parabola determined by the focus $F(p, 0)[F(0, p)]$ and the directrix $l: x = -p[l: y = -p] \Leftrightarrow$*

$$y^2 = 4px \tag{3}$$

$$[x^2 = 4py]. \tag{4}$$

A final remark about the equation of a parabola. Some writers use $(p/2, 0)$ as the coordinates of the focus and $x = -(p/2)$ as the equation of the directrix (i.e., in this convention $|p|$ is the distance between focus and directrix, rather than $2|p|$ as in ours). When this is done the equation is $y^2 = 2px$.

Equation [3] is easily analyzed by the techniques of Section 4.3. This analysis produces the following:

1. The only intercept is $(0, 0)$.
2. Since $y^2 > 0$, we must have $px > 0$; i.e.,

$$p > 0 \Rightarrow x > 0$$
$$p < 0 \Rightarrow x < 0.$$

(In other words, the curve lies entirely in one half-plane.)
3. There is symmetry with respect to the x-axis, since $(-y)^2 = y^2$.

We observe also that if we take square roots we have $y = \pm 2\sqrt{px}$. For $|x| > 1$ we know that $\sqrt{|x|}$ increases more slowly than $|x|$; thus $|x| > 1 \Rightarrow |y|$ increases more slowly than does $|x|$. Even so, $|y|$ increases beyond bounds, which is to say that the curve "goes off to infinity." The sketch for $p = \frac{1}{4}$ is shown in Figure 2.

In Figure 2 the x-axis, the line with respect to which the curve is symmetric, can also be described as the line through the focus perpendicular to the directrix. It is easy to see from Definition 1 (i.e., from strictly geometric considerations) that a parabola will always have this line as an *axis of symmetry*. The point of intersection of this line with the curve (the origin in Figure 2) is called the *vertex*.

Equations [3] and [4] give the simplest representations for the parabola. Situations may occur where the coordinate system cannot be so favorably chosen as to produce these forms. For the present we restrict ourselves to the case where the axis of symmetry is parallel to one of the coordinate axes and the vertex is at the point $V(h, k)$. (See Exercise C1, however.) In this case we can easily use a translation of coordinates, making the vertex the new origin

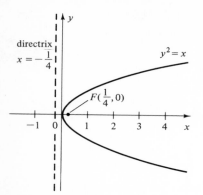

Figure 2

and the axis of symmetry one of the new coordinate axes. Suppose, to be specific, the vertex is at $V(h, k)$ and the axis of symmetry is the line $x = h$ (parallel to the y-axis). See Figure 3. The translation of coordinates is achieved by the equations

$$\begin{cases} x' = x - h \\ y' = y - k \end{cases}.$$ [5]

Clearly, in the $x'y'$ system the equation of the parabola is $x'^2 = 4py'$, which, as a result of [5], becomes

$$(x - h)^2 = 4p(y - k).$$ [6]

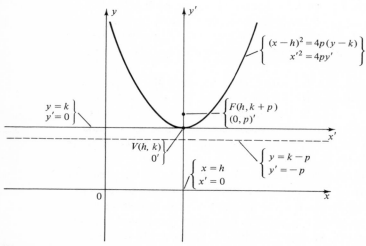

Figure 3

If the vertex is at $V(h, k)$ and the axis of symmetry is the line $y = k$, parallel to the x-axis, a similar discussion produces

$$(y - k)^2 = 4p(x - h), \qquad\qquad [7]$$

analogous to [3].

If we expand and rearrange Equation [6], we can write it as

$$x^2 - 2hx - 4py + (h^2 + 4pk) = 0. \qquad\qquad [8]$$

This is in the general form

$$Ax^2 + Dx + Ey + F = 0, \qquad AE \neq 0, \qquad\qquad [9]$$

since $p \neq 0$. Similarly, Equation [7] when rewritten takes the general form

$$Cy^2 + Dx + Ey + F = 0, \qquad CD \neq 0. \qquad\qquad [10]$$

The essential facts about [9] and [10] are these: each has exactly one second-degree term, not xy, and a nonzero first-degree term in the other variable—thus the conditions $AE \neq 0$ and $CD \neq 0$. Conversely, given an equation such as [9] or [10], it is always possible by completing the square in the second-degree variable to put it into the form of [6] or [7], respectively, thus showing that Equations [9] and [10] represent parabolas with axis of symmetry parallel to the y- and x-axis, respectively.

A final comment is in order about Equation [9]. Since $E \neq 0$, we can divide both sides by E to get

$$y = \left(-\frac{A}{E}\right)x^2 + \left(-\frac{D}{E}\right)x + \left(-\frac{F}{E}\right),$$

or

$$y = ax^2 + bx + c, \quad \text{where } a = -\frac{A}{E} \neq 0. \qquad\qquad [11]$$

The right-hand side of this equation is in the form of a polynomial of degree two in x; we thus see that its graph is a parabola with axis of symmetry parallel to the y-axis. (Cf. Exercise B2 after Section 2.5.) Analogous remarks can be made about Equation [10].

Example 1.   We consider the equation

$$x^2 - 4x - 4y + 8 = 0.$$

Completing the square in x gives

$$(x - 2)^2 = 4y - 8 + 4,$$

or

$$(x - 2)^2 = 4(y - 1),$$

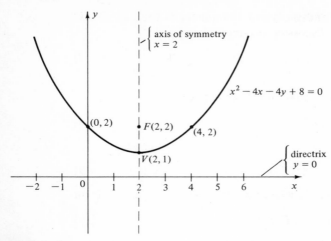

Figure 4

disclosing that the parabola has vertex at $(2, 1)$, axis of symmetry $x = 2$, and $p = 1$. Thus the focus is $F(2, 2)$ and the directrix is $y = 0$. See Figure 4.

Example 2. We graph

$$3y^2 + 2x + 6y - 3 = 0.$$

We begin by completing the square in y:

$$3(y + 1)^2 = -2x + 3 + 3,$$

or

$$(y + 1)^2 = -\frac{2}{3}(x - 3).$$

Thus the parabola has vertex $V(3, -1)$, axis of symmetry $y + 1 = 0$. The value of p is $(-1)/6$, enabling one to calculate the coordinates of F and the equation of the directrix (exercise for student). The graph is shown in Figure 5.

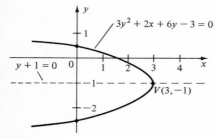

Figure 5

From the original equation we can easily find the intercepts to be $(\frac{3}{2}, 0)$ and $(0, -1 \pm \sqrt{2})$.

Example 3. Find the equation of a parabola that has vertex at $(-1, 2)$, axis of symmetry parallel to the x-axis, and goes through the point $P_1(-3, -4)$.

From the first two pieces of information we conclude that the equation of the parabola, in the form of [7], is

$$(y - 2)^2 = 4p(x + 1).$$

To find the value of p we use the last piece of information: $P_1(-3, -4)$ is on the curve. Thus

$$(-4 - 2)^2 = 4p(-3 + 1),$$

whence $4p = -18$. Thus the desired equation is

$$(y - 2)^2 = -18(x + 1).$$

Exercises

A. **1.** Sketch the parabola $y^2 = 4px$ for each of the following values of p.
    (a) $\frac{1}{4}$.
    (b) 1.
    (c) 2.
    (d) $-\frac{1}{4}$.
    (e) -1.
    (f) -2.
  2. Same as Exercise A1, except for the parabola $x^2 = 4py$.
  3. See Exercise A1. For the parabola $y^2 = 4px$:
    (a) Describe verbally the geometric effect of increasing $|p|$.
    (b) Describe the geometric significance of taking $p > 0$.
    (c) Describe the geometric significance of taking $p < 0$.
  4. Same as Exercise A3 only for the parabola $x^2 = 4py$. See Exercise A2.

In Exercises 5–14 transform the equation into the form of either [6] or [7], find the coordinates of the focus, find the equation of the directrix, and sketch.
  5. $y = x^2 + 4x$.
  6. $y^2 - 2x + 6y + 1 = 0$.
  7. $2x^2 - 4x + y + 4 = 0$.
  8. $x = (y + 1)(y - 3)$.
  9. $3y^2 + 5x - 12y - 8 = 0$.
  10. $y = (4 - x)(x + 2)$.
  11. $x^2 - 2x - y = 0$.
  12. $y^2 - x - 2y = 0$.

13. $y^2 + x - 2y + 1 = 0$.
14. $y^2 - x - 2y + 1 = 0$.

In Exercises 15–22 find the equation of the parabola described and sketch.

15. Vertex $(3, 0)$, axis of symmetry parallel to y-axis, through $(0, -3)$.
16. Vertex $(-2, -2)$, focus $(-2, 0)$.
17. Vertex $(-2, -2)$, directrix $x = 0$.
18. Vertex $(4, 5)$, axis of symmetry parallel to x-axis, through the origin.
19. Focus $(3, -1)$, directrix $y + 3 = 0$.
20. Focus $(-2, 4)$, directrix $x - 2 = 0$.
21. Directrix $x + 4 = 0$, vertex $(-2, 0)$.
22. Directrix $y = 0$, vertex $(3, -1)$.
23. (a) Find the equation of the parabola that has axis of symmetry parallel to the y-axis and that goes through $(1, 1)$, $(2, 0)$, and $(0, -2)$.
 (b) Same as (a) except axis of symmetry is parallel to the x-axis.
 (c) Sketch the parabolas of (a) and (b) on the same coordinate system.
24. (a) Find the equation of the parabola that has axis of symmetry parallel to the y-axis and that goes through $(0, 0)$, $(2, 2)$, and $(4, 0)$.
 (b) Same as (a) except axis of symmetry is parallel to the x-axis.
 (c) Can you explain what happened in (b)?

B. **1.** A *chord* of a parabola is the line segment joining two points on the parabola. The *latus rectum* of a parabola is the chord through the focus parallel to the directrix.

 (a) Prove that the length of the latus rectum of a parabola is $4|p|$.

Hints: (i) Prove first for the parabola $y^2 = 4px$. (ii) Is there any more to be done?

 (b) Find the length of the latus rectum for each of the parabolas in Exercises A5–14.

2. This refers to Equation [2]. Show that $d(P, l) = |x + p|$ in any of the different cases that may arise.

3. Derive Equation [4].

4. Consider the equation $y = ax^2 + bx + c$, where $a \neq 0$.
 (a) Show that the graph is a parabola with vertex at

$$\left(-\frac{b}{2a}, \frac{4ac - b^2}{4a}\right),$$

 axis of symmetry parallel to the y-axis, and $p = 1/(4a)$.
 (b) What is the geometric significance of the sign of a?

(c) Prove the following:

(i) $a > 0 \Rightarrow y \geqslant \dfrac{4ac - b^2}{4a}$ and $y_{min} = \dfrac{4ac - b^2}{4a}$ occurs for

$x = \dfrac{-b}{2a}.$

(ii) $a < 0 \Rightarrow y \leq \dfrac{4ac - b^2}{4a}$ and $y_{max} = \dfrac{4ac - b^2}{4a}$ occurs for

$x = \dfrac{-b}{2a}.$

C. **1.** Let the directrix of a parabola be the line $ax + by + c = 0$, where $a^2 + b^2 \neq 0$, and let the focus be the point $F(h, k)$ not on the directrix.

(a) If $P(x, y)$ is an arbitrary point on the parabola, show that x and y must satisfy

$$(bx - ay)^2 - 2(ac + h(a^2 + b^2))x - 2(bc + k(a^2 + b^2))y + (a^2 + b^2)(h^2 + k^2) - c^2 = 0.$$

(b) Thus show that the equation of a parabola has no xy term if and only if the directrix is parallel to one of the coordinate axes. (Alternatively, the equation has no xy term if and only if the axis of symmetry is parallel to one of the coordinate axes.)

2. In this exercise we intrude into the domain of calculus. We consider the parabola $y^2 = 4px$ and a point $P_1(x_1, y_1)$ on the parabola, arbitrary except that P_1 is not the vertex. We define the *tangent* to the parabola at P to be the nonhorizontal line through P_1 that has no other point in common with the parabola.

(a) Show that the slope m of the tangent line is $m = 2p/y_1$.

Hints: (i) Write the point-slope form of the equation of a line through P_1. (ii) Since $m \neq 0$ (why?), it is possible to solve this equation for x. Do this. (iii) Substitute this value of x into the equation for the parabola and write as a quadratic in y. (iv) The definition of the tangent line to the parabola requires that the two roots of this quadratic be real and equal. This is true $\Leftrightarrow$ the discriminant of the quadratic is zero. Impose this condition, remember that P_1 is on the parabola, and conclude that m must equal $2p/y_1$.

(b) Show that the equation of the tangent to the parabola at $P_1(x_1, y_1)$ is

$y_1 y = 2p(x + x_1).$ [12]

(c) Prove that the intercepts of the tangent line are $(-x_1, 0)$ and $(0, \tfrac{1}{2}y_1)$.

(d) What should be the tangent line to the parabola at the vertex?

3. The parabola has a property which is useful in applications. We describe it in simplified form. If a reflecting surface is parabolical, then a light ray parallel to the axis of symmetry hitting the surface at any point will be reflected in to the focus. (Or, to turn it around, if a light source is at the focus of a parabola, the beams bouncing off the surface will all be parallel to the axis of symmetry of the parabola.) The only physical principle needed is the following. When a light ray is reflected from a surface the angle of incidence equals the angle of reflection. The angle of incidence is the angle between the "outgoing" ray and the normal. Prove that the parabola does have the stated property.

Hints: (i) Refer to Figure 6. It must be shown that $\phi_2 = \phi_1$. Why? (ii) Observe that $\phi_2 = \phi_1 \Leftrightarrow \beta = \alpha$. Why? (iii) Note that $\beta = \gamma - \alpha$ (why?) and $\tan \gamma = m_{\overline{FP_1}}$. (iv) Your turn. Use Exercise C2.

4. Let $S = \{(x, y) \mid x^2 \leqslant 4py, p > 0\}$. Show that S is convex.

Hints.   (i) Use Equations [2.7]. (ii) Use the fact that, for all $x_1, x_2 \in$ **R**, $2x_1x_2 \leqslant x_1^2 + x_2^2$. [*Proof:* $(x_1 - x_2)^2 \geqslant 0$.]

5.2 The Ellipse

We begin by remarking that, roughly, the pattern we established in studying the parabola in Section 1 can—and will be—followed in this section.

DEFINITION 2.   *Given two fixed points F_1 and F_2, called* foci, *and a positive number a, an* ellipse *is the set of all points the sum of whose distances*

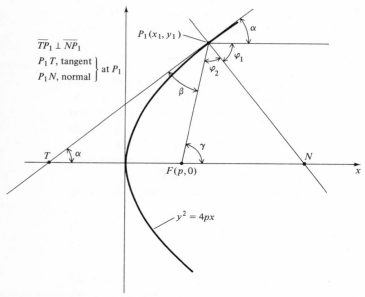

$$\overline{TP_1} \perp \overline{NP_1}$$
$$\left.\begin{array}{l} P_1T, \text{ tangent} \\ P_1N, \text{ normal} \end{array}\right\} \text{ at } P_1$$

Figure 6

from F_1 and F_2 equals 2a. In symbols, a point P is on the ellipse determined by F_1, F_2, and a $\Leftrightarrow$

$$|\overline{F_1P}| + |\overline{F_2P}| = 2a. \tag{13}$$

To obtain an analytic representation of an ellipse we set up a coordinate system as follows. The x-axis is the line determined by the foci F_1 and F_2, the origin is the midpoint of the segment $\overline{F_1F_2}$, and we label (relabel, if necessary) the foci so that F_1 is on the positive x-axis, its coordinates being $F_1(c, 0)$; then F_2 is at $(-c, 0)$, where $c > 0$. See Figure 7.

For a point $P(x, y)$ on the ellipse, the condition of Equation [13] takes the form

$$\sqrt{(x - c)^2 + y^2} + \sqrt{(x + c)^2 + y^2} = 2a. \tag{14}$$

We transfer the second radical to the right and then square:

$$\sqrt{(x - c)^2 + y^2} = 2a - \sqrt{(x + c)^2 + y^2},$$

or

$$x^2 - 2cx + c^2 + y^2 =$$
$$4a^2 - 4a\sqrt{(x + c)^2 + y^2} + x^2 + 2cx + c^2 + y^2.$$

Upon clearing away the unnecessary debris and rewriting, we have

$$a\sqrt{(x + c)^2 + y^2} = cx + a^2.$$

Squaring again gives, with some rearranging,

$$(a^2 - c^2)x^2 + a^2y^2 = a^2(a^2 - c^2). \tag{15}$$

Now it is clear from Definition 2 (see Figure 7) that a must satisfy $2a \geqslant 2c$. In fact, $2a = 2c$ would produce for us only the segment F_1F_2. Since we are aiming higher than that we assume $a > c$. It follows that $a^2 - c^2 > 0$, and we achieve some notational simplification by defining a number $b > 0$ by

$$b^2 = a^2 - c^2 \quad \text{or} \quad b^2 + c^2 = a^2. \tag{16}$$

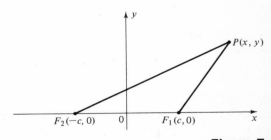

Figure 7

Equation [15] can then be written as

$$b^2x^2 + a^2y^2 = a^2b^2,$$

or, as is customarily done, dividing by a^2b^2,

$$\frac{x^2}{a^2} + \frac{y^2}{b^2} = 1. \tag{17}$$

Conversely, starting with a point $P(x, y)$ that satisfies [17], we can easily reverse the steps to obtain [14], showing that P is indeed on the ellipse determined by F_1, F_2, and a.

Clearly, choosing the y-axis as the line determined by the foci, again taking the origin as the midpoint of $\overline{F_1F_2}$, and putting F_1 at $(0, c)$ and F_2 at $(0, -c)$, where $c > 0$, would simply interchange the roles of x and y, producing instead of Equation [17]

$$\frac{y^2}{a^2} + \frac{x^2}{b^2} = 1, \tag{18}$$

where, as before, a, b, and c satisfy [16].

Equations [17] and [18] are the two standard forms for the equation of an ellipse.

We summarize the preceding discussion in a formal way.

THEOREM 2. *A point $P(x, y)$ is on the ellipse determined by the number $a > 0$ and the foci $F_1(c, 0)$, $F_2(-c, 0)$ $[F_1(0, c), F_2(0, -c)] \Leftrightarrow$*

$$\frac{x^2}{a^2} + \frac{y^2}{b^2} = 1 \tag{17}$$

$$\left[\frac{y^2}{a^2} + \frac{x^2}{b^2} = 1\right], \tag{18}$$

where a, b, and c satisfy $a^2 = b^2 + c^2$.

To carry out a geometric analysis of [17] we write it in two equivalent forms:

$$y = \pm\frac{b}{a}\sqrt{a^2 - x^2} \tag{19}$$

and

$$x = \pm\frac{a}{b}\sqrt{b^2 - y^2}. \tag{20}$$

The following facts are now readily apparent:

1. Intercepts: $(a, 0)$, $(-a, 0)$, $(0, b)$, $(0, -b)$.
2. Extent: $-a \leqslant x \leqslant a$, $-b \leqslant y \leqslant b$. (The curve lies entirely within the $2a \times 2b$ rectangle centered at the origin.)

3. Symmetry: With respect to x-axis, y-axis, origin.
4. Equation [19] shows that as x increases from 0 to a, $|y|$ decreases from b to 0. The actual behavior of the curve in the neighborhoods of the intercepts is not clear from this analysis but can be learned from calculus techniques.

The sketch is in Figure 8. Notice that the triangle OF_1W_1 gives the relation between a, b, and c.

The following terminology is standard for the ellipse. The segment $\overline{V_1V_2}$ is the *major axis* (of length $2a$; thus a is the length of the *semimajor axis $\overline{OV_1}$* or $\overline{OV_2}$). The ends V_1 and V_2 of the major axis are the *vertices*. The segment $\overline{W_1W_2}$ is the *minor axis* (of length $2b$). Either segment $\overline{OW_1}$ or $\overline{OW_2}$, of length b, is a semiminor axis. The intersection of the two axes of symmetry is the *center*. The chord through either focus perpendicular to the major axis is a *latus rectum* ($\overline{Q_1Q_2}$ in Figure 8 is one of the two *latera recta*); from [19] one can compute its length to be $(2b^2)/a$.

The *eccentricity* of an ellipse is defined to be the number

$$e = \frac{c}{a} = \frac{\sqrt{a^2 - b^2}}{a}. \qquad [21]$$

Clearly, e satisfies the inequalities $0 < e < 1$. Its geometric significance can be made evident by considering a fixed a. Then e close to zero means that c is small compared to a (or that b is close to a): the ellipse will be "close to" a circle. Near the other extreme, e close to one means that c is close to a (b is small compared to a): the ellipse will be quite flat. *At* the extremes, $e = 0 \Rightarrow b = a$ and the ellipse is a circle; $e = 1 \Rightarrow c = a$ and the "ellipse" is the line segment $\overline{V_1V_2} = \overline{F_1F_2}$, as already mentioned.

If the center of an ellipse is at the point (h, k) rather than the origin, its axes of symmetry being parallel to the coordinate axes, we could perform a translation which would put the new origin at the center and would make the

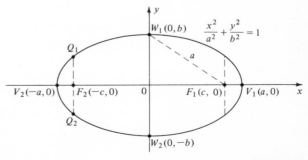

Figure 8

new coordinate axes the axes of symmetry. Then the equation of the ellipse in the new system would be either

$$\frac{x'^2}{a^2} + \frac{y'^2}{b^2} = 1$$

or

$$\frac{y'^2}{a^2} + \frac{x'^2}{b^2} = 1.$$

If we return to the original coordinate system by using $x' = x - h$ and $y' = y - k$ in the preceding two equations, we would have

$$\frac{(x - h)^2}{a^2} + \frac{(y - k)^2}{b^2} = 1 \qquad\qquad [22]$$

and

$$\frac{(y - k)^2}{a^2} + \frac{(x - h)^2}{b^2} = 1, \qquad\qquad [23]$$

respectively.

Upon simplifying [23], say, we obtain

$$a^2x^2 + b^2y^2 - 2a^2hx - 2b^2ky + a^2h^2 + b^2k^2 - a^2b^2 = 0. \qquad [24]$$

An equation of similar type would result from [22], the essentials of the form being

$$Ax^2 + Cy^2 + Dx + Ey + F = 0, \qquad AC > 0. \qquad\qquad [25]$$

Thus the coefficients of x^2 and y^2 must be of like sign and there is no xy term.

Conversely, given an equation of type [25], one can, by completing the squares in x and y, reduce it to either [22] or [23] or their equivalents in $x'\ y'$.

Example 4.   Consider the equation

$$4x^2 + 9y^2 - 16x + 18y - 11 = 0.$$

Completing the squares in x and y, we have

$$4(x^2 - 4x + 4) + 9(y^2 + 2y + 1) = 11 + 16 + 9,$$

or

$$4(x - 2)^2 + 9(y + 1)^2 = 36,$$

or

$$\frac{(x - 2)^2}{9} + \frac{(y + 1)^2}{4} = 1.$$

Thus we see that $h = 2, k = -1, a = 3, b = 2, c = \sqrt{5}, e = \sqrt{5}/3 \approx 0.745.$

The major axis is on $y + 1 = 0$ and the minor axis lies on $x - 2 = 0$. The sketch is shown in Figure 9.

Example 5. We find the equation of the ellipse which has vertices $V_1(-2, 6)$, $V_2(-2, -4)$ and foci $F_1(-2, 4)$, $F_2(-2, -2)$. See Figure 10.

Evidently the major axis is on $x = -2$, and the center is at $C(-2, 1)$, the midpoint of $\overline{V_1 V_2}$. It follows that $a = 5$, and, from the coordinates of the foci, we see that $c = 3$. This means that $b = 4$ and the ends of the minor axis, on $y = 1$, are at $W_1(2, 1)$ and $W_2(-6, 1)$. From these data we can write the equation as

$$\frac{(y - 1)^2}{25} + \frac{(x + 2)^2}{16} = 1,$$

or

$$25x^2 + 16y^2 + 100x - 32y - 284 = 0.$$

Exercises

A.   1. The equation $(x^2/25) + (y^2/b^2) = 1$ represents a family of ellipses.
     (a) Sketch on the same graph the members for $b = \frac{1}{2}, 1, 2, 3, 4, \frac{9}{2}$.
     (b) Find the value of e for each of the ellipses in (a).
     (c) What do all members of the family have in common?

   2. Consider the equation

$$\frac{y^2}{a^2} + \frac{x^2}{a^2 - 9} = 1.$$

     (a) Sketch the ellipses for $a = 4, 5, 6$.
     (b) Find the value of e for each of the ellipses in (a).
     (c) What is the family characteristic?

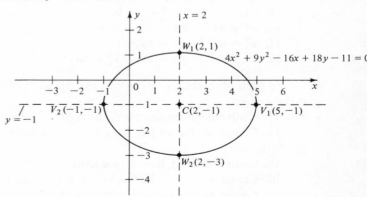

Figure 9

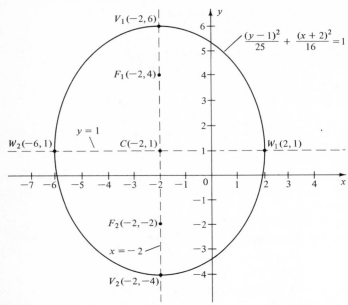

Figure 10

For each of Exercises 3–12 sketch the ellipse and find the value of e and the coordinates of the vertices and foci.

3. $3x^2 + 4y^2 = 12$.

4. $5x^2 + 3y^2 = 15$.

5. $2x^2 + y^2 = 1$.

6. $36x^2 + 64y^2 = 2{,}304$.

7. $x^2 + 9y^2 - 6x = 0$.

8. $9x^2 + 4y^2 + 18x + 8y - 23 = 0$.

9. $64x^2 + 60y^2 + 960y = 0$.

10. $x^2 + 4y^2 - 4x - 8y + 4 = 0$.

11. $x^2 + 4y^2 - 4x - 8y + 8 = 0$.

12. $x^2 + 4y^2 - 4x - 8y + 12 = 0$.

In each of Exercises 13–24 find the equation of the ellipse defined and make a sketch.

13. Center at the origin, one focus at $(0, -3)$, length of semimajor axis 4.

14. Center at the origin, length of semiminor axis 7, one vertex at $(-10, 0)$.

15. Center at $(5, 3)$, $a = 3$, one focus at $(5, 2)$.

16. Center at $(-3, -2)$, one vertex at $(0, -2)$, b $= 1$.

17. Center at $(0, 4)$, $e = \frac{1}{2}$, a focus at $(0, 2)$.

18. Vertices at $(-10, 2)$ and $(2, 2)$, $e = \frac{1}{3}$.

19. Vertices at $(1, 7)$ and $(1, -1)$, a focus at $(1, 5)$.
20. Ends of minor axis at $(4, 4)$ and $(4, 0)$, $e = \sqrt{2}/2$.
21. Center at $(-5, 0)$, $b = 3$, $e = \frac{1}{3}$.
22. Foci at $(-6, -1)$ and $(2, -1)$, $e = \frac{4}{5}$.
23. Foci at $(0, 6)$ and $(0, 0)$, $e = \frac{1}{4}$.
24. Foci at $(0, 0)$ and $(2, 0)$, one vertex at $(3, 0)$.

B.   **1.** Consider the ellipse $b^2x^2 + a^2y^2 = a^2b^2$. Let F_1 be $(c, 0)$ and let l_1 be the line $x = a/e$. Prove that a point $P(x, y)$ is on the ellipse $\Leftrightarrow |\overline{F_1P}| = e \cdot d(P, l_1)$. [The line l_1 is a *directrix* of the ellipse. Clearly, by the symmetry property of the ellipse, an analogous statement would hold for $F_2(-c, 0)$ and $l_2 : x = (-a)/e$, the other directrix. Compare this property with the defining property (Definition 1) of a parabola.]
   2. See Exercise B1. If a parabola were to have an eccentricity e, what should its value be? (The same for all parabolas?)

C.   **1.** Another tangent problem. Consider a point $P_1(x_1, y_1)$ on the ellipse $b^2x^2 + a^2y^2 = a^2b^2$. A *tangent* to the ellipse at P_1 is a line through P_1 with no other point on the ellipse. Prove that if $y_1 \neq 0$, there is a tangent at P_1, its slope is $m = (-b^2x_1)/(a^2y_1)$ and its equation can be put in the form

$$\frac{x_1x}{a^2} + \frac{y_1y}{b^2} = 1.$$

   2. See Exercise C1. The *normal* to the ellipse at P_1 is the line through P_1 perpendicular to the tangent. Prove that the normal at P_1 bisects the angle $F_1P_1F_2$. See Figure 11.
   3. See Exercise C3 after Section 5.1. Interpret the result of Exercise C2 in terms of a light ray emanating from a source at F_1 (or F_2) and being reflected at an arbitrary point P_1 on the ellipse.

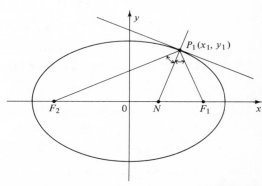

Figure 11

4. Prove that the set of points

$$S = \{(x, y) \mid \frac{x^2}{a^2} + \frac{y^2}{b^2} \leqslant 1\}$$

is convex.

Hints: (i) Use Equations [2.7]. (ii) Use the inequality

$$2uv \leqslant u^2 + v^2, \qquad\qquad [26]$$

valid for all u, $v \in \mathbf{R}$. First prove [26] by considering $(u - v)^2$ and the fact that it is always non-negative.

5.3 The Hyperbola

The structure of this section will be similar to that of Sections 5.1 and 5.2: we define a curve by a geometric property, obtain its equation in a fixed coordinate system, and study the geometric behavior of the curve from its equation.

DEFINITION 3. *The* hyperbola *determined by the two points F_1 and F_2 (the foci) and the positive number a is the set of all points P with the property that the absolute value of the difference of the distances $|\overline{PF_1}|$ and $|\overline{PF_2}|$ is equal to 2a. In symbols, P is on the hyperbola determined by F_1, F_2, and $a \Leftrightarrow*$

$$||\overline{PF_1}| - |\overline{PF_2}|| = 2a. \qquad\qquad [27]$$

To get an analytic representation for the hyperbola we choose a coordinate system in exactly the same way as for the ellipse: the x-axis is the line determined by the foci, the origin is midway between F_1 and F_2, and we denote the coordinates of the foci as $(c, 0)$ and $(-c, 0)$, respectively, where $c > 0$. See Figure 7.

In terms of this coordinate system Equation [27] becomes

$$\sqrt{(x - c)^2 + y^2} - \sqrt{(x + c)^2 + y^2} = \pm 2a.$$

If we carry out the same algebraic procedure on this equation (exercise for student) as was done for the ellipse, we obtain

$$(c^2 - a^2)x^2 - a^2y^2 = a^2(c^2 - a^2).$$

Now, in the present case the relation which must hold between a and c is $c > a$ (why?). For this reason we now define the number $b > 0$ by

$$b^2 = c^2 - a^2 \quad \text{or} \quad a^2 + b^2 = c^2. \qquad\qquad [28]$$

When this is done the equation preceding Equation [28] becomes

$$b^2x^2 - a^2y^2 = a^2b^2,$$

or, upon dividing by a^2b^2,

$$\frac{x^2}{a^2} - \frac{y^2}{b^2} = 1. \tag{29}$$

If the line determined by the foci had been chosen as the y-axis, the foci being $(0, c)$ and $(0, -c)$, the roles of x and y would have been interchanged and the resulting equation would have been

$$\frac{y^2}{a^2} - \frac{x^2}{b^2} = 1. \tag{30}$$

We summarize the foregoing discussion.

THEOREM 3.   *A point $P(x, y)$ is on the hyperbola determined by the number $a > 0$ and the foci $F_1(c, 0)$, $F_2(-c, 0)$ $[F_1(0, c), F_2(0, -c)]$* ⇔

$$\frac{x^2}{a^2} - \frac{y^2}{b^2} = 1 \tag{29}$$

$$\left[\frac{y^2}{a^2} - \frac{x^2}{b^2} = 1\right], \tag{30}$$

where a, b, and c satisfy $a^2 + b^2 = c^2$.

For a geometric analysis of Equation [29] we write it in the following three equivalent forms:

$$y = \pm\frac{b}{a}\sqrt{x^2 - a^2} \tag{31}$$

$$y = \pm\frac{b}{a}x\sqrt{1 - \frac{a^2}{x^2}} \tag{32}$$

$$x = \pm\frac{a}{b}\sqrt{y^2 + b^2}. \tag{33}$$

We can then assert that

1. The intercepts are at $(\pm a, 0)$. There are no y-intercepts.
2. From [31] we see that $x^2 \geqslant a^2$, i.e., $x \leqslant -a$ or $x \geqslant a$; similarly, [33] shows that there is no restriction on y. [The curve is of infinite extent, lying outside the vertical strip $\{(x, y) \mid -a < x < a\}$.]
3. There is symmetry with respect to x-axis, y-axis, and origin.
4. Because of the symmetry we can focus attention on the behavior of the curve in the first quadrant. From [31] we see that as x increases from a, y increases from 0. Moreover, [32] shows that the values of y on the curve will always be slightly less than those on the line $y = (b/a)x$; further, the same equation shows that the factor $\sqrt{1 - (a^2/x^2)}$ approaches 1 as x gets big beyond bounds. In other

words, the line $y = (b/a)x$ is an asymptote. So too is $y = -(b/a)x$ in quadrants II and IV. Notice that replacing the one with zero on the right-hand side of [29] gives the equation of the asymptotes, $(x^2/a^2) - (y^2/b^2) = 0$.

These observations suggest a convenient sketching device. Draw the rectangle with vertices (a, b), $(-a, b)$, $(-a, -b)$, and $(a, -b)$. The diagonals, extended, of this rectangle are the asymptotes. The curve can now be easily sketched as in Figure 12. Notice that the curve is in two pieces, or *branches*; however, the set of points described by [29] is one curve.

We give now a brief summary of the usual terminology for the hyperbola, referring to the sketch in Figure 12. The line V_1V_2 is the *transverse axis*; the points V_1 and V_2 of intersection of the curve with this axis are the *vertices*. The other axis (the y-axis) of symmetry is the *conjugate axis*. The intersection of transverse and conjugate axes (the origin in this sketch) is the *center*. The chord through either focus perpendicular to the transverse axis is the *latus rectum*; its length is easily found from [31] and [28] to be $(2b^2)/a$.

The relation [28] between a, b, and c is different for the hyperbola from the corresponding one [16] for the ellipse and care must be taken not to confuse them. Specifically, for the hyperbola $c > a$ and $c > b$ (note the position of the foci with respect to the vertices in Figure 12). Also, for the ellipse $b < a$, whereas [28] imposes no such relation on a and b for the hyperbola. Thus it is possible to have $a > b$ or $a < b$ or $a = b$. In the last case, $a = b$, the rectangle sketched in Figure 12 becomes a square, and the hyperbola is called an *equilateral* hyperbola. Example: $x^2 - y^2 = 1$.

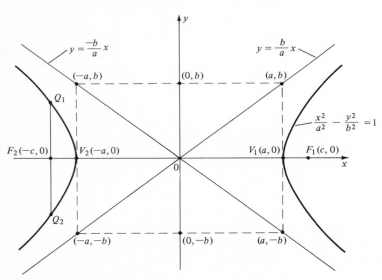

Figure 12

The *eccentricity* of a hyperbola is defined to be the number

$$e = \frac{c}{a} = \frac{\sqrt{a^2 + b^2}}{a}.$$ [34]

It is clear from [34] that $e > 1$. For further interpretation we hold a fixed. Then e close to one means b is small compared to a (the rectangle is flat), whereas large e means b is large compared to a (the rectangle is tall). What is the value of e for the equilateral hyperbola?

If the center of the hyperbola is at (h, k) and the axes of symmetry are parallel to the coordinate axes, the equation would be

$$\frac{(x - h)^2}{a^2} - \frac{(y - k)^2}{b^2} = 1,$$ [35]

or

$$\frac{(y - k)^2}{a^2} - \frac{(x - h)^2}{b^2} = 1,$$ [36]

depending on whether the transverse axis is horizontal or vertical. If [35] is expanded and rewritten it becomes

$$b^2x^2 - a^2y^2 - 2b^2hx + 2a^2ky + b^2h^2 - a^2k^2 - a^2b^2 = 0,$$ [37]

and similarly for [36]. The essential type of either of these equations is

$$Ax^2 + Cy^2 + Dx + Ey + F = 0, \qquad AC < 0.$$ [38]

Thus the coefficients of x^2 and y^2 must have opposite signs and there is no xy term.

Conversely, by completing the squares one can convert an equation of type [38] into either [35] or [36].

Example 6.   Consider the equation

$$x^2 - 4y^2 + 4x + 8y + 4 = 0.$$

Completing the squares, we have

$$(x^2 + 4x + 4) - 4(y^2 - 2y + 1) = -4 + 4 - 4,$$

or

$$\frac{(y - 1)^2}{1} - \frac{(x + 2)^2}{4} = 1.$$

We see that the center is at $C(-2, 1)$, that $a = 1$, and that $b = 2$. Thus we can compute that $c = \sqrt{5}$ and $e = \sqrt{5}$. The transverse axis is $x + 2 = 0$ and the conjugate axis is $y - 1 = 0$. The vertices are at $(-2, 1 \pm 1)$, i.e., $(-2, 2)$ and $(-2, 0)$; the foci are $(-2, 1 \pm \sqrt{5})$. The coordinates of the vertices of the fundamental rectangle are $(0, 2)$, $(-4, 2)$, $(-4, 0)$, and $(0, 0)$.

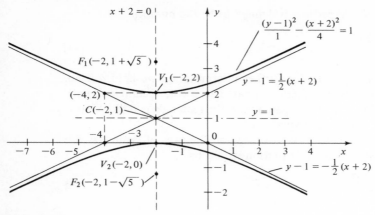

Figure 13

The equation of the asymptotes is $4(y - 1)^2 - (x + 2)^2 = 0$, or $y - 1 = \pm\frac{1}{2}(x + 2)$, The sketch is shown in Figure 13.

Example 7. We find the equation of the hyperbola with vertices $V_1(8, 0)$, $V_2(2, 0)$ and eccentricity $e = 2$.

The information about the vertices tells us that $2a = 6$, or $a = 3$, that the center is at $C(5, 0)$, that the transverse axis is the x-axis, and that the conjugate axis is $x = 5$. Also, since $e = c/a$, we have $c = ea = 2 \times 3 = 6$, and therefore $b = \sqrt{c^2 - a^2} = \sqrt{36 - 9} = \sqrt{27} \approx 5.2$. The equation is

$$\frac{(x - 5)^2}{9} - \frac{y^2}{27} = 1,$$

or

$$3x^2 - y^2 - 30x + 48 = 0.$$

The sketch is shown in Figure 14.

Exercises

A. **1.** Consider the family of hyperbolas

$$\frac{x^2}{25} - \frac{y^2}{b^2} = 1.$$

    (a) Sketch, on the same graph, the members of the family for $b = 1, 4, 5, 12$.

    (b) Find the value of e for each of the hyperbolas in (a).

    (c) What is the family characteristic?

2. Consider the equation

$$\frac{y^2}{a^2} - \frac{x^2}{25 - a^2} = 1.$$

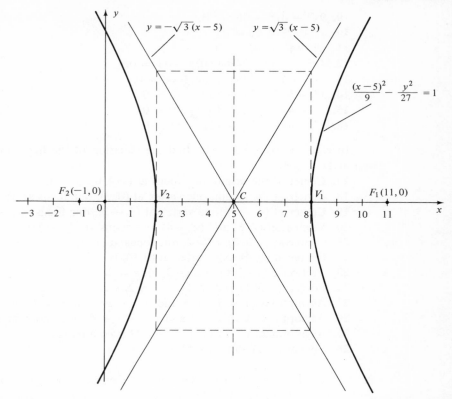

$y = -\sqrt{3}\,(x-5)$ $y = \sqrt{3}\,(x-5)$

$$\frac{(x-5)^2}{9} - \frac{y^2}{27} = 1$$

$F_2(-1,0)$ V_2 C V_1 $F_1(11,0)$

Figure 14

   (a) Sketch the hyperbolas for $a = 1, 3, 4$.
   (b) Find the value of e for each hyperbola in (a).
   (c) What do all members of the family have in common?
  3. Sketch on the same axes:
   (a) $x^2 - y^2 = 1$.
   (b) $x^2 - y^2 = -1$.
  4. Sketch on the same axes:
   (a) $4x^2 - y^2 = 4$.
   (b) $4x^2 - y^2 = -4$.

    In each of Exercises 5–16 find the coordinates of the center, the vertices, and the foci; find the value of e; and sketch the hyperbola.
  5. $4x^2 - 3y^2 = 12$.
  6. $4y^2 - 3x^2 = 12$.
  7. $7y^2 - 12x^2 = 84$.
  8. $4x^2 - 9y^2 = 36$.

9. $9x^2 - 4y^2 - 36x = 0.$
10. $x^2 - y^2 + 6y = 0.$
11. $x^2 - y^2 - 10x = 0.$
12. $4x^2 - 5y^2 - 24x - 10y + 11 = 0.$
13. $9x^2 - 4y^2 + 36x + 8y + 68 = 0.$
14. $x^2 - 4y^2 - 2x - 16y - 15 = 0.$
15. $x^2 - 4y^2 - 2x - 16y - 19 = 0.$
16. $x^2 - 4y^2 - 2x - 16y - 11 = 0.$

In each of Exercises 17–28 find the equation of the hyperbola defined and make a sketch.

17. Center at the origin, one focus at $(-4, 0)$, $a = 3$.
18. Center at the origin, one vertex at $(0, 3)$, one focus at $(0, -5)$.
19. Center at $(4, -2)$, one vertex at $(0, -2)$, one focus at $(-1, -2)$.
20. Vertices at $(2, 6)$ and $(2, -4)$, one focus at $(2, -6)$.
21. Center at $(-3, 2)$, $b = 2$, one focus at $(1, 2)$.
22. Center at $(0, 4)$, one vertex at $(0, 0)$, b $= 4$.
23. Vertices at $(-2, 6)$ and $(-2, 0)$, $e = 2$.
24. Foci at $(-2, 1)$ and $(4, 1)$, $e = \sqrt{2}$.
25. Asymptotes: $y = 2x + 5$ and $y = -2x - 3$, $a = 1$ (two answers).
26. Asymptotes: $y = x - 4$ and $y = -x + 4$, one vertex at the origin.
27. Asymptotes: $y = \pm(x + 2)$, $b = 3$ (two answers).
28. Foci at $(1, 5)$ and $(1, -5)$, $e = 3$.

B.   **1.** See Exercise B1 after Section 5.2. Consider the hyperbola $b^2x^2 - a^2y^2 = 1$. Let F_1 be $(c, 0)$ and let l_1 be the line $x = a/e$. Prove that a point $P(x, y)$ is on the hyperbola $\Leftrightarrow |\overline{F_1P}| = e \cdot d(P, l_1)$. [The line l_1 is a *directrix* of the hyperbola. By symmetry, the line $l_2: x = (-a)/e$ is the directrix associated with the focus $F_2(-c, 0)$ and P is on the hyperbola $\Leftrightarrow |\overline{F_2P}| = e \cdot d(P, l_2)$.]

 2. See Exercises A3 and 4. The hyperbolas $b^2x^2 - a^2y^2 = a^2b^2$ and $b^2x^2 - a^2y^2 = -a^2b^2$ are called *conjugate hyperbolas*.

 (a) Prove that conjugate hyperbolas share the same asymptotes.
 (b) What is the hyperbola conjugate to $4x^2 - 9y^2 = 36$? Sketch both curves.

Note that the traditional use of a as distance from center to a vertex is lost when we write the equation for the hyperbola conjugate to $b^2x^2 - a^2y^2 = a^2 b^2$, but we shall not worry about that.)

C.   **1.** Time for the tangent problem. Consider the point $P_1(x_1, y_1)$ on the hyperbola $b^2x^2 - a^2y^2 = a^2b^2$.

 (a) Look at the equation of the tangent to the ellipse $b^2x^2 + a^2y^2 = a^2b^2$ as given in Exercise C1 after Section 5.2. Make an intelligent guess about the equation of the tangent to the hyperbola at P_1. [*Hint:* The slope is $m = (b^2x_1)/(a^2y_1)$.]

    (b) Prove that the tangent line in (a) has no point other than P_1 in common with the hyperbola.

    2. See Exercise C2 after Section 5.2. Prove that the *tangent* (not the normal) of Exercise C1 bisects the angle $F_1P_1F_2$. Make a sketch.

5.4 Rotation of Axes

We begin this section with a brief remark about the name *conic section curves*. As the geometers of classical Greece well knew (Apollonius wrote an eight-volume treatise on the subject in the third century B.C.), the curves we have just been considering can all be obtained as intersections of planes with a circular cone, the particular curve depending on the relation of the plane to the cone. In Figure 15 we show how different curves occur.

    Exhaustive study of the properties of these curves had been made by synthetic (i.e., noncoordinate) methods. With the introduction of coordinates it was found that this same family of curves was described by the equations of second degree in x and y, i.e., by equations of the type

$$Ax^2 + Bxy + Cy^2 + Dx + Ey + F = 0, \qquad\qquad [39]$$

where at least one of A, B, C is not zero. The fact is that all of the equations of this type encountered in this chapter have had $B = 0$. We can assert, on the basis of what has already been said, that if an axis of symmetry of a conic section curve is parallel to one of the coordinate axes, then $B = 0$. Conversely,

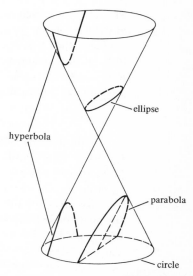

ellipse

hyperbola

parabola

circle

Figure 15

as we shall see, if $B \neq 0$ in [39] then the curve (if it is not "degenerate" —see the following paragraph) is a conic section with axis of symmetry not parallel to either coordinate axis. Example: $xy = 1$.

Equation [39] includes all the conic section curves in the plane; it also includes degenerate cases thereof: (1) pairs of intersecting lines, (2) pairs of coincident lines, (3) pairs of parallel lines, (4) points, and (5) the empty set. As examples of these respective cases we cite

1. $x^2 - y^2 = 0$ $(A = 1, C = -1, B = D = E = F = 0)$.
2. $x^2 = 0$ $(A = 1, B = C = D = E = F = 0)$.
3. $y^2 - 3y + 2 = 0$ $(A = B = D = 0, C = 1, E = -3, F = 2)$.
4. $x^2 + y^2 = 0$ $(A = C = 1, B = D = E = F = 0)$.
5. $x^2 + y^2 + 1 = 0$ $(A = C = F = 1, B = D = E = 0)$.

We now consider the presence of an xy term in [39].

As an indication of what is involved, we recall that the equations of the central conics (those with a center: circle, ellipse, hyperbola), in their simplest form, do not have terms of the first degree. The form of these equations is

$$Ax^2 + Cy^2 + F = 0, \qquad AC \neq 0. \qquad [40]$$

We recall further that if first-degree terms do occur they can be eliminated by a transformation of coordinates, namely, a translation of axes of the sort

$$\begin{Bmatrix} x' = x - h \\ y' = y - k \end{Bmatrix} \quad \text{or} \quad \begin{Bmatrix} x = x' + h \\ y = y' + k \end{Bmatrix}. \qquad [41]$$

The effect of such a transformation is to introduce new axes which are parallel to the original axes. Then if h and k are chosen so that (h, k) is the center of the conic the new equation in x' and y' will be of the same type as [40]. [If the conic is a parabola, its equation will in any case have first-degree terms; a translation of coordinates chosen so that (h, k) is the vertex of the parabola will reduce it to one of the following types, but in x' and y':

$$Ax^2 + Ey = 0 \quad \text{or} \quad Cy^2 + Dx = 0.]$$

Now it turns out that an xy term can also be eliminated by a transformation of coordinates—but of a different sort. The effective transformation in this case is a *rotation* of the axes (keeping the origin fixed) through a suitably chosen angle γ.

We first obtain relations between the old (unprimed) and the new (primed) coordinates for such a transformation. Thus suppose a new set of (x', y') axes has been superimposed on the original set, the origins being the same, the angle between the x- and x'-axes being γ, where $0 < \gamma < \pi/2$. See Figure 16. Each point P will now have two sets of coordinates (x, y) and (x', y'). To obtain relations between these coordinates, we let θ and θ' be,

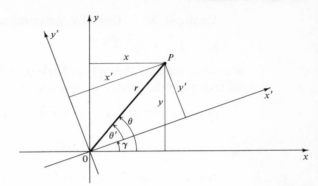

Figure 16

respectively, the angles between the x- and x'-axes and the segment $\overline{OP}$. Also, let $|\overline{OP}| = r$. We then have

$$\left.\begin{cases} x = r \cos \theta \\ y = r \sin \theta \end{cases}\right\},$$ [42a]

$$\left.\begin{cases} x' = r \cos \theta' \\ y' = r \sin \theta' \end{cases}\right\},$$ [42b]

$$\left.\begin{cases} \theta = \theta' + \gamma \\ \quad \text{or} \\ \theta' = \theta - \gamma \end{cases}\right\}.$$ [42c]

Using these relations and two familiar trigonometric identities, we have

$$x = r \cos \theta = r \cos(\theta' + \gamma) = r \cos \theta' \cos \gamma - r \sin \theta' \sin \gamma$$
$$y = r \sin \theta = r \sin(\theta' + \gamma) = r \sin \theta' \cos \gamma + r \cos \theta' \sin \gamma,$$

or, because of [42b],

$$\left.\begin{cases} x = x' \cos \gamma - y' \sin \gamma \\ y = x' \sin \gamma + y' \cos \gamma \end{cases}\right\}.$$ [43]

These are the relations we mainly need, but for the sake of completeness we remark that a similar technique [or, alternatively, solving [43] for x' and y'] will lead to

$$\left.\begin{cases} x' = x \cos \gamma + y \sin \gamma \\ y' = -x \sin \gamma + y \cos \gamma \end{cases}\right\}.$$ [44]

Before turning to the general theory we shall illustrate the use of a rotation of coordinates to eliminate the xy term from a second-degree equation.

Example 8.   Consider the equation

$$x^2 - 3xy + 2y^2 = 1.$$

We rotate the axes through an angle γ, to be determined shortly. Using [43] we transform the preceding equation to

$$(x' \cos \gamma - y' \sin \gamma)^2 - 3(x' \cos \gamma - y' \sin \gamma)(x' \sin \gamma + y' \cos \gamma) + 2(x' \sin \gamma + y' \cos \gamma)^2 = 1,$$

or

$$\cos^2 \gamma x'^2 - \sin 2\gamma x'y' + \sin^2 \gamma y'^2 - 3 \sin \gamma \cos \gamma x'^2$$
$$- 3 \cos 2\gamma x'y' + 3 \sin \gamma \cos \gamma y'^2 + 2 \sin^2 \gamma x'^2$$
$$+ 2 \sin 2\gamma x'y' + 2 \cos^2 \gamma y'^2 = 1.$$

Collecting terms, we have

$$(\cos^2 \gamma - \tfrac{3}{2} \sin 2\gamma + 2 \sin^2 \gamma)x'^2 + (\sin 2\gamma - 3 \cos 2\gamma)x'y' +$$
$$(\sin^2 \gamma + \tfrac{3}{2} \sin 2\gamma + 2 \cos^2 \gamma)y'^2 = 1.$$

Now the identities $\cos 2\gamma = 1 - 2 \sin^2 \gamma = 2 \cos^2 \gamma - 1$ can be solved to give

$$\sin^2 \gamma = \tfrac{1}{2}(1 - \cos 2\gamma) \quad \text{and} \quad \cos^2 \gamma = \tfrac{1}{2}(1 + \cos 2\gamma). \tag{45}$$

Thus we can further modify the above equation to

$$\tfrac{1}{2}(3 - 3 \sin 2\gamma - \cos 2\gamma)x'^2 + (\sin 2\gamma - 3 \cos 2\gamma)x'y' +$$
$$\tfrac{1}{2}(3 + 3 \sin 2\gamma + \cos 2\gamma) = 1.$$

Now, we choose γ so that the coefficient of $x'y'$ is zero; i.e., we choose γ so that $\tan 2\gamma = 3$. Then $\sin 2\gamma = 3/\sqrt{10}$ and $\cos 2\gamma = 1/\sqrt{10}$. With this choice the equation becomes

$$\tfrac{1}{2}\left(3 - \frac{9}{\sqrt{10}} - \frac{1}{\sqrt{10}}\right)x'^2 + \tfrac{1}{2}\left(3 + \frac{9}{\sqrt{10}} + \frac{1}{\sqrt{10}}\right)y'^2 = 1,$$

or

$$\tfrac{1}{2}(\sqrt{10} + 3)y'^2 - \tfrac{1}{2}(\sqrt{10} - 3)x'^2 = 1.$$

By rationalizing the coefficients of y'^2 and x'^2 this can be written as

$$\frac{y'^2}{2(\sqrt{10} - 3)} - \frac{x'^2}{2(\sqrt{10} + 3)} = 1,$$

the equation of a hyperbola with the y'-axis as transverse axis, $a^2 = 2(\sqrt{10} - 3)$, $b^2 = 2(\sqrt{10} + 3)$.

We now apply this technique to the general equation [39]. However, since we want to focus attention on the second-degree terms, we consider only the expression

$$Q(x, y) = Ax^2 + Bxy + Cy^2, \qquad B > 0. \tag{46}$$

(Adjusting the coefficients so that $B > 0$ makes the subsequent calculations easier.)

We can make—and prove—the following assertion.

THEOREM 4.   *Let $Q(x, y)$ be defined as in [46]. Then*

1. *If $C = A$, a rotation of the axes through an angle $\gamma = \pi/4$ will transform $Q(x, y)$ into*

$$(A + \tfrac{1}{2}B)x'^2 + (A - \tfrac{1}{2}B)y'^2. \tag{47}$$

2. *If $A - C \neq 0$, a rotation of the axes through an angle γ, $0 < \gamma < \pi/2$, determined by*

$$\tan 2\gamma = \frac{B}{A - C}, \tag{48}$$

will transform $Q(x, y)$ into

$$A'x'^2 + C'y'^2, \tag{49}$$

where

$$\begin{cases} A' = \tfrac{1}{2}(A + C + \sqrt{B^2 + (A - C)^2}) \\ C' = \tfrac{1}{2}(A + C - \sqrt{B^2 + (A - C)^2}) \end{cases}. \tag{50}$$

PROOF.   Using [43], we have

$$\begin{aligned}
Q(x, y) &= A(x' \cos \gamma - y' \sin \gamma)^2 + B(x' \cos \gamma - y' \sin \gamma) \\
&\quad (x' \sin \gamma + y' \cos \gamma) + C(x' \sin \gamma + y' \cos \gamma)^2 \\
&= A \cos^2 \gamma x'^2 - 2A \sin \gamma \cos \gamma x'y' + A \sin^2 \gamma y'^2 \\
&\quad + B \sin \gamma \cos \gamma x'^2 + B(\cos^2 \gamma - \sin^2 \gamma)x'y' - B \sin \gamma \cos \gamma y'^2 \\
&\quad + C \sin^2 \gamma x'^2 + 2C \sin \gamma \cos \gamma x'y' + C \cos^2 \gamma y'^2 \\
&= A'x'^2 + B'x'y' + C'y'^2,
\end{aligned}$$

where

$$\begin{cases} A' = A \cos^2 \gamma + B \sin \gamma \cos \gamma + C \sin^2 \gamma \\ B' = B(\cos^2 \gamma - \sin^2 \gamma) - (A - C)(2 \sin \gamma \cos y) \\ C' = A \sin^2 \gamma - B \sin \gamma \cos \gamma + C \cos^2 \gamma \end{cases}.$$

Using [45] we can write the expressions for A' and C' as

$$A' = \tfrac{1}{2}A(1 + \cos 2\gamma) + \tfrac{1}{2}B \sin 2\gamma + \tfrac{1}{2}C(1 - \cos 2\gamma)$$
$$C' = \tfrac{1}{2}A(1 - \cos 2\gamma) - \tfrac{1}{2}B \sin 2\gamma + \tfrac{1}{2}C(1 + \cos 2\gamma).$$

Then a slight rearrangement of these expressions and use of standard identities for sin 2γ and cos 2γ in the expression for B' gives

$$\begin{cases} A' = \frac{1}{2}[(A + C) + B\sin 2\gamma + (A - C)\cos 2\gamma] \\ B' = B\cos 2\gamma - (A - C)\sin 2\gamma \\ C' = \frac{1}{2}[(A + C) - (B\sin 2\gamma + (A - C)\cos 2\gamma)] \end{cases}. \qquad [51]$$

If we let

$$H = B\sin 2\gamma + (A - C)\cos 2y, \qquad [52]$$

the equations for A' and C' become

$$\begin{cases} A' = \frac{1}{2}[A + C + H] \\ C' = \frac{1}{2}[A + C - H] \end{cases}. \qquad [53]$$

To eliminate the crossproduct term $x'y'$ we want to choose γ so that $B' = 0$, i.e., we want to select γ so that

$$B\cos 2\gamma - (A - C)\sin 2\gamma = 0. \qquad [54]$$

We first note that if $A = C$ this equation reduces to $B\cos 2\gamma = 0$, or cos $2\gamma = 0$, or $\gamma = \pi/4$. Then, from [52] we have $H = B$, and, since $A = C$, the expressions for A' and C' in [53] become

$$\begin{cases} A' = A + \frac{1}{2}B \\ C' = A - \frac{1}{2}B \end{cases}. \qquad [55]$$

This proves assertion 1.

If $A - C \neq 0$, Equation [54] can be written as

$$\tan 2\gamma = \frac{B}{A - C}. \qquad [56]$$

We can always choose 2γ to lie between 0 and π, which means we can choose γ to satisfy [56] and $0 < \gamma < \pi/2$.

We easily find from [56] that

$$\sin 2\gamma = \frac{B}{\sqrt{B^2 + (A - C)^2}}, \quad \cos 2\gamma = \frac{A - C}{\sqrt{B^2 + (A - C)^2}}, \qquad [57]$$

(Recall that $B > 0$; thus the sign of tan 2γ and of cos 2γ depends on that of $A - C$.)

It follows from [57] and [52] that when γ is chosen so as to satisfy [56]

$$H = \frac{B^2 + (A - C)^2}{\sqrt{B^2 + (A - C)^2}} = \sqrt{B^2 + (A - C)^2}.$$

Using this value of H in [53] gives the values of A' and C' of [50] in the statement of the theorem. ∎

Example 9. Consider the equation

$$2x^2 - 5xy - y^2 = 3.$$

As we have agreed that $B > 0$, we multiply by -1 and work with

$$-2x^2 + 5xy + y^2 = -3, \qquad [58]$$

where

$$A = -2, \quad B = 5, \quad C = 1, \quad A - C = -3, \quad A + C = -1.$$

Thus,

$$H = \sqrt{25 + 9} = \sqrt{34}, \quad A' = \tfrac{1}{2}(-1 + \sqrt{34}), \quad C' = \tfrac{1}{2}(-1 - \sqrt{34}).$$

Accordingly, we know by Theorem 4 that if the axes are rotated through an angle γ such that $\tan 2\gamma = 5/(-3)$, the equation in [58] will be transformed into

$$\tfrac{1}{2}(\sqrt{34} - 1)x'^2 - \tfrac{1}{2}(\sqrt{34} + 1)y'^2 = -3,$$

or

$$\tfrac{1}{6}(\sqrt{34} + 1)y'^2 - \tfrac{1}{6}(\sqrt{34} - 1)x'^2 = 1,$$

a hyperbola.

To obtain the equations of transformation [43], we note that if $A = C$, $\gamma = \pi/4$. Since $\sin(\pi/4) = \cos(\pi/4) = 1/\sqrt{2}$, equations [43] become

$$\begin{cases} x = \dfrac{1}{\sqrt{2}}(x' - y') \\[2mm] y = \dfrac{1}{\sqrt{2}}(x' + y') \end{cases}. \qquad [59]$$

If $A - C \neq 0$ we can use (see [45])

$$\sin \gamma = \sqrt{\frac{1 - \cos 2\gamma}{2}}, \quad \cos \gamma = \sqrt{\frac{1 + \cos 2\gamma}{2}} \qquad [60]$$

and the second equation in [57] to write the desired transformation equations.

Example 10. We consider the equation

$$10x^2 + 24xy + 3y^2 = 19, \qquad [61]$$

where

$$A = 10, \quad B = 24, \quad C = 3, \quad A - C = 7.$$

Thus,

$$\tan 2\gamma = \tfrac{24}{7}, \quad \cos 2\gamma = \tfrac{7}{25},$$

and

$$\sin \gamma = \sqrt{\frac{1 - \tfrac{7}{25}}{2}} = \sqrt{\frac{9}{25}} = \frac{3}{5}, \quad \cos \gamma = \frac{4}{5}.$$

Equations [43] become

$$\begin{cases} x = \tfrac{1}{5}(4x' - 3y') \\ y = \tfrac{1}{5}(3x' + 4y') \end{cases}.$$

Substituting these into [61] produces, after a few calculations,

$$19x'^2 - 6y'^2 = 19.$$

The technique of Example 10, utilizing the transformation equations [43], enables one to avoid the cumbersome formulas of Theorem 4. However, the expressions for $\sin \gamma$ and $\cos \gamma$ will usually *not* be rational and the calculations become very messy. Consequently it is generally simpler to use the formulas of Theorem 4, as was done in Example 9.

If first-degree terms are present in an equation such as [39], they can be removed first by a translation of axes, as we now illustrate.

Example 11.   Consider the equation

$$x^2 + 2xy + 3y^2 - 2x + 4y + 5 = 0.$$

We first eliminate the first-degree terms by a translation of axes. To this end, let $x = x' + h$, $y = y' + k$, where the values of h and k will be chosen later. The equation then becomes

$$(x' + h)^2 + 2(x' + h)(y' + k) + 3(y' + k)^2 - 2(x' + h) + \\ 4(y' + k) + 5 = 0,$$

or

$$x'^2 + 2x'y' + 3y'^2 + (2h + 2k - 2)x' + (2h + 6k + 4)y' + h^2 \\ 2hk + 3k^2 - 2h + 4k + 5 = 0.$$

To eliminate the x' and y' terms we want to make their coefficients zero, i.e., we choose h and k to satisfy

$$\begin{cases} 2h + 2k - 2 = 0 \\ 2h + 6k + 4 = 0 \end{cases}.$$

The solution of this system is $h = 5/2$, $k = (-3)/2$, i.e., the $x'y'$-origin is at $(5/2, (-3)/2)$. The transformed equation then becomes

$$x'^2 + 2x'y' + 3y'^2 = \tfrac{1}{2},$$

the left-hand side of which is (in x', y') like [46] with

$$A = 1, \quad B = 2, \quad C = 3, \quad A - C = -2, \quad A + C = 4.$$

Thus, to remove the $x'y'$ term by a rotation, the angle γ must satisfy

$$\tan 2\gamma = \frac{2}{-2} = -1, \quad \cos 2\gamma = \frac{-1}{\sqrt{2}},$$

$$\sin \gamma = \sqrt{\frac{1 - (-1/\sqrt{2})}{2}} = \sqrt{\frac{\sqrt{2} + 1}{2\sqrt{2}}}$$

$$= \frac{1}{2}\sqrt{2 + \sqrt{2}}, \quad \cos \gamma = \frac{1}{2}\sqrt{2 - \sqrt{2}}.$$

We obtain the transformed equation by calculating H and (using [50]) A' and C':

$$H = \sqrt{B^2 + (A - C)^2} = \sqrt{4 + 4} = 2\sqrt{2}$$
$$A' = \tfrac{1}{2}(A + C + H) = \tfrac{1}{2}(4 + 2\sqrt{2}) = 2 + \sqrt{2}$$
$$C' = \tfrac{1}{2}(A + C - H) = \tfrac{1}{2}(4 - 2\sqrt{2}) = 2 - \sqrt{2}.$$

Consequently, by first translating and then rotating the axes, we have transformed the original equation to

$$(2 + \sqrt{2})x''^2 + (2 - \sqrt{2})y''^2 = \tfrac{1}{2},$$

which can be rewritten as

$$\frac{y''^2}{\tfrac{1}{4}(2 + \sqrt{2})} + \frac{x''^2}{\tfrac{1}{4}(2 - \sqrt{2})} = 1,$$

an ellipse. Figure 17 shows the three sets of axes and the graph.

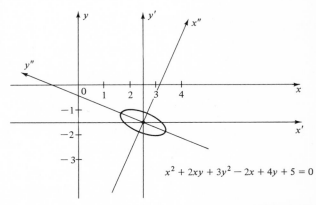

$$x^2 + 2xy + 3y^2 - 2x + 4y + 5 = 0$$

Figure 17

We return to Equations [53] and remark that it is evident that

$$A' + C' = A + C,$$

this result being independent of γ. Thus the sum $A + C$ is *invariant* under a rotation of axes. This is interesting, but more essential to our immediate purposes is the existence of another, but less obvious invariant. We refer to the discriminant $\Delta = B^2 - 4AC$: as we shall ask you to show in Exercise B1, if the axes are rotated through an angle γ, then

$$B'^2 - 4A'C' = B^2 - 4AC. \tag{62}$$

We state this formally.

THEOREM 5.   *If the axes are rotated through an angle γ (Equations [43]), transforming*

$$Ax^2 + Bxy + Cy^2 \quad into \quad A'x'^2 + B'x'y' + C'y'^2,$$

then

1. $A' + C' = A + C$.
2. $B'^2 - 4A'C' = B^2 - 4AC$.

PROOF.   As already remarked, assertion 1 follows from Equations [53]. For assertion 2, see Exercise B1.   ∎

An immediate advantage of Theorem 5 is that by means of the invariance of the discriminant $\Delta = B^2 - 4AC$ we can identify the type of conic section curve without removing the xy term. Specifically, the criteria are described in the following assertion.

THEOREM 6.   *Consider the equation*

$$Ax^2 + Bxy + Cy^2 + Dx + Ey + F = 0, \tag{63}$$

where $B \neq 0$. Then

1. $B^2 - 4AC = 0 \Rightarrow$ *the curve is a parabola.*
2. $B^2 - 4AC < 0 \Rightarrow$ *the curve is an ellipse.*
3. $B^2 - 4AC > 0 \Rightarrow$ *the curve is a hyperbola.*

Degenerate cases may occur in any of the three possibilities.

PROOF.   We apply Theorem 4 to the equation, rotating the axes through the appropriate angle γ so that $B' = 0$, giving

$$A'x'^2 + C'y'^2 + D'x' + E'y' + F' = 0. \tag{64}$$

Now we can easily relate the discriminant and the type of curve. Recall that, since $B' = 0$, $\Delta = -A'C'$.

1. $\Delta = 0 \Rightarrow A'C' = 0$. There are three possibilities:

(a) $\begin{cases} A' \neq 0 \\ C' = 0 \end{cases}$.

(b) $\begin{cases} A' = 0 \\ C' \neq 0 \end{cases}$.

(c) $\begin{cases} A' = 0 \\ C' = 0 \end{cases}$.

We assert that the curve in [64] is a parabola for both (a) and (b). We further assert (see Exercise B2) that (c) cannot occur.

2. $\Delta < 0 \Rightarrow -A'C' < 0 \Rightarrow A'C' > 0$. This means that A' and C' agree in sign, and that the curve in [64] is an ellipse.

3. $\Delta > 0 \Rightarrow -A'C' > 0 \Rightarrow A'C' < 0$. This means that A' and C' have opposite signs, and that the curve in [64] is a hyperbola.

But, by Theorem 5, Δ is invariant under a rotation, i.e., $B^2 - 4AC = B'^2 - 4A'C'$, and the assertion of the theorem follows. ∎

As illustrations of Theorem 6, we note that for the equation in Example 9, $\Delta = 33 > 0$, indicating that the curve is a hyperbola; in Example 10, $\Delta = 456 > 0$, again a hyperbola; whereas for Example 11, $\Delta = -8 < 0$, showing that the curve there is an ellipse.

Exercises

A. In Exercises 1–8 assume the conic section curve is nondegenerate and identify *without* a transformation of coordinates.

1. $3x^2 + 5xy + 2y^2 = 1$.
2. $2x^2 + 3xy + 4y^2 = 5$.
3. $x^2 + 4xy + 5y^2 = 2$.
4. $x^2 + 6xy + 9y^2 = 1$.
5. $2x^2 - 4xy - 3y^2 = 3$.
6. $16x^2 + 8xy + y^2 = 4$.
7. $x^2 + 2xy + y^2 = 0$.
8. $x^2 + 3xy - 10y^2 = 0$.
9. Is the assumption about nondegeneracy valid for Exercise A7? What *is* the graph?
10. Same as Exercise A9, only for the graph of Exercise A8.

In Exercises 11–16 use a rotation of coordinates to remove the xy term.

11. $x^2 + 4xy + y^2 = 1$.
12. $x^2 + 4xy - y^2 = 1$.
13. $7x^2 + 12xy + 2y^2 = 4$.
14. $2x^2 + 3xy + 2y^2 = 3$.
15. $3x^2 + 4xy = 8$.
16. $6x^2 + 4xy + 3y^2 = 14$.

17. Give an example of an equation of type [39] which is a degenerate parabola ($\Delta = 0$) and which is the null set.

18. Same as Exercise A17, only for a degenerate ellipse ($\Delta < 0$).

19. Can Equation [39] represent the null set and be a degenerate hyperbola ($\Delta > 0$)? Why?

20. If Equation [39] is a degenerate ellipse, what must it be?

21. Same as Exercise A20, only for a degenerate hyperbola.

22. Same as Exercise A20, only for a degenerate parabola.

B. **1.** Prove the invariance of the discriminant under a rotation, i.e., show that

$$B'^2 - 4A'C' = B^2 - 4AC,$$

the letters referring to the coefficients of a general second-degree equation.

Hints: (i) Use Equations [51], [52], and [53].

(ii) Show that

$$-4A'C' = H^2 - (A + C)^2;$$

hence

$$B'^2 - 4A'C' = B'^2 + H^2 - (A + C)^2.$$

(iii) Next show that

$$B'^2 + H^2 = B^2 + (A - C)^2.$$

(iv) Now use the results of (ii) and (iii) to show that

$$B'^2 - 4A'C' = B^2 - 4AC.$$

2. This exercise refers to the case $\Delta = 0$ in the proof of Theorem 6. We ask you to show that $A' = C' = 0$ is inconsistent with $\Delta = 0$ and with the hypothesis that $B \neq 0$.

Hints:

(i) $\Delta = B'^2 - 4A'C' = 0 \xrightarrow{\text{why?}} B^2 - 4AC = 0 \xrightarrow{\text{why?}}$
$$B^2 = 4AC \xrightarrow{\text{why?}} AC > 0.$$

(ii) $A' = C' = 0 \xrightarrow{\text{why?}} A' + C' = 0 \xrightarrow{\text{why?}} A + C = 0$
$$\xrightarrow{\text{why?}} AC \leqslant 0.$$

3. The two invariants under a rotation are $\Delta = B^2 - 4AC$ and $S = A + C$. Show that the value of $H = \sqrt{B^2 + (A - C)^2}$ can be written in terms of Δ and S as $H = \sqrt{\Delta + S^2}$.

6

Polar Coordinates

The use of coordinates enables us to associate points in the plane with ordered pairs of real numbers and thus use arithmetic, algebraic, or, more generally, analytic methods in the study of the geometric properties of curves and other sets of points in the plane. Thus far we have made the association between points and ordered pairs of numbers in just one way, leading to what is usually called a rectangular cartesian coordinate system. There are, however, other ways of establishing the correspondence between points and ordered pairs of numbers—other types of coordinate systems. For example, one could use a pair of axes which intersect at some angle other than $\pi/2$. The fact is, though, that only one system other than rectangular cartesian coordinates is widely used in plane geometry, the system of *polar coordinates*, which we now describe and proceed to study.

The basic scheme is as follows: one chooses a point O, called the *pole*, and, using O as the initial point, draws a ray, or half-line, called the *polar axis*. Customarily one draws the polar axis horizontally to the right from O. Finally, one must choose a unit of distance. Now let P be an arbitrary point in the plane and draw the line segment OP. The polar coordinates of P are the numbers (r, θ), where r is the length of OP and θ is the angle measured from the polar axis in a counterclockwise direction to OP. See Figure 1.

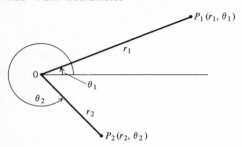

Figure 1

Conversely, given an ordered pair $(2, 3\pi/4)$, say, one associates a point P with it by drawing the terminal side of the angle $3\pi/4$ (the initial side being the polar axis, the vertex being the pole O) and measuring 2 units from O along this terminal side. Figure 2 shows this point $(2, 3\pi/4)$ and several others.

Although the polar axis is, by definition, a half-line, it is customary to draw the entire line, indicating the position of the pole.

A little reflection shows that it is possible to "cover" the entire plane by using values of $r \geqslant 0$ and values of θ in the interval $0 \leqslant \theta < 2\pi$. In fact, these restrictions on r and θ *almost* give a one-to-one correspondence between the points in the plane and the set of ordered pairs $\{(r, \theta) \mid r \geqslant 0, 0 \leqslant \theta < 2\pi\}$. The exception, of course, is the pole, for which $r = 0$ but for which θ could have any value. As it turns out, however, such limitations on r and θ would be too restrictive for our purposes, and the usual convention is to allow both r and θ to have any value in **R**. However, we must now establish agreements for the use of negative values of r and θ. In the case of θ there is no problem: if $\theta < 0$ we simply measure the angle in the clockwise direction from the polar axis. To interpret negative values of r we take our cue from the treat-

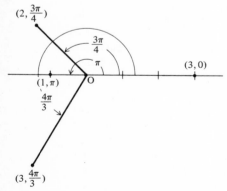

Figure 2

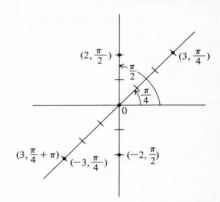

Figure 3

ment of numbers on the x-axis: a and $-a$ are equidistant from O, but in opposite directions. Thus if $r < 0$ we agree to extend the terminal side of the angle θ "backward" through the pole and locate P on this segment $|r|$ units from the pole. In this way (r, θ) and $(-r, \theta)$ are symmetric to each other with respect to the pole. We illustrate in Figure 3.

We can also describe the convention regarding negative values of r by saying that $(-r, \theta)$ and $(r, \theta + \pi)$ refer to the same point in the plane. See Figure 3.

With these conventions we lose all hope of a one-to-one correspondence between the points in the plane and the ordered pairs (r, θ). In fact, it is now the case that every point in the plane has infinitely many sets of coordinates. For, the two infinite sets

$$(r, \theta + 2n\pi), \qquad\qquad n = 0, \pm 1, \pm 2, \ldots$$

and

$$(-r, \theta + (2n + 1)\pi), \qquad n = 0, \pm 1, \pm 2, \ldots$$

all describe the same point. We illustrate in Figure 4.

When considering any coordinate system it is informative to investigate the sets of points obtained by letting each coordinate equal a constant. These

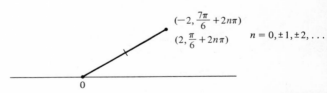

Figure 4

sets are called (in the plane) the *coordinate curves*. In this case the coordinate curves are

$$r = c$$

and

$$\theta = c.$$

For each c the equation $r = c$ is a circle with center at the pole and radius $|c|$; for each value of c the equation $\theta = c$ is a line through the pole. Thus, some of the coordinate curves are as shown in Figure 5.

Polar coordinate graph paper simply contains some of the coordinate curves, with the values of c equally spaced.

Exercises

A.   1. Plot each of the following points—the context is polar coordinates.

(a) $(3, \pi/6)$ 　　　　　　(g) $(-2, 0)$
(b) $(3, -(\pi/6))$ 　　　　(h) $(1, 1)$
(c) $(3, 5\pi/6)$ 　　　　　(i) $(1, \pi/2)$
(d) $(3, 7\pi/6)$ 　　　　　(j) $(1, -(\pi/2))$
(e) $(-3, \pi/6)$ 　　　　　(k) $(1, 3\pi/2)$
(f) $(2, \pi)$ 　　　　　　(l) $(3, 13\pi/6)$.

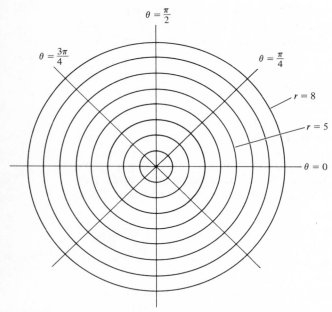

Figure 5

2. This question refers to the points in Exercise A1. What symmetry properties do the following pairs of points have?

    (a) Those in (a) and (b).

    (b) Those in (a) and (c).

    (c) Those in (a) and (d).

3. What set of points is represented by $r = -2$?

4. Give values to θ, compute the corresponding values of r, and obtain a sketch of the set of points (r, θ) such that

    (a) $r = \theta$.

    (b) $r = \theta + 1$.

    (c) $r\theta = 1$.

    (d) $r = \sin \theta, 0 \leqslant \theta < \pi$.

    (e) $r = \sin \theta, \pi \leqslant \theta < 2\pi$.

5. What are the coordinate curves $x = c$ and $y = c$ in rectangular coordinates?

6.2 Curves in Polar Coordinates

An equation or inequality involving r and θ will determine a set of points in the plane: the points whose coordinates satisfy the equation or inequality. Frequently we shall be interested in sets such as

$$\{(r, \theta) \mid r = f(\theta), \text{ where } f \text{ is a function}\}.$$

Our immediate concern will be to indicate and illustrate how geometric information can sometimes be extracted from the formula for f.

    INTERCEPTS.   The intersections (if any) of the curve with the polar axis can be found by setting $\theta = n\pi, n = 0, \pm 1, \pm 2, \ldots$. Also, intersections with the line through the pole perpendicular to the polar axis, the $\pi/2$-axis, can be obtained by setting $\theta = (2n + 1)(\pi/2), n = 0, \pm 1, \pm 2, \ldots$. Intersections with the pole are found by solving the equation $f(\theta) = 0$.

    SYMMETRY.   As the points (r, θ) and $(r, -\theta)$ are symmetric to each other with respect to the polar axis, a curve will be symmetric with respect to the polar axis if $f(-\theta) = f(\theta)$. In particular, since $\cos(-\theta) = \cos \theta$, if θ appears in the formula for f only as $\cos \theta$, the curve will be symmetric with respect to the polar axis.

    Symmetry with respect to the $\pi/2$-axis can be useful also. The points (r, θ) and $(r, \pi - \theta)$ are symmetric with respect to this line, so a curve will have such symmetry if $f(\pi - \theta) = f(\theta)$. In particular, since $\sin(\pi - \theta) = \sin \theta$, if θ appears in the formula for f only as $\sin \theta$, the curve will be symmetric with respect to the $\pi/2$-axis.

    Finally, we mention symmetry with respect to the pole. Two ways of describing the point symmetric to (r, θ) with respect to the pole are $(r, \theta + \pi)$ and $(-r, \theta)$. Thus if $f(\theta + \pi) = f(\theta)$—this would be the case if θ appeared

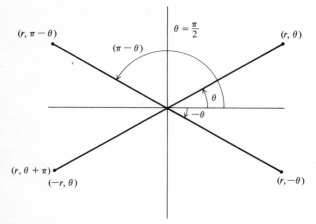

Figure 6

in the formula for f only as $\tan \theta$ or $\cot \theta$—or if the relation between r and θ were not explicitly a functional one and r appeared as r^2 or as an even power only (example: $r^2 = \cos 2\theta$), then the resulting curve would be symmetric with respect to the pole.

The various types of symmetry are illustrated in Figure 6.

Because of the multiplicity of coordinates for a given point there are various tests for the different types of symmetry: the ones mentioned above are some of the more useful—but by no means the only—ones. Others will be introduced later.

Frequently one can easily discern from the formula for f whether or not r is bounded for all values of θ, in which case the curve will lie entirely within a circle with center at the pole, or whether r—and hence the curve—will be unbounded. For example, the curve described by $r = \theta$ is clearly unbounded, whereas the curve described by $r = 1 + \cos \theta$ is readily seen to lie entirely within the circle $r = 2$.

We shall illustrate the above points, as well as some others, in a few examples.

Example 1.   We begin with $r = \theta$. In this example we consider $\theta \geqslant 0$ only. Clearly r is unbounded; there is, for $\theta \geqslant 0$, none of the symmetry discussed above, and the curve intersects the polar axis infinitely many times ($\theta = n\pi$, $n = 0, 1, 2, \ldots$) and the $\pi/2$-axis infinitely many times (at all odd multiples of $\pi/2$). It is easy to see that the graph is a spiral. See Figure 7; see also Exercise A21.

Example 2.   We graph $r = 2 \cos \theta$.
The following facts are readily discernible:

1. Because of the periodicity of cos, we need consider only values of θ in $[0, 2\pi)$. In fact, as we shall see, the interval $0 \leqslant \theta < \pi$ will suffice.

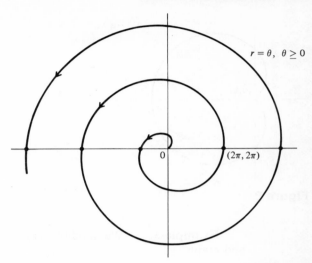

$r = \theta, \ \theta \geq 0$

$(2\pi, 2\pi)$

Figure 7

2. Intersections with the pole and polar axis occur at $(0, \pi/2)$, $(0, 3\pi/2)$, and $(2, 0)$, $(-2, \pi)$, respectively.
3. Clearly $|r| \leqslant 2$ for all θ, so the entire curve lies within the circle of radius 2, center at 0.
4. Since for all θ, $\cos \theta = -\cos(\theta - \pi)$, it follows that for $\pi < \theta < 2\pi$ the points obtained are identical with those already found for $0 < \theta < \pi$. Thus, the entire curve is described once for $0 \leqslant \theta < \pi$.
5. The curve is symmetric with respect to the polar axis.

We show a sketch in Figure 8. As *appears* to be the case (and, as we shall show in Section 6.3, unquestionably *is* the case), the curve is a circle.

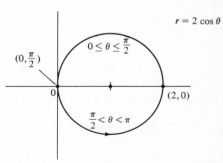

$r = 2 \cos \theta$

$0 \leq \theta \leq \dfrac{\pi}{2}$

$\left(0, \dfrac{\pi}{2}\right)$

$(2, 0)$

$\dfrac{\pi}{2} < \theta < \pi$

Figure 8

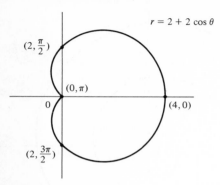

Figure 9

Example 3.   We modify very slightly the formula of Example 2 and graph

$$r = 2 + 2 \cos \theta = 2(1 + \cos \theta).$$

DISCUSSION

1. There is symmetry with respect to the polar axis, so we need consider only values of θ in $[0, \pi]$.
2. Intercepts occur at $(4, 0)$, $(2, \pi/2)$, $(0, \pi)$.
3. The values of r are bounded: $|r| \leqslant 4$.
4. Table 1 may help.
5. The curve, shown in Figure 9, is called a *cardioid*.

Table 1

θ	$2 \cos \theta$	$r = 2 + 2 \cos \theta$
increases from 0 to $\pi/2$	decreases from 2 to 0	decreases from 4 to 2
increases from $\pi/2$ to π	decreases from 0 to -2	decreases from 2 to 0

Example 4.   We find the graph of $r = \sin 3\theta$. For this curve we use the following method. It is clear that r varies between -1 and 1, and we record, in Table 2, this variation.

Now, using the last two columns of Table 2, we obtain the sketch as shown in Figure 10.

Notice that Table 2 takes θ only between 0 and π; it is not hard to see that the interval $[\pi, 2\pi]$ will simply produce a retracing of the curve already obtained.

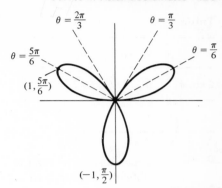

$\theta = \dfrac{2\pi}{3}$ $\theta = \dfrac{\pi}{3}$

$\theta = \dfrac{5\pi}{6}$ $\theta = \dfrac{\pi}{6}$

$(1, \dfrac{5\pi}{6})$

$(-1, \dfrac{\pi}{2})$

Figure 10

This is an example of a *rose curve*, the general equations of which are $r = a \sin n\theta$ and $r = a \cos n\theta$, where n is a positive integer. It will be found that the curve has n leaves if n is odd and $2n$ leaves if n is even.

Table 2

3θ	$\sin 3\theta = r$	θ
0 to $\pi/2$	0 to 1	0 to $\pi/6$
$\pi/2$ to π	1 to 0	$\pi/6$ to $\pi/3$
π to $3\pi/2$	0 to -1	$\pi/3$ to $\pi/2$
$3\pi/2$ to 2π	-1 to 0	$\pi/2$ to $2\pi/3$
2π to $5\pi/2$	0 to 1	$2\pi/3$ to $5\pi/6$
$5\pi/2$ to 3π	1 to 0	$5\pi/6$ to π

Example 5.   We consider $r = 1 + 2 \sin \theta$. General considerations tell us that $-1 \leqslant r \leqslant 3$, i.e., that the curve is bounded, lying entirely within and on the circle $r = 3$. There is symmetry with respect to the 90°-axis. Also $r = 0$ when $\sin \theta = -\frac{1}{2}$, i.e., for $\theta = 7\pi/6$ and $11\pi/6$. It is reasonably clear that the entire curve is obtained exactly once as θ runs from 0 to 2π. Because of the symmetry we consider values of θ between 0 and $\pi/2$ and between $3\pi/2$ and 2π. See Table 3.

Once this portion of the curve has been found one can use the symmetry with respect to the 90°-axis to complete the sketch, as shown in Figure 11.

The curves $r = a + b \sin \theta$ and $r = a + b \cos \theta$, where $ab \neq 0$, are called *limaçons*. When $a = b$ the limaçon is a cardioid (Example 3). When $|b| > |a|$, $r = 0$ for the values of θ such that $\cos \theta = (-a/b)$ and r changes sign at these values of θ; in this case the curve has an inner loop, as in the present example. If $|a| > |b|$, r is bounded but never zero: the curve is a kind of distorted circle. But there is a variation in its geometric behavior,

Table 3

θ	0	$\pi/6$	$\pi/4$	$\pi/3$	$\pi/2$	$3\pi/2$	$5\pi/3$	$7\pi/4$	$11\pi/6$	2π
$2\sin\theta$	0	1	$\sqrt{2}$	$\sqrt{3}$	2	-2	$-\sqrt{3}$	$-\sqrt{2}$	-1	0
r		1	2	$1+\sqrt{2}$	$1+\sqrt{3}$	3	-1	$1-\sqrt{3}$	$1-\sqrt{2}$	0	1

depending on whether $|a| < 2|b|$ or $|a| > 2|b|$; however, these properties are difficult to detect without calculus.

Example 6. We consider the graph of $r^2 = 4\cos 2\theta$. As will be seen shortly, the essential features of the curve are easily obtained. Before investigating them we call attention to the fact that the given equation involves a relation between r and θ which is not a function. We also point out that, since $r^2 \geqslant 0$, only values of θ are admissible for which $\cos 2\theta \geqslant 0$. Since

$$\frac{\pi}{2} < 2\theta < \frac{3\pi}{2} \Rightarrow \cos 2\theta < 0,$$

we conclude that values of θ between $\pi/4$ and $3\pi/4$ give no points on the curve. Considerations of symmetry indicate that the same is true for θ between $5\pi/4$ and $7\pi/4$.

The analysis of the graph is easily made if we use identities for $\cos 2\theta$ to write the equation $r^2 = 4\cos 2\theta$ in the equivalent forms

$$r = \pm 2\sqrt{2\cos^2\theta - 1} = \pm 2\sqrt{1 - 2\sin^2\theta}.$$

From these equations the following facts are apparent:

1. The curve is symmetric with respect to the polar axis, the 90°-axis, and the pole.
2. Since $|r| \leqslant 2$, the curve is bounded.

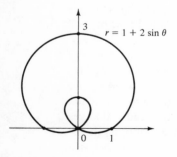

Figure 11

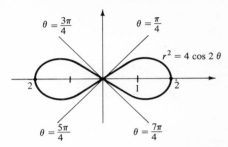

Figure 12

3. Intercepts with the axes occur at $(\pm 2, 0)$ and at $(0, \pi/4)$, $(0, 3\pi/4)$, $(0, 5\pi/4)$, $(0, 7\pi/4)$.

Because of the symmetry, we need consider only values of θ between 0 and $\pi/4$; it is easily seen that r decreases from 2 to 0. This gives the portion of the curve in quadrant I and symmetry gives the remainder, as shown in Figure 12. The figure suggests that as the curve comes into the pole for $\theta = \pi/4$ it has the line $\theta = \pi/4$ as tangent. This is indeed the case, but the proof requires the use of the limit techniques of calculus.

This curve is called the *lemniscate* of Bernoulli. (Why lemniscate? Try a dictionary.)

We conclude this section with one more illustration.

Example 7.   We consider $r = \sin \frac{1}{2}\theta$. (Should this be a rose curve? See Example 4.)

The equation as given does not enable us to draw any conclusions about symmetry (see, however, the sketch). We can say that the curve lies on and within the circle $r = 1$ and that, as $\frac{1}{2}\theta$ runs from 0 to 2π, θ will run from 0 to 4π. We resort to a table (Table 4).

Table 4

$\frac{1}{2}\theta$	0	$\pi/6$	$\pi/4$	$\pi/3$	$\pi/2$	$2\pi/3$	$3\pi/4$	$5\pi/6$	π	$7\pi/6$	$5\pi/4$	$4\pi/3$
$r = \sin \frac{1}{2}\theta$	0	$\frac{1}{2}$	$\sqrt{2}/2$	$\sqrt{3}/2$	1	$\sqrt{3}/2$	$\sqrt{2}/2$	$\frac{1}{2}$	0	$-\frac{1}{2}$	$-(\sqrt{2}/2)$	$-(\sqrt{3}/2)$
θ	0	$\pi/3$	$\pi/2$	$2\pi/3$	π	$4\pi/3$	$3\pi/2$	$5\pi/3$	2π	$7\pi/3$	$5\pi/2$	$8\pi/3$

$3\pi/2$	$5\pi/3$	$7\pi/4$	$11\pi/6$	2π
-1	$-(\sqrt{3}/2)$	$-(\sqrt{2}/2)$	$-\frac{1}{2}$	0
3π	$10\pi/3$	$7\pi/2$	$11\pi/3$	4π

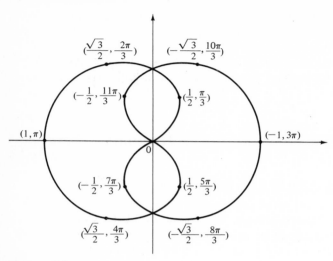

Figure 13

Using the second and third rows, we get a few points on the curve, as shown in Figure 13.

Exercises

A. In Exercises 1–20 sketch the graphs of the functions given.

 1. $r = 2 \sin \theta$.

 2. $r = 1 - \cos \theta$.

 3. $r = 1 - \sin \theta$.

 4. $r = 1 + \sin \theta$.

 5. $r = 1 - 2 \cos \theta$. [*Hint:* be sure to find all θ such that $r = 0$.]

 6. $r = \cos 3\theta$.

 7. $r = \sin 2\theta$ (four-leaved rose).

 8. $r = \sin 4\theta$ (eight-leaved rose).

 9. $r = \cos 2\theta$.

 10. $r \cos \theta = 2$.

 11. $r = 2 + \cos \theta$.

 12. $r = \tan \theta$. [*Hints:* $\tan(\theta + \pi) = \tan \theta \Rightarrow$ sym. with respect to? $\tan(\pi - \theta) = -\tan \theta \Rightarrow$ sym. with respect to?]

 13. $r = 2/(1 - \cos \theta)$.

 14. $r = \cos(\theta/2)$.

 15. $r^2 = 2 \sin 2\theta$.

 16. $r = 1 + 2 \cos \theta$.

 17. $r = 2 + \sin \theta$.

 18. $r = 3 + \sin \theta$.

 19. $r = \cos(\theta/4)$.

 20. $r = \cos(\theta/3)$.

21. Draw $r = \theta$ for $\theta \leqslant 0$. How is this portion of the curve related to the part drawn in Example 1?

B. **1.** Suppose that f is a function (of θ) and suppose that f is an *odd* function, i.e., $f(-\theta) = -f(\theta)$. Show that the graph is symmetric with respect to the $\pi/2$-axis.

6.3 Relation Between Polar and Rectangular Coordinates

We now consider the relation between polar and rectangular coordinates. If the two systems are superimposed with the pole and the origin coincident and the polar axis and positive x-axis coincident, then every point will have a set of coordinates in each system, as shown in Figure 14.

We note that

$$\left.\begin{array}{l} x = r \cos \theta \\ y = r \sin \theta \end{array}\right\}.$$ [1]

Conversely, we can write

$$\left.\begin{array}{l} r^2 = x^2 + y^2 \\ \tan \theta = y/x \end{array}\right\}.$$ [2]

The equations in (2) *can* be solved explicitly for r and θ:

$$\left.\begin{array}{l} r = \pm \sqrt{x^2 + y^2} \\ \theta = \tan^{-1} y/x + n\pi, \qquad n = 0, \pm 1, \pm 2, \ldots \end{array}\right\},$$ [3]

but in many cases it is preferable to work with the form in [2]. With regard to the expression for θ in [3] recall that $\tan^{-1}(y/x) \in (-(\pi/2), \pi/2)$, and θ in polar coordinates need not lie in this interval.

It is useful to have some facility in translating back and forth between the two systems. For example, suppose we find the cartesian equivalent of $r = 2 \cos \theta$. If we multiply both sides by r [the geometric effect of this is to

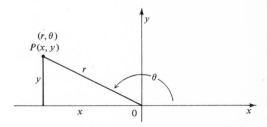

Figure 14

add the pole to the curve, but it was there already as $(0, \pi/2)$ so the locus is unchanged] we have

$$r^2 = 2r \cos \theta,$$

or, using one equation from each of [2] and [1],

$$x^2 + y^2 = 2x,$$

the equation of a circle with center $(1, 0)$, radius 1 (see Example 2).

Similarly, consider the cardioid of Example 3:

$$r = 2 + 2 \cos \theta. \qquad [4]$$

Again we multiply through by r:

$$r^2 = 2r + 2r \cos \theta,$$

or, using [2] and [1],

$$x^2 + y^2 = 2r + 2x.$$

This can be written

$$x^2 + y^2 - 2x = 2r,$$

or

$$x^2 + y^2 - 2x = 2\sqrt{x^2 + y^2};$$

squaring both sides gives

$$(x^2 + y^2 - 2x)^2 = 4(x^2 + y^2). \qquad [5]$$

The student should compare the graphing of $r = 2 + 2 \cos \theta$, as carried out in Example 3, with the prospect of graphing the curve defined by Equation [5].

To emphasize the point of the preceding remark consider the function graphed in Example 1: $r = \theta$. It takes only a little thought to discern the nature of the curve in polar coordinates, a spiral of infinite extent. Now an explicit use of Equations [3] would give, as a rectangular equivalent of $r = \theta$,

$$\pm \sqrt{x^2 + y^2} = \tan^{-1} \frac{y}{x} + n\pi, \qquad n = 0, \pm 1, \pm 2, \dots.$$

But the somewhat ambiguous nature of the right-hand side suggests a different approach: we take the tangent of both sides *before* translating. This gives

$$\tan r = \tan \theta,$$

or using [3] and [2],

$$\tan(\pm \sqrt{x^2 + y^2}) = \frac{y}{x},$$

which can also be written

$$\tan\sqrt{x^2 + y^2} = \pm\frac{y}{x}. \tag{6}$$

It is hardly an understatement to say that the geometric nature of the curve described by [6] is not immediately apparent.

The translation from rectangular to polar coordinates can usually be achieved by means of Equations [1] and [2]. Consider, for example, the parabola $y^2 = 4x$; using [1] we have

$$r^2 \sin^2 \theta = 4r \cos \theta.$$

We can safely divide by r since the pole also appears as $(0, \pi/2)$; this gives

$$r \sin^2 \theta = 4 \cos \theta,$$

or, solving for r,

$$r = \frac{4 \cos \theta}{\sin^2 \theta} = 4 \csc \theta \cot \theta.$$

(Is it "obvious" what sort of curve this equation represents?)

Finally, we consider the straight line $y = mx + b$. A direct use of equations [1] gives

$$r \sin \theta = mr \cos \theta + b,$$

or

$$r(\sin \theta - m \cos \theta) = b.$$

Solving for r we have

$$r = \frac{b}{\sin \theta - m \cos \theta}.$$

In summary, we remark that it is frequently essential to be able to translate back and forth between polar and rectangular coordinates. A by-product of our illustrations is a demonstration of the fact that certain curves are much more easily sketched in polar coordinates whereas other curves are more readily analyzed for their geometric features in rectangular coordinates. This provides one answer to the question "Why bother with a second coordinate system when we already have a perfectly good one?"

Exercises

A. In Exercises 1–10 translate to rectangular coordinates and sketch each curve from one of the two forms.

    1. $r = 4 \sin \theta$.
    2. $r = 1 - 2 \sin \theta$.
    3. $r \cos \theta = 2$.

4. $r = \tan \theta$.
5. $r = \cos 2\theta$.
6. $r = 3 - \cos \theta$.
7. $r = 2/(\sin \theta - \cos \theta)$.
8. $r = 2 \cos \theta - 4 \sin \theta$.
9. $r = 1/(1 - \cos \theta)$.
10. $r = 4 \csc \theta$.

In Exercises 11–19 translate to polar coordinates, then draw a sketch of the curve, using whichever coordinate system seems preferable.
11. $y = 3\sqrt{x}$.
12. $y = 4x^2 + 8x + 5$.
13. $x^2 + y^2 - 2y = 0$.
14. $(x^2 + y^2 + 2y)^2 = 4(x^2 + y^2)$.
15. $2x - 3y + 4 = 0$.
16. $x^2 - y^2 = 1$.
17. $(x^2 + y^2)^2 = x^2 - y^2$.
18. $y = 1/(x^2 + 1)$.
19. $x + y = 0$.

B.   **1.** We turn our attention to a circle with center at $C(h, k) = C(c, \gamma)$ and radius a; see Figure 15. Use the law of cosines to show that in polar coordinates the equation is

$$r^2 - 2c \cos(\theta - \gamma)r = a^2 - c^2.$$

2. Let $P_1(r_1, \theta_1)$ and $P_2(r_2, \theta_2)$ be two points. Show that the distance $|\overline{P_1P_2}|$ between them is given by

$$|\overline{P_1P_2}|^2 = r_1^2 + r_2^2 - 2r_1r_2 \cos(\theta_1 - \theta_2).$$

C.   **1.** Transform $r = \sin 3\theta$ to rectangular coordinates.

Hint:

$$\sin 3\theta = \sin(2\theta + \theta)$$
$$= 3 \sin \theta - 4 \sin^3 \theta.$$

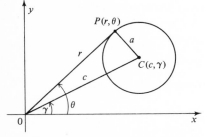

Figure 15

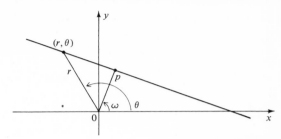

Figure 16

2. Consider the normal form of the equation of a straight line (see Exercise C1 after Section 3.2):

$$(\cos \omega)x + (\sin \omega)y - p = 0;$$

see Figure 16. Show that the polar coordinate equation is

$$r = \frac{p}{\cos(\theta - \omega)}.$$

3. Use whatever techniques seem appropriate to sketch the following curves:

  (a) $r = a(\sec \theta - \cos \theta)$, the *cissoid of Diocles*.
  (b) $r = a \cos 2\theta \sec \theta$, the *strophoid*.
  (c) $r = a \sin \theta \cos^2 \theta$, the *bifolium*.
  (d) $r = \csc \theta + 2$, the *conchoid of Nicomedes*.
  (e) $r = 2\csc \theta + 1$.

6.4 The Conic Section Curves (alternative definition)

We have already indicated, in Exercises B1 after Sections 5.2 and 5.3, that it is possible to give one definition that encompasses all three of the conic section curves, the distinction between the different types being made in terms of the eccentricity. It turns out to be especially convenient to describe the equation that results from this definition in terms of polar coordinates, and this we shall do.

DEFINITION 1.   *Let l be a fixed line (the* directrix*), F a fixed point (the* focus*) not on l, and e > 0 a fixed number. The set of points*

$$\{P \mid |\overline{PF}| = e \cdot d(P, l)\}$$

is called a conic section curve.

To obtain a polar coordinate equation of a conic section curve we take the focus at the pole and the directrix perpendicular to the polar axis and

$2p(p > 0)$ units to the left of the line $\theta = \pi/2$ (thus the directrix is the line $r \cos \theta + 2p = 0$). See Figure 17.

Let $P(r, \theta)$ be a point on the curve. Then, by Definition 1,

$$|\overline{OP}| = e|\overline{MP}|,$$

i.e.,

$$r = e|\overline{MP}|.$$

Now, for all possible positions of P it is possible to prove (see Exercise B1) that $|\overline{MP}| = |r \cos \theta + 2p|$. Thus the preceding equation can be written as

$$r = \pm e(r \cos \theta + 2p).$$

Using first the plus sign and then the minus sign and solving for r, we get, respectively,

$$r = \frac{2ep}{1 - e \cos \theta} \tag{7}$$

and

$$r = \frac{-2ep}{1 + e \cos \theta}. \tag{7a}$$

It is not hard to show (see Exercise B2) that a point (r, θ) satisfies [7a] $\Leftrightarrow (r, \theta)$ satisfies [7]; in other words, the two equations are equivalent and we can work, as we shall, with [7].

Other choices could have been made in setting up the coordinate system. For example, if we had taken the focus at the pole and the directrix perpendicular to the polar axis but $2p$ units to the *right* of $\theta = \pi/2$ (i.e., l is $r \cos \theta - 2p = 0$), then the equation would have been

$$r = \frac{2ep}{1 + e \cos \theta}. \tag{8}$$

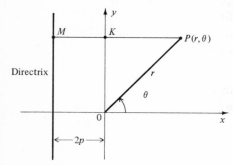

Figure 17

Or, by taking the directrix parallel to and either $2p$ units below or $2p$ units above the polar axis, the focus still being at the pole, one would obtain

$$r = \frac{2ep}{1 - e \sin \theta},$$ [9]

or

$$r = \frac{2ep}{1 + e \sin \theta},$$ [10]

respectively. We shall discuss only Equation [7]; clearly each of [8], [9], and [10] can be treated in an entirely analogous manner.

As a rough indication of how e determines the nature of the curve described by [7], we write that equation in the equivalent form:

$$r = \frac{2p}{(1/e) - \cos \theta}.$$ [11]

It follows that

1. $0 < e < 1 \Rightarrow (1/e) > 1 \Rightarrow (1/e) - \cos \theta \neq 0$ and r is bounded.
2. $e = 1 \Rightarrow r$ is unbounded in a neighborhood of $\theta = 0$.
3. $e > 1 \Rightarrow (1/e) < 1 \Rightarrow r$ is unbounded in neighborhoods of $\theta = \theta_1$ and $\theta = -\theta_1$, where θ_1 is in quadrant I and $\cos \theta_1 = e^{-1}$.

It is obvious that Definition 1, with $e = 1$, agrees with Definition 5.1 for the parabola. We illustrate this fact and a useful sketching hint.

Example 8. We discuss Equation [7] with $e = p = 1$:

$$r = \frac{2}{1 - \cos \theta}$$ [12]

The curve is clearly symmetric with respect to the polar axis and has intercepts with the polar and vertical axes at $(1, \pi)$, $(2, \pi/2)$, and $(2, 3\pi/2)$. We see that r is undefined for $\theta = 0$ and that values of θ close to zero produce large values of r. To obtain more specific information about points on the curve for small values of θ we study the behavior of the ordinate $y = r \sin \theta$ for small θ. From [12] we have

$$y = r \sin \theta = \frac{2 \sin \theta}{1 - \cos \theta}.$$

Now both numerator and denominator of this fraction are close to zero for θ near zero, so this form does not help. But by "rationalizing" the denominator we find

$$y = \frac{(2 \sin \theta)(1 + \cos \theta)}{(1 - \cos \theta)(1 + \cos \theta)} = \frac{2(1 + \cos \theta)}{\sin \theta}.$$

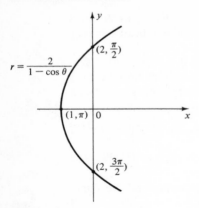

$$r = \frac{2}{1 - \cos \theta}$$

Figure 18

Since θ close to zero makes the numerator close to 4 and the denominator close to zero, we see that $|y|$ gets big beyond bounds in a neighborhood of $\theta = 0$. The sketch is in Figure 18.

We now prove that [7] represents a conic section curve in the sense of Chapter 5 for all $e > 0$.

THEOREM 1.   *The curve described by Equation [7] is a parabola if $e = 1$, an ellipse if $0 < e < 1$, and a hyperbola if $e > 1$. The same assertions hold for the curves given by [8], [9], and [10].*

PROOF.   We consider only [7]; the steps for the other forms would be entirely analogous. In view of the discussion in Chapter 5 we need only convert the equation to rectangular coordinates. From [7] we have

$$r - er \cos \theta = 2ep,$$

or, since $r \cos \theta = x$,

$$r = e(x + 2p).$$

Squaring this equation and then replacing r^2 by $x^2 + y^2$, we have

$$x^2 + y^2 = e^2(x^2 + 4px + 4p^2),$$

or

$$(1 - e^2)x^2 + y^2 - 4e^2px - 4e^2p^2 = 0. \qquad [13]$$

If $e = 1$, [13] becomes

$$y^2 = 4p(x + p), \qquad [14]$$

a parabola with vertex at $(-p, 0)$, axis of symmetry the x-axis.

If $0 < e < 1$, then $1 - e^2 > 0$ and [13] has the same form as Equation [5.25]: the curve is an ellipse (nondegenerate, as we shall see).

Finally, if $e > 1$, [13] can be rewritten as

$$(e^2 - 1)x^2 - y^2 + 4e^2px + 4e^2p^2 = 0, \qquad\qquad [15]$$

which has the same form as Equation [5.38]: the curve is a hyperbola. ∎

It is possible to be more explicit than Theorem 1 is about Equation [7] in the cases of ellipses and hyperbolas. The proofs of the following assertions are simple but messy and we leave them for the exercises.

THEOREM 2.   *The following are true about the curves of Equations* [7] *and* [13]:

1. *If* $0 < e < 1$ *they can be put in the form*

$$\frac{(x - c)^2}{a^2} + \frac{y^2}{b^2} = 1, \qquad\qquad [16]$$

   where

$$a = \frac{2ep}{1 - e^2}, \quad b = \frac{2ep}{\sqrt{1 - e^2}}, \quad c = \frac{2e^2p}{1 - e^2}. \qquad\qquad [17]$$

2. *If* $e > 1$ *they can be expressed as*

$$\frac{(x + c)^2}{a^2} - \frac{y^2}{b^2} = 1, \qquad\qquad [18]$$

   where

$$a = \frac{2ep}{e^2 - 1}, \quad b = \frac{2ep}{\sqrt{e^2 - 1}}, \quad c = \frac{2e^2p}{e^2 - 1}. \qquad\qquad [19]$$

It follows from Theorems 1 and 2 that Equation [7] represents a non-degenerate conic section curve for all values of $e > 0$ and $p > 0$.

Sketching an ellipse from Equation [7] is straightforward: the curve is traced out, as θ increases from 0 to 2π, in a counterclockwise fashion starting with the right-hand vertex. Although the nature of the curve is less evident from this analytic representation than from those in Chapter 5, there is some point in knowing about such an equation; recall that the orbit of the earth (or any planet) about the sun is, approximately, an ellipse with the sun at one focus.

Sketching a hyperbola, however, from Equation [7] presents a small challenge, as we now illustrate.

Example 9   We consider [7] with $p = 1$ and $e = 2$:

$$r = \frac{4}{1 - 2\cos\theta}.$$

First we remark that, because of the symmetry with respect to the polar axis (why?), we need consider only the interval $0 \leqslant \theta \leqslant \pi$.

We next look at the way in which r varies with θ, as described in Table 5.

Table 5

θ	r
$0 \to \pi/3$	$-4 \to -\infty$
$\pi/3 \to \pi/2$	$+\infty \to 4$
$\pi/2 \to \pi$	$4 \to \frac{4}{3}$

Now it would seem that the lines $\theta = \pi/3$ and $\theta = 5\pi/3$ [or, alternatively, $\theta = -(\pi/3)$] are asymptotes for the curve. This, however, is not the case: the asymptotes are in fact lines parallel to the ones just mentioned but intersecting on the polar axis at the point $(\frac{8}{3}, \pi)$. The curve, sketched by using the information already detailed, is shown in Figure 19.

As the figure shows, the lower half of the left branch is obtained for θ between 0 and $\pi/3$; the whole right branch comes from the interval $\pi/3 < \theta < 5\pi/3$; and, finally, the points on the upper half of the left branch are obtained for θ between $5\pi/3$ and 2π.

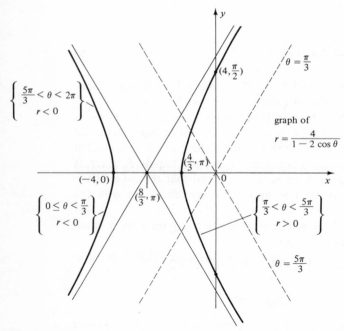

Figure 19

Exercises

A. In Exercises 1–12 sketch each of the curves. It may help to write the equation in one of the forms

$$r = \frac{2ep}{1 \pm e \cos \theta} \quad \text{or} \quad r = \frac{2ep}{1 \pm e \sin \theta}.$$

1. $r = 1/(2 - \cos \theta)$.
2. $r + r \cos \theta = 2$.
3. $r - r \sin \theta = 4$.
4. $2r + r \sin \theta = 2$.
5. $r = 6/(3 + 2 \sin \theta)$.
6. $10r + r \cos \theta = 1$.
7. $r = 9/(10 + 9 \cos \theta)$.
8. $r = 4 - 2r \sin \theta$.
9. $r = 8/(1 + 2 \cos \theta)$.
10. $r = 10/(1 - 5 \sin \theta)$.
11. $r + 3r \sin \theta = 12$.
12. $9r - 10r \cos \theta = 20$.

In Exercises 13–20 find the equation of each of the conic section curves described, and sketch. In each case the focus is at the pole.
13. Directrix: $r = 3 \csc \theta$, $e = 1$.
14. Directrix: $r = -2 \sec \theta$, $e = \frac{1}{2}$.
15. Directrix: $r = -4 \csc \theta$, $e = 0.01$.
16. Directrix: $r = \sec \theta$, $e = \frac{4}{5}$.
17. Directrix: $r = -2 \csc \theta$, $e = \frac{1}{3}$.
18. Directrix: $r = 2 \csc \theta$, $e = \frac{7}{4}$.
19. Directrix: $r = -4 \sec \theta$, $e = \frac{5}{3}$.
20. Directrix: $r = 2 \sec \theta$, $e = \frac{5}{2}$.

B. **1.** Prove the assertion made in the text about the length of the segment $\overline{MP}$ in Figure 17, that

$$|\overline{MP}| = |r \cos \theta + 2p|.$$

Note that P can lie to the left of the directrix.

2. Prove the assertion made in the text to the effect that Equations [7a] and [7] are equivalent.

Hints: (i) Let the point $P_0(r_0, \theta_0)$ satisfy [7a]:

$$r_0 = \frac{-2ep}{1 + e \cos \theta_0}.$$

(ii) Multiply both sides by -1 and use the fact that $\cos \theta_0 = -\cos(\theta_0 + \pi)$ to obtain

$$-r_0 = \frac{2ep}{1 - e\cos(\theta_0 + \pi)}.$$

(iii) What is the relation between the points (r_0, θ_0) and $(-r_0, \theta_0 + \pi)$?
(iv) Reverse the steps.

    3. Prove assertion 1 of Theorem 2.

    Hints: (i) Complete the square in x in [13]. You should get

$$(1 - e^2)\left(x - \frac{2e^2p^2}{1 - e^2}\right)^2 + y^2 = \frac{4e^2p^2}{1 - e^2}.$$

(ii) Divide both sides by $(4e^2p^2)/(1 - e^2)$:

$$\frac{\left(x - \dfrac{2e^2p}{1 - e^2}\right)^2}{\dfrac{4e^2p^2}{(1 - e^2)^2}} + \frac{y^2}{\dfrac{4e^2p^2}{1 - e^2}} = 1.$$

(iii) Set

$$a^2 = \frac{4e^2p^2}{(1 - e^2)^2}, \quad b^2 = \frac{4e^2p^2}{1 - e^2}.$$

Find $c^2 = a^2 - b^2$ and show that $c/a = e$.
(iv) Prove that $2p = b^2/c$. Note that $2p = (a/e) - ae$, the distance between the directrix and the focus (see Exercise B1 after Section 5.2).

    4. Prove assertion 2 of Theorem 2. The hints given in Exercise B3 should suffice.

Vectors and Parametric Equations

7

In the previous chapters we have already made extensive use of line segments. It is frequently useful in geometric problems to attach a direction to a line segment, which is then called a vector. A line segment can be described by specifying its two endpoints, in either order (i.e., $\overline{AB} = \overline{BA}$); to describe a vector, a *directed* line segment, we assign the direction, or orientation, by the order in which the points are listed. See Figure 1.

DEFINITION 1. *A* vector *is a directed line segment. If the vector is determined by the points A and B, the direction (orientation) being from A toward B, we denote it by $\overrightarrow{AB}$. We call A the* initial point *and B the* terminal point *of $\overrightarrow{AB}$.*

Although much can be done with vectors without introducing co-ordinates, such a procedure would be contrary to both the spirit of this work and to our future purposes. Consequently we shall give a coordinate-free

Figure 1

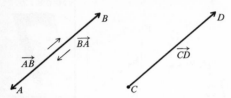

Figure 2

definition of equality of vectors and then proceed to discover how to represent vectors in terms of a coordinate system.

DEFINITION 2. *Two vectors are equal ⇔ they have the same length, lie on parallel lines, and have the same orientation.*

In Figure 2 $\overrightarrow{AB}$ and $\overrightarrow{CD}$ are the same length and lie on parallel lines; also, the orientation from A to B is the same as that from C to D. Thus $\overrightarrow{AB} = \overrightarrow{CD}$. But $\overrightarrow{AB} \neq \overrightarrow{BA}$.

We shall denote the length or magnitude of $\overrightarrow{AB}$ by $|\overrightarrow{AB}|$.

We now assume we have introduced a coordinate system and we consider a vector $\overrightarrow{AB}$, where A and B have coordinates (a_1, a_2) and (b_1, b_2), respectively. We know we can describe the length d of $\overrightarrow{AB}$ in terms of the coordinates by

$$d = |\overrightarrow{AB}| = \sqrt{(b_1 - a_1)^2 + (b_2 - a_2)^2}. \qquad [1]$$

As an aid in describing the direction of $\overrightarrow{AB}$ we introduce the direction angles and their cosines.

DEFINITION 3. *The direction angles α and β of a vector $\overrightarrow{OB}$ are the angles from the positive x- and y-axes, respectively, to the vector. The cosines of these angles are the direction cosines. The direction angles and cosines of a vector $\overrightarrow{AB}$ are the direction angles and cosines of that vector equal to $\overrightarrow{AB}$ with initial point at the origin.*

We agree that α and β will always satisfy $0 \leqslant \alpha \leqslant \pi$, $0 \leqslant \beta \leqslant \pi$. See Figure 3, where we have drawn the vector with A at the origin.

It is clear from Figure 3(i) that

$$\begin{cases} b_1 - a_1 = d \cos \alpha \\ b_2 - a_2 = d \cos \beta \end{cases}. \qquad [2]$$

Moreover, we assert that [2] holds in every case (Exercise B2). Notice that, although we have, for the sake of simplicity, shown A at the origin, we have written the equations in [2] for the general case; where A is not at the origin we could translate the axes so that the new origin is at A.

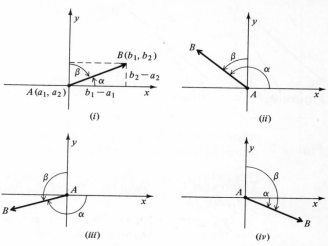

Figure 3

Clearly the direction cosines distinguish between the directions of $\overrightarrow{AB}$ and $\overrightarrow{BA}$. For (see Figure 4), if $\overrightarrow{AB}$ has direction cosines α and β and $\overrightarrow{BA} = \overrightarrow{AB'}$ α' and β', then

$$\left.\begin{array}{l} \alpha' = \pi - \alpha \\ \beta' = \pi - \beta \end{array}\right\} \Rightarrow \begin{cases} \cos\alpha' = -\cos\alpha \\ \cos\beta' = -\cos\beta. \end{cases}$$

Let A and B have coordinates (a_1, a_2) and (b_1, b_2), respectively. Then, since the numbers d, $\cos\alpha$, and $\cos\beta$ determine uniquely the length and direction of the vector $\overrightarrow{AB}$, and since, by [1] and [2], these numbers can be expressed in terms of $b_1 - a_1$ and $b_2 - a_2$, we can make the following assertion. See Figure 5. For the proof, see Exercise B3.

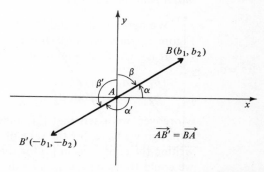

Figure 4

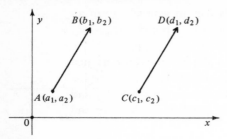

Figure 5

THEOREM 1. *Consider the points* $A(a_1, a_2)$, $B(b_1, b_2)$, $C(c_1, c_2)$, *and* $D(d_1, d_2)$. *Then*

$$\overrightarrow{AB} = \overrightarrow{CD} \Leftrightarrow \begin{cases} b_1 - a_1 = d_1 - c_1 \\ b_2 - a_2 = d_2 - c_2 \end{cases}. \tag{3}$$

As a result of Theorem 1, we know that given a coordinate system, the vector $\overrightarrow{AB}$ is uniquely described by the pair of numbers $b_1 - a_1$ and $b_2 - a_2$, and we shall in the future write

$$\overrightarrow{AB} = [b_1 - a_1, b_2 - a_2]. \tag{4}$$

The numbers $b_1 - a_1$ and $b_2 - a_2$ are called the *coordinates* or the *components* of the vector $\overrightarrow{AB}$. We have thus achieved, in Equation [4], an analytic representation of a vector.

Example 1. Consider the points $A(3, 1)$ and $B(5, 4)$. Then the vector $\overrightarrow{AB}$ is represented by

$$\overrightarrow{AB} = [5 - 3, 4 - 1] = [2, 3].$$

If we denote by P_0 the point $(2, 3)$, then clearly $\overrightarrow{OP_0} = [2, 3]$, and $\overrightarrow{AB} = \overrightarrow{OP_0}$. See Figure 6.

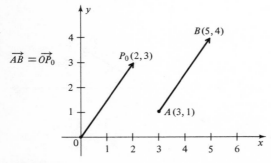

Figure 6

The situation illustrated in Example 1 holds true in general: given an arbitrary vector $\overrightarrow{AB} = [b_1 - a_1, b_2 - a_2]$, there exists a point $P_0(b_1 - a_1, b_2 - a_2)$ such that $\overrightarrow{OP_0} = \overrightarrow{AB}$. In other words, each vector, described by a pair of numbers, determines a point, related to the given vector as just described. Conversely, each point $P_0(x_0, y_0)$ determines the vector $\overrightarrow{OP_0} = [x_0, y_0]$. Notice that, following Murdoch [*Analytic Geometry*, John Wiley and Sons, Inc., New York, 1966] and others, we use brackets for vectors and parentheses for points.

We see, then, that a vector can be specified as an ordered pair of numbers, independent of a specific pair of points. When this is done we shall denote the vector in boldface. Thus we can consider the vector $\mathbf{a} = [a_1, a_2]$, with magnitude

$$|\mathbf{a}| = \sqrt{a_1^2 + a_2^2} \qquad [5]$$

and direction angles defined by

$$\left. \begin{array}{l} a_1 = |\mathbf{a}| \cos \alpha \\ a_2 = |\mathbf{a}| \cos \beta \end{array} \right\}. \qquad [6]$$

The geometric counterpart of the analytic vector $\mathbf{a}$ is the directed line segment $\overrightarrow{OA}$, where A is the point with coordinates (a_1, a_2), i.e., $\mathbf{a} = \overrightarrow{OA}$.

A word is in order about Definition 2, defining equal vectors. Usually in mathematics equality means "identically the same." In the present instance we have gone counter to this custom: two vectors are equal if they have the same length and the same direction, but they may have different positions in the plane. The term *free vectors* is used to describe the scheme we use. If we defined equality of vectors to mean same length, same direction, and same initial point (i.e., identically the same), then the vectors would be called *fixed*. See Exercise B1 for an alternative approach.

We return to the direction cosines of Definition 3.

THEOREM 2. *The direction cosines of a vector satisfy*

$$\cos^2 \alpha + \cos^2 \beta = 1. \qquad [7]$$

PROOF. One need only square each equation in [6], add the results, and use Equation [5]. ∎

There are two special cases related to this discussion. First of all, the brief proof given for Theorem 2 fails (why?) if the length d of the vector is zero. If $\overrightarrow{AB}$ has $d = 0$, it must follow that $B = A$, or $\overrightarrow{AB} = [0, 0]$. We refer to $[0, 0]$ as the *zero vector* and denote it by $\mathbf{0}$; its length is zero. Its direction is obviously ambiguous; we shall agree that it has *all* directions. Second, if the length is one, we call the vector a *unit vector*. Notice from [6] that if $d = 1$ the components of the vector are the direction cosines. Notice also that corresponding to every nonzero vector $\mathbf{a} = [a_1, a_2]$ there is a unit vector $\mathbf{u}_a$ with the same direction as $\mathbf{a}$; for

$$\mathbf{u}_a = \left[\frac{a_1}{\sqrt{a_1^2 + a_2^2}}, \frac{a_2}{\sqrt{a_1^2 + a_2^2}}\right] = \left[\frac{a_1}{d}, \frac{a_2}{d}\right] = [\cos \alpha, \cos \beta].$$

Thus, if $\mathbf{a} = [3, -4]$, then $\mathbf{u}_a = [3/5, (-4)/5]$ and, for both $\mathbf{a}$ and $\mathbf{u}_a$, $\cos \alpha = 3/5$, $\cos \beta = (-4)/5$ (see Figure 7).

Exercises

A. In each of Exercises 1–8 find the components, the length, and the direction cosines of $\overrightarrow{AB}$; find, also the components of the unit vector corresponding to it.

    1. $A(2, 4)$, $B(-6, 1)$.
    2. $A(3, 1)$, $B(3, 5)$.
    3. $A(-2, 1)$, $B(6, 1)$.
    4. $A(-1, -2)$, $B(3, 2)$.
    5. $A(3, 2)$, $B(-1, -2)$.
    6. $A(4, 0)$, $B(-2, -4)$.
    7. $A(3, 2)$, $B(3, 2)$.
    8. $A(0, -2)$, $B(0, 6)$.

In each of Exercises 9–16 find the direction cosines of the vector $\mathbf{v}$ given and find the terminal point B if the initial point is at the given point A.

    9. $\mathbf{v} = [-4, 3]$, $A(2, -1)$.
    10. $\mathbf{v} = [-5, -1]$, $A(0, 3)$.
    11. $\mathbf{v} = [3, 0]$, $A(-3, 0)$.
    12. $\mathbf{v} = [2, -7]$, $A(-4, 3)$.
    13. $\mathbf{v} = [a, b]$, $A(-a, -b)$.

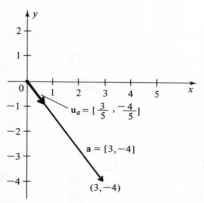

Figure 7

14. $v = [-2, 4]$, $A(-2, 4)$.
15. $v = [3, -4]$, $A(2, 0)$.
16. $v = [v_1, v_2]$, $A(a_1, a_2)$.

B. **1.** A correct approach to the definition of equality for vectors is the following. We consider the set of all directed line segments in the plane and define two directed line segments to be *equivalent* ⇔ they have the same length and the same direction. Using ~ (tilde) for equivalent, show that this relation has the following properties:

1. $\overrightarrow{AB} \sim \overrightarrow{AB}$. (reflexive)
2. $\overrightarrow{AB} \sim \overrightarrow{CD} \Rightarrow \overrightarrow{CD} \sim \overrightarrow{AB}$ (symmetric)
3. $\left.\begin{array}{c}\overrightarrow{AB} \sim \overrightarrow{CD}\\ \overrightarrow{CD} \sim \overrightarrow{EF}\end{array}\right\} \Rightarrow \overrightarrow{AB} \sim \overrightarrow{EF}$ (transitive).

A relation on a set S satisfying these properties is called an *equivalence relation*. It divides S into *equivalence classes*, mutually exclusive sets whose union is S, where two elements of S are in the same class ⇔ they are equivalent. Thus, in the present case the equivalence classes would be the sets of equivalent directed line segments.

We now define a *vector* to be such an equivalence class of directed line segments. We then define length and direction (angles, cosines) of a vector as the length and direction (angles, cosines) of any directed line segment in the class.

Frequently in more advanced mathematics definitions are made in terms of equivalence relations and equivalence classes.

2. Verify that Equation [2] holds for all cases of Figure 3.
3. Carry out the details for the proof of Theorem 1 (there are two statements to prove).
4. Is the direction angle α of a directed line segment the same as the angle of inclination of a line?

7.2 Addition and Scalar Multiplication

There are several operations on vectors which prove to be useful. In this section we shall discuss two of these, addition of vectors and multiplication of a vector by a number. It is customary, when working with vectors, to use the term *scalar* to mean number. Thus the second of these operations could also be called multiplication by a scalar, or scalar multiplication.

DEFINITION 4. *Let* $a = [a_1, a_2]$ *and* $b = [b_1, b_2]$ *be vectors and let* $c \in R$ *be a scalar. The sum* $a + b$ *and scalar multiple* ca *are defined by*

$$a + b = [a_1 + b_1, a_2 + b_2] \tag{8}$$
$$ca = [ca_1, ca_2], \tag{9}$$

respectively.

The geometric effect of scalar multiplication is easily described: it involves a change of length by the factor $|c|$; if $c > 0$, then $\mathbf{a}$ and $c\mathbf{a}$ have the same direction; whereas if $c < 0$, then $\mathbf{a}$ and $c\mathbf{a}$ lie on the same line but are oppositely directed, or have opposite *sense*. We prove the assertion about length as follows:

$$|c\mathbf{a}| = |[ca_1, ca_2]| = \sqrt{c^2a_1^2 + c^2a_2^2} = |c|\sqrt{a_1^2 + a_2^2},$$

or

$$|c\mathbf{a}| = |c|\,|\mathbf{a}|. \tag{10}$$

To prove the statement about the direction of $c\mathbf{a}$, let α and β be the direction angles of $\mathbf{a}$ and α_1 and β_1 those of $c\mathbf{a}$. Then, by [6], we have

$$a_1 = |\mathbf{a}|\cos\alpha$$
$$a_2 = |\mathbf{a}|\cos\beta$$

and

$$ca_1 = |c\mathbf{a}|\cos\alpha_1 = |c|\,|\mathbf{a}|\cos\alpha_1$$
$$ca_2 = |c\mathbf{a}|\cos\beta_1 = |c|\,|\mathbf{a}|\cos\beta_1.$$

From these equations we see that $c > 0 \Rightarrow \cos\alpha_1 = \cos\alpha$ and $\cos\beta_1 = \cos\beta$, whereas $c < 0 \Rightarrow \cos\alpha_1 = -\cos\alpha$ and $\cos\beta_1 = -\cos\beta$. In other words, $c > 0 \Rightarrow \mathbf{a}$ and $c\mathbf{a}$ have the same direction, while $c < 0 \Rightarrow c\mathbf{a}$ is directed oppositely to $\mathbf{a}$.

In Figure 8 we illustrate by showing $\mathbf{a}$, $3\mathbf{a}$, and $-2\mathbf{a}$.

The geometric interpretation of the sum of two vectors is often succinctly described by the phrase "parallelogram law": if $\mathbf{a}$ and $\mathbf{b}$ are drawn with the same initial point and if the parallelogram determined by these two sides is completed, then the vector $\mathbf{a} + \mathbf{b}$ is the diagonal from the common initial point of $\mathbf{a}$ and $\mathbf{b}$ to the opposite vertex. Figure 9 shows this. It also shows that

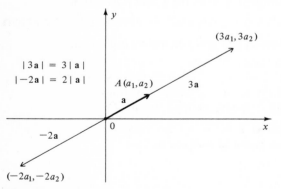

Figure 8

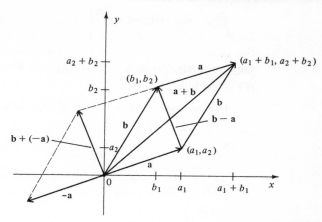

Figure 9

a + **b** can be obtained by drawing **b** with initial point at the terminal point of **a** and then drawing the segment from initial point of **a** to terminal point of **b**.

Figure 9 shows several additional facts about vector addition. We see that **b** + **a** = **a** + **b**, and that the second diagonal of the parallelogram is the vector which when added to **a** results in **b**; thus this diagonal should be **b** − **a** or, as is also illustrated in Figure 9, **b** + (−**a**). As regards length, it appears that

$$|\mathbf{a} + \mathbf{b}| < |\mathbf{a}| + |\mathbf{b}|.$$

These observations will soon be verified analytically; for complete generality, equality must be allowed in the statement about lengths (why?).

It will be useful to describe the algebraic properties of these vector operations. We do this in the following assertion, calling attention to the fact that the first five agree with the five addition properties for a field (Definition 1.1).

THEOREM 3.   *Let* **a**, **b**, *and* **c** *be vectors, let r and s be scalars in* **R**. *Then the following are true.*

1. **a** + **b** *is a vector.*
2. **a** + **b** = **b** + **a**.
3. **a** + (**b** + **c**) = (**a** + **b**) + **c**.
4. *There exists* **0** *such that* **a** + **0** = **a**.
5. *For every* **a** *there exists* −**a** *such that* **a** + (−**a**) = **0**.
6. *r***a** *is a vector.*
7. *r*(**a** + **b**) = *r***a** + *r***b**.
8. (*r* + *s*)**a** = *r***a** + *s***a**.

9. $(rs)\mathbf{a} = r(s\mathbf{a})$.

10. $1\mathbf{a} = \mathbf{a}$.

PROOF. These assertions follow easily from Definition 4 and the field properties for **R**, but to go through all of the details would be tedious. We shall prove 4, 5, and 7 and ask you to do several others as exercises.

4. The vector **0** is of course $[0, 0]$. Thus

$$\mathbf{a} + \mathbf{0} = [a_1, a_2] + [0, 0] = [a_1, a_2] = \mathbf{a}.$$

5. The vector $-\mathbf{a}$ is $(-1)\mathbf{a} = [-a_1, -a_2]$. Then

$$\mathbf{a} + (-\mathbf{a}) = [a_1, a_2] + [-a_1, -a_2] = [0, 0] = \mathbf{0}.$$

7. We have

$$
\begin{aligned}
r(\mathbf{a} + \mathbf{b}) &= r([a_1, a_2] + [b_1, b_2]) \\
&= r[a_1 + b_1, a_2 + b_2] && \text{(Def. 4)} \\
&= [r(a_1 + b_1), r(a_2 + b_2)] && \text{(Def. 4)} \\
&= [ra_1 + rb_1, ra_2 + rb_2] && \text{(?)} \\
&= [ra_1, ra_2] + [rb_1, rb_2] && \text{(Def. 4)} \\
&= r[a_1, a_2] + r[b_1, b_2] && \text{(Def. 4)} \\
&= r\mathbf{a} + r\mathbf{b}. \quad\blacksquare
\end{aligned}
$$

Subtraction for vectors can be handled as suggested in the discussion of Figure 9: we define $\mathbf{a} - \mathbf{b}$ by

$$\mathbf{a} - \mathbf{b} = \mathbf{a} + (-\mathbf{b}) = \mathbf{a} + (-1)\mathbf{b}. \tag{11}$$

Thus in terms of components we have

$$\mathbf{a} - \mathbf{b} = [a_1 - b_1, a_2 - b_2]. \tag{12}$$

There is a simple but important geometric fact about vector addition that should be made explicit.

THEOREM 4. *Given any three points A, B, and C, the following vector equation holds (see Figure 10):*

$$\overrightarrow{AB} + \overrightarrow{BC} = \overrightarrow{AC}.$$

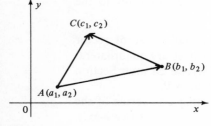

Figure 10

PROOF. Let the points A, B, and C be (a_1, a_2), (b_1, b_2), and (c_1, c_2), respectively. Then

$$\overrightarrow{AB} + \overrightarrow{BC} = [b_1 - a_1, b_2 - a_2] + [c_1 - b_1, c_2 - b_2]$$
$$= [c_1 - a_1, c_2 - a_2]$$
$$= \overrightarrow{AC}. \ \blacksquare$$

The previous discussion of the scalar multiple $c\mathbf{a}$ of a vector $\mathbf{a}$ showed that $c\mathbf{a}$ has the same or opposite direction as $\mathbf{a}$, depending on whether $c > 0$ or $c < 0$. In either case it is clear that $\mathbf{a}$ and $c\mathbf{a}$ are parallel. Moreover, the converse is true, as we now show.

THEOREM 5. *Two nonzero vectors $\mathbf{a}$ and $\mathbf{b}$ are parallel $\Leftrightarrow$ there exists a scalar c such that $\mathbf{b} = c\mathbf{a}$.*

PROOF. For the $\Rightarrow$ assertion, let $\mathbf{a} = [a_1, a_2]$ have direction cosines $\cos \alpha$ and $\cos \beta$ and let $\mathbf{b} = [b_1, b_2]$ have direction cosines $\cos \alpha'$ and $\cos \beta'$. Then, by [6] assuming $\mathbf{a} \neq 0$, $\mathbf{b} \neq 0$,

$$\left. \begin{array}{l} \cos \alpha = \dfrac{a_1}{|\mathbf{a}|}, \quad \cos \beta = \dfrac{a_2}{|\mathbf{a}|} \\[2mm] \text{and} \\[2mm] \cos \alpha' = \dfrac{b_1}{|\mathbf{b}|}, \quad \cos \beta' = \dfrac{b_2}{|\mathbf{b}|} \end{array} \right\}. \qquad [13]$$

The hypothesis that $\mathbf{b}$ is parallel to $\mathbf{a}$ implies that

$$\left. \begin{array}{l} \cos \alpha' = \pm \cos \alpha, \\ \cos \beta' = \pm \cos \beta \end{array} \right\}, \qquad [14]$$

the same sign holding in both cases. Using [13] in [14] we have

$$b_1 = \pm \frac{|\mathbf{b}|}{|\mathbf{a}|} a_1$$

and

$$b_2 = \pm \frac{|\mathbf{b}|}{|\mathbf{a}|} a_2,$$

i.e., $\mathbf{b} = c\mathbf{a}$, where $c = \pm (|\mathbf{b}|/|\mathbf{a}|)$.

The $\Leftarrow$ assertion has already been proven, as noted just prior to the statement of the theorem. $\blacksquare$

Example 2. As an illustration of the utility and power of vector methods we show that the midpoints of the sides of an arbitrary quadrilateral are the vertices of a parallelogram. Compare with Exercise C1 after Section 2.3.

First of all we choose the coordinate system so that one vertex of the quadrilateral $OABC$ is at the origin and one side lies along the positive x-axis. See Figure 11.

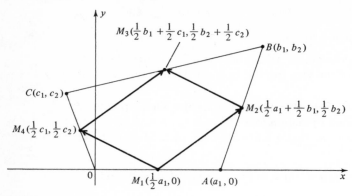

Figure 11

We compute the coordinates of the midpoints M_1, M_2, M_3, and M_4 as shown in Figure 11. It is then a simple matter to calculate the vectors $\overrightarrow{M_1M_2}$, $\overrightarrow{M_2M_3}$, $\overrightarrow{M_4M_3}$, and $\overrightarrow{M_1M_4}$:

$$\overrightarrow{M_1M_2} = [\tfrac{1}{2}b_1, \tfrac{1}{2}b_2] = \tfrac{1}{2}[b_1, b_2] = \overrightarrow{M_4M_3}$$
$$\overrightarrow{M_2M_3} = [\tfrac{1}{2}c_1 - \tfrac{1}{2}a_1, \tfrac{1}{2}c_2] = \tfrac{1}{2}[c_1 - a_1, c_2] = \overrightarrow{M_1M_4}.$$

Since the opposite sides are equal vectors, hence parallel and of equal length, the figure $M_1M_2M_3M_4$ is a parallelogram. Notice that the use of vector methods enabled us to bypass the formula for lengths.

We conclude this section by introducing a widely used and occasionally helpful notation for the unit vectors in the direction of the positive axes.

DEFINITION 5.   *The vectors* **i** *and* **j** *are defined by*

$$\mathbf{i} = [1, 0], \quad \mathbf{j} = [0, 1].$$

Every vector in the plane can be written uniquely as a linear combination of **i** and **j**. For, let $\mathbf{a} = [a_1, a_2]$; then

$$\begin{aligned}\mathbf{a} = [a_1, a_2] &= [a_1, 0] + [0, a_2]\\ &= a_1[1, 0] + a_2[0, 1]\\ &= a_1\mathbf{i} + a_2\mathbf{j}.\end{aligned}$$

Moreover, addition of vectors and multiplication by a scalar are easily carried out in terms of **i** and **j**. Thus, if $\mathbf{a} = [a_1, a_2]$ and $\mathbf{b} = [b_1, b_2]$, then

$$\mathbf{a} + \mathbf{b} = [a_1 + b_1, a_2 + b_2] = (a_1 + b_1)\mathbf{i} + (a_2 + b_2)\mathbf{j},$$

or

$$(a_1\mathbf{i} + a_2\mathbf{j}) + (b_1\mathbf{i} + b_2\mathbf{j}) = (a_1 + b_1)\mathbf{i} + (a_2 + b_2)\mathbf{j}.$$

Similarly,

$$ca = c(a_1\mathbf{i} + a_2\mathbf{j}) = (ca_1)\mathbf{i} + (ca_2)\mathbf{j}.$$

Example 3. Given the points $A(2, 1)$ and $B(5, 7)$, we find the point $P_0(x_0, y_0)$ that is one third of the way from A to B on the line segment $\overline{AB}$. See Figure 12.

Let $\mathbf{v} = \overrightarrow{AB} = [5 - 2,\ \ 7 - 1] = [3, 6] = 3\mathbf{i} + 6\mathbf{j}$. Then points P between A and B are described by the vector

$$\begin{aligned}
\overrightarrow{OP} = \overrightarrow{OA} + t\overrightarrow{AB} &= \overrightarrow{OA} + t\mathbf{v} \\
&= (2\mathbf{i} + \mathbf{j}) + t(3\mathbf{i} + 6\mathbf{j}) \\
&= (2 + 3t)\mathbf{i} + (1 + 6t)\mathbf{j}, \quad 0 \leqslant t \leqslant 1.
\end{aligned}$$

In particular, the desired point P_0 is found by using $t = \frac{1}{3}$:

$$\overrightarrow{OP_0} = 3\mathbf{i} + 3\mathbf{j} = [3, 3].$$

Thus the coordinates of P_0 are $(3, 3)$.

Exercises

A.   **1.** Let $\mathbf{a} = [5, 9]$, $\mathbf{b} = [4, 2]$, and $\mathbf{c} = [3, -5]$. Find
       (a) $\mathbf{a} + \mathbf{b}$.
       (b) $(\mathbf{a} + \mathbf{b}) + \mathbf{c}$ and $\mathbf{a} + (\mathbf{b} + \mathbf{c})$.
       (c) $(-1)\mathbf{a}$.
       (d) $\mathbf{a} - \mathbf{b}$ and $\mathbf{b} - \mathbf{a}$.
       (e) $2\mathbf{a} + 3\mathbf{b}$.
       (f) $3\mathbf{a} - 4\mathbf{b}$.
       (g) $\mathbf{a} - 2\mathbf{b} + \mathbf{c}$.
       (h) $2\mathbf{b} - \mathbf{c}$. Compare with $\mathbf{a}$.

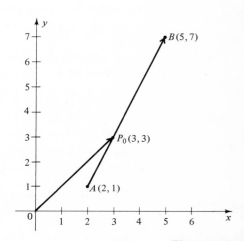

Figure 12

2. Given the points $A(-2, -3)$, $B(4, 0)$, $C(6, 6)$, and $D(-4, 1)$.

(a) Find the vectors $\overrightarrow{AB}$, $\overrightarrow{BC}$, $\overrightarrow{CD}$, and $\overrightarrow{DA}$.

(b) What can be said about $\overrightarrow{AB}$ and $\overrightarrow{CD}$?

(c) Find $|\overrightarrow{AD}|$.

(d) Find $\overrightarrow{AB} + \overrightarrow{BC} + \overrightarrow{CD} + \overrightarrow{DA}$. [*Hint:* Theorem 4.]

(e) Find a unit vector parallel to $\overrightarrow{BC}$.

3. Let $\mathbf{v}_1 = [1, 1]$, $\mathbf{v}_2 = [-1, 2]$. For each vector $\mathbf{a}$ given below find scalars c_1 and c_2 such that $\mathbf{a} = c_1\mathbf{v}_1 + c_2\mathbf{v}_2$.

(a) $\mathbf{a} = [3, 0]$.

(b) $\mathbf{a} = [-4, 3]$.

(c) $\mathbf{a} = [2, 5]$.

(d) $\mathbf{a} = [0, -4]$.

4. Given the points $A(-4, -3)$, $B(2, -2)$, $C(4, 5)$, $D(-1, 8)$, and $E(-7, 4)$. Find

(a) $\overrightarrow{AB} + \overrightarrow{BC} + \overrightarrow{CD}$.

(b) $\overrightarrow{AE} + \overrightarrow{ED}$.

(c) $\overrightarrow{AD}$.

5. Let $\mathbf{v}_1 = -3\mathbf{i} + 2\mathbf{j}$, $\mathbf{v}_2 = 6\mathbf{i} - 4\mathbf{j}$. Find scalars c_1 and c_2 such that $c_1\mathbf{v}_1 + c_2\mathbf{v}_2 = \mathbf{0}$.

6. Find the point P_0:

(a) P_0 is one seventh of the way from $A(-3, 2)$ to $B(4, -5)$.

(b) P_0 is two fifths of the way from $A(-2, -4)$ to $B(3, 1)$.

(c) P_0 is two thirds of the way from $A(-4, 2)$ to $B(8, 5)$.

(d) P_0 is on the line determined by $A(2, 1)$ and $B(6, 5)$, and A is the midpoint of $\overline{P_0 B}$.

7. Find the point P_0:

(a) P_0 is one fourth of the way from $A(-1, 5)$ to $B(3, 1)$.

(b) P_0 is three fifths of the way from $A(-2, -1)$ to $B(3, 9)$.

(c) P_0 is on the line determined by $A(-3, 0)$ and $B(4, 5)$, and B is the midpoint of $\overline{AP_0}$.

B. **1.** Prove parts 2, 3, and 8 of Theorem 3.

2. Let $\mathbf{v}_1$ and $\mathbf{v}_2$ be vectors; suppose there exist scalars c_1 and c_2, not both zero, such that $c_1\mathbf{v}_1 + c_2\mathbf{v}_2 = \mathbf{0}$. Prove that $\mathbf{v}_1$ and $\mathbf{v}_2$ are parallel.

3. Let $\mathbf{v}_1$ and $\mathbf{v}_2$ be given nonzero vectors, and let $\mathbf{a} = [a_1, a_2]$ be an arbitrary vector. Is it possible to find scalars c_1 and c_2 such that $\mathbf{a} = c_1\mathbf{v}_1 + c_2\mathbf{v}_2$? [*Hints:* (i) See Exercise A3. (ii) What if $\mathbf{v}_1$ and $\mathbf{v}_2$ are the two vectors of Exercise A5?

C. **1.** Consider the point $A(-3, 2)$ and the vector $\mathbf{v} = [3, -4]$. Find the point $B(b_1, b_2)$ such that $\overrightarrow{AB}$ is parallel to $\mathbf{v}$ and $|\overrightarrow{AB}| = 10$. How many such points are there?

2. Same as Exercise C1, except A is $(3, 2)$ and $\mathbf{v} = [2, 1]$.

7.3 The Inner Product

In this section we shall introduce a form of multiplication for vectors, the *inner product* (also called the *dot product* or *scalar product*). The utility of this concept will be amply demonstrated.

DEFINITION 6. *Let* $\mathbf{a} = [a_1, a_2] = a_1\mathbf{i} + a_2\mathbf{j}$, $\mathbf{b} = [b_1, b_2] = b_1\mathbf{i} + b_2\mathbf{j}$. The *inner product* $\mathbf{a} \cdot \mathbf{b}$ of $\mathbf{a}$ and $\mathbf{b}$ is defined by

$$\mathbf{a} \cdot \mathbf{b} = a_1b_1 + a_2b_2. \qquad [15]$$

Notice that the right-hand side of [15] is a number: the inner product of two *vectors* is a *scalar*.

We mention some other algebraic properties of the inner product.

THEOREM 6. *Let* $\mathbf{a}$, $\mathbf{b}$, *and* $\mathbf{c}$ *be (arbitrary) vectors; let* $h \in \mathbf{R}$. *Then*

1. $\mathbf{a} \cdot \mathbf{b} = \mathbf{b} \cdot \mathbf{a}$.
2. $h(\mathbf{a} \cdot \mathbf{b}) = (h\mathbf{a}) \cdot \mathbf{b} = \mathbf{a} \cdot (h\mathbf{b})$.
3. $\mathbf{a} \cdot (\mathbf{b} + \mathbf{c}) = \mathbf{a} \cdot \mathbf{b} + \mathbf{a} \cdot \mathbf{c}$.
4. $\mathbf{a} \cdot \mathbf{a} = |\mathbf{a}|^2$.
5. $\mathbf{a} \cdot \mathbf{a} \geqslant 0$ and $\mathbf{a} \cdot \mathbf{a} = 0 \Leftrightarrow \mathbf{a} = \mathbf{0}$.

PROOF. The commutativity is an immediate consequence of commutativity of multiplication in $\mathbf{R}$.

For assertion 2, let $\mathbf{a} = [a_1, a_2]$, $\mathbf{b} = [b_1, b_2]$. Then

$$h(\mathbf{a} \cdot \mathbf{b}) = h(a_1b_1 + a_2b_2) = ha_1b_1 + ha_2b_2$$
$$(h\mathbf{a}) \cdot \mathbf{b} = [ha_1, ha_2] \cdot [b_1, b_2] = ha_1b_1 + ha_2b_2$$
$$\mathbf{a} \cdot (h\mathbf{b}) = [a_1, a_1] \cdot [hb_1, hb_2] = ha_1b_1 + ha_2b_2.$$

The equality of the three left members follows from that of the three right-hand sides.

We leave the proof of the distributivity as an exercise.

For assertion 4, we have

$$\mathbf{a} \cdot \mathbf{a} = a_1^2 + a_2^2 = |\mathbf{a}|^2,$$

by Equation [5].

Finally, assertion 5 follows immediately from assertion 4. ∎

It is worth calling attention to the behavior of the inner products of the unit vectors $\mathbf{i}$ and $\mathbf{j}$:

$$\left\{ \begin{array}{c} \mathbf{i} \cdot \mathbf{i} = \mathbf{j} \cdot \mathbf{j} = 1 \\ \mathbf{i} \cdot \mathbf{j} = 0 \end{array} \right\}. \qquad [16]$$

We next describe the geometric interpretation of the inner product.

THEOREM 7. *Let* **a** *and* **b** *be arbitrary vectors. Then*

$$\mathbf{a} \cdot \mathbf{b} = |\mathbf{a}|\,|\mathbf{b}|\cos\theta, \tag{17}$$

where $\theta, 0 \leqslant \theta \leqslant \pi$, *is the angle between the vectors when they are drawn with the same initial point.*

PROOF. See Figure 13. We use the law of cosines on triangle *OAB*, writing it in vector form:

$$|\mathbf{b} - \mathbf{a}|^2 = |\mathbf{a}|^2 + |\mathbf{b}|^2 - 2|\mathbf{a}|\,|\mathbf{b}|\cos\theta.$$

If we use assertion 4 of Theorem 6 we can write this equation as

$$(\mathbf{b} - \mathbf{a}) \cdot (\mathbf{b} - \mathbf{a}) = \mathbf{a} \cdot \mathbf{a} + \mathbf{b} \cdot \mathbf{b} - 2|\mathbf{a}|\,|\mathbf{b}|\cos\theta. \tag{18}$$

Now we use assertions 1, 2, and 3 of Theorem 6 on the left-hand side of [18]:

$$\begin{aligned}
(\mathbf{b} - \mathbf{a}) \cdot (\mathbf{b} - \mathbf{a}) &= (\mathbf{b} - \mathbf{a}) \cdot \mathbf{b} - (\mathbf{b} - \mathbf{a}) \cdot \mathbf{a} \\
&= \mathbf{b} \cdot (\mathbf{b} - \mathbf{a}) - \mathbf{a} \cdot (\mathbf{b} - \mathbf{a}) \\
&= \mathbf{b} \cdot \mathbf{b} - \mathbf{b} \cdot \mathbf{a} - \mathbf{a} \cdot \mathbf{b} + \mathbf{a} \cdot \mathbf{a} \\
&= \mathbf{a} \cdot \mathbf{a} + \mathbf{b} \cdot \mathbf{b} - 2\mathbf{a} \cdot \mathbf{b}.
\end{aligned}$$

It follows from this equation and from [18] that

$$\mathbf{a} \cdot \mathbf{b} = |\mathbf{a}|\,|\mathbf{b}|\cos\theta. \quad\blacksquare$$

[As the preceding development of $(\mathbf{b} - \mathbf{a}) \cdot (\mathbf{b} - \mathbf{a})$ illustrates, assertions 1, 2, and 3 of Theorem 6 enable us to manipulate inner products of vectors the same way we would manipulate products of numbers. Exception: since $\mathbf{a} \cdot \mathbf{b}$ is a scalar, none of the following is meaningful: $\mathbf{a} \cdot \mathbf{b} \cdot \mathbf{c}$, $(\mathbf{a} \cdot \mathbf{b}) \cdot \mathbf{c}$, $\mathbf{a} \cdot (\mathbf{b} \cdot \mathbf{c})$.]

There are two important consequences of Theorem 7, both of which we state formally.

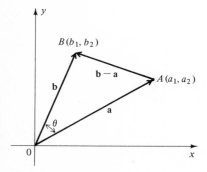

Figure 13

THEOREM 8.   *The vectors* **a** *and* **b** *are perpendicular if and only if their inner product is zero. In symbols,*

$$\mathbf{a} \perp \mathbf{b} \Leftrightarrow \mathbf{a} \cdot \mathbf{b} = 0. \tag{19}$$

PROOF.   Suppose first that **a** and **b** are perpendicular. Then $\theta = \pi/2$ and $\cos \theta = 0$, so, by [17], $\mathbf{a} \cdot \mathbf{b} = 0$.

For the $\Leftarrow$ we assume $\mathbf{a} \cdot \mathbf{b} = 0$. Then, by [17],

$$|\mathbf{a}|\,|\mathbf{b}| \cos \theta = 0. \tag{20}$$

Now, if either $\mathbf{a} = \mathbf{0}$ or $\mathbf{b} = \mathbf{0}$, then we agree that **a** and **b** are perpendicular (we have said that the zero vector will have all directions in part so that we could say that the zero vector is perpendicular to every vector). And if neither $\mathbf{a} = \mathbf{0}$ nor $\mathbf{b} = \mathbf{0}$, then $|\mathbf{a}|\,|\mathbf{b}| \neq 0$; it must follow from [20] that $\cos \theta = 0$, or $\theta = \pi/2$, which implies that **a** and **b** are perpendicular. ∎

THEOREM 9 (CAUCHY-SCHWARZ INEQUALITY).   *For any two vectors* **a** *and* **b**

$$(\mathbf{a} \cdot \mathbf{b})^2 \leqslant |\mathbf{a}|^2\,|\mathbf{b}|^2. \tag{21}$$

Equality holds if and only if **a** *and* **b** *are parallel.*

PROOF.   (See Exercise B4 for a proof which holds in a more general context and for some ramifications thereof.) From [17] we have, squaring both sides,

$$\begin{aligned}(\mathbf{a} \cdot \mathbf{b})^2 &= |\mathbf{a}|^2\,|\mathbf{b}|^2 \cos^2 \theta \\ &\leqslant |\mathbf{a}|^2\,|\mathbf{b}|^2,\end{aligned}$$

since $\cos^2 \theta \leqslant 1$. Moreover $\cos^2 \theta = 1 \Leftrightarrow \theta = 0$ or $\theta = \pi$, which correspond exactly to the cases of parallel vectors. ∎

We turn now to some illustrations.

Example 4.   We shall find the angle between $\overrightarrow{AB}$ and $\overrightarrow{AC}$, where A, B, and C are $(2, 1)$, $(5, 3)$, and $(4, 7)$, respectively. See Figure 14.

Let

$$\begin{aligned}\mathbf{b} &= \overrightarrow{AB} = [5 - 2, 3 - 1] = [3, 2] \\ \mathbf{c} &= \overrightarrow{AC} = [4 - 2, 7 - 1] = [2, 6].\end{aligned}$$

Then $\mathbf{b} \cdot \mathbf{c} = 3 \cdot 2 + 2 \cdot 6 = 18$; also

$$\begin{aligned}|\mathbf{b}| &= \sqrt{\mathbf{b} \cdot \mathbf{b}} = \sqrt{9 + 4} = \sqrt{13} \\ |\mathbf{c}| &= \sqrt{\mathbf{c} \cdot \mathbf{c}} = \sqrt{4 + 36} = \sqrt{40} = 2\sqrt{10}.\end{aligned}$$

Since, by [17], $\mathbf{b} \cdot \mathbf{c} = |\mathbf{b}|\,|\mathbf{c}| \cos \theta$, we have

$$\cos \theta = \frac{\mathbf{b} \cdot \mathbf{c}}{|\mathbf{b}|\,|\mathbf{c}|} = \frac{18}{(\sqrt{13})(2\sqrt{10})} = \frac{9}{\sqrt{130}} \approx 0.789,$$

whence $\theta \approx 37° - 50'$.

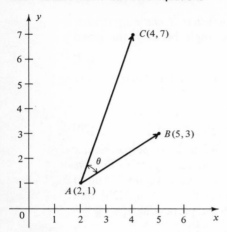

Figure 14

Example 5. We use the inner product to determine whether the angle between $\mathbf{a} = 3\mathbf{i} + 4\mathbf{j}$ and $\mathbf{b} = -7\mathbf{i} + 5\mathbf{j}$ is acute or obtuse. See Figure 15.

Since $\mathbf{a} \cdot \mathbf{b} = -21 + 20 = -1 < 0$, it follows that $\cos \theta < 0$; thus θ lies between $\pi/2$ and π.

Example 6. We find the value of c such that the vectors $\mathbf{a} = [1, 3]$ and $\mathbf{b} = [2, c]$ are (1) perpendicular, (2) parallel.

1. By Theorem 8, $\mathbf{a}$ and $\mathbf{b}$ are perpendicular $\Leftrightarrow \mathbf{a} \cdot \mathbf{b} = 0 \Leftrightarrow 2 + 3c = 0 \Leftrightarrow c = -\frac{2}{3}$.
2. By Theorem 9, $\mathbf{a}$ and $\mathbf{b}$ are parallel $\Leftrightarrow (\mathbf{a} \cdot \mathbf{b})^2 = |\mathbf{a}|^2 |\mathbf{b}|^2 \Leftrightarrow (2 + 3c)^2 = 10(4 + c^2) \Leftrightarrow c = 6$.

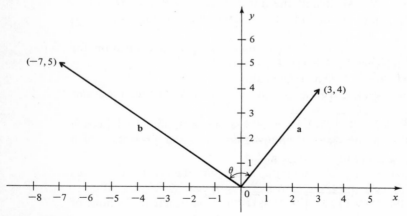

Figure 15

Exercises

A. In Exercises 1–10 find $\cos \theta$, where θ is the angle between the given vectors.

   1. $\mathbf{a} = [3, -1], \mathbf{b} = [-2, 5]$.
   2. $\mathbf{a} = [1, 4], \mathbf{b} = [-3, 2]$.
   3. $\mathbf{a} = 2\mathbf{i} + 7\mathbf{j}, \mathbf{b} = -14\mathbf{i} + 4\mathbf{j}$.
   4. $\mathbf{a} = 4\mathbf{i} - 3\mathbf{j}, \mathbf{b} = 6\mathbf{i} + 8\mathbf{j}$.
   5. $\overrightarrow{AB}, \overrightarrow{CD}$, for $A(3, -2), B(3, 4), C(-4, 1), D(-1, -1)$.
   6. $\overrightarrow{AB}, \overrightarrow{CD}$, for $A(0, 3), B(3, 4), C(-2, 0), D(0, -4)$.
   7. $\mathbf{a} = [1, 1], \mathbf{b} = [1, -1]$.
   8. $\mathbf{a} = [3, 4], \mathbf{b} = [5, -12]$.
   9. $\mathbf{a} = -4\mathbf{i} - 3\mathbf{j}, \mathbf{b} = 7\mathbf{i} + 24\mathbf{j}$.
   10. $\mathbf{a} = -3\mathbf{i} + 5\mathbf{j}, \mathbf{b} = -3\mathbf{i} + 4\mathbf{j}$.
   11. Find the cosines of the angles of the triangle with vertices $A(-3, -2)$, $B(5, 1)$, and $C(2, 4)$.
   12. Find c such that $\mathbf{a} = [3, -4]$ and $\mathbf{b} = [c, 1]$ are perpendicular.
   13. Find c such that the vectors of Exercise A12 intersect at an angle of $\pi/3$.
   14. Find c such that the vectors $\mathbf{a} = -4\mathbf{i} + 3\mathbf{j}$ and $\mathbf{b} = \mathbf{i} + c\mathbf{j}$ intersect at an angle of $3\pi/4$.
   15. Find b_1 and b_2 so that $\mathbf{b} = [b_1, b_2]$ is a unit vector perpendicular to $\mathbf{a} = [6, -8]$.
   16. Let $\mathbf{a} = [4, 3], \mathbf{b} = [-1, 2]$, and $\mathbf{v} = [-13, 4]$. Find scalars h and k such that $\mathbf{v} = h\mathbf{a} + k\mathbf{b}$.

   Hint: Using both expressions for $\mathbf{v}$, calculate $\mathbf{v} \cdot \mathbf{a}$ and $\mathbf{v} \cdot \mathbf{b}$, and solve the resulting system of linear equations for h and k.

B.   **1.** Prove the "triangle inequality"

$$|\mathbf{a} + \mathbf{b}| \leqslant |\mathbf{a}| + |\mathbf{b}|. \tag{22}$$

   Hint: (i) Use assertion 4 of Theorem 6 to get an expression for $|\mathbf{a} + \mathbf{b}|^2$. (ii) Use the Cauchy-Schwarz inequality [21].
   2. Explain the name "triangle inequality" for [22].
   3. If $\mathbf{a}$ is a unit vector, then $\mathbf{a} \cdot \mathbf{b} = |\mathbf{b}| \cos \theta$, which is called the *scalar projection* of $\mathbf{b}$ *along* $\mathbf{a}$. See Figure 16.
   (a) The term scalar projection of $\mathbf{b}$ along $\mathbf{a}$ applies to $|\mathbf{b}| \cos \theta$, whether or not $|\mathbf{a}| = 1$. Show that the scalar projection of $\mathbf{b}$ along $\mathbf{a}$ is $(\mathbf{a} \cdot \mathbf{b})/\sqrt{\mathbf{a} \cdot \mathbf{a}}$, if $\mathbf{a} \neq \mathbf{0}$.
   (b) Let $\mathbf{a} = [a_1, a_2]$. Show that a_1 and a_2 are the scalar projections of $\mathbf{a}$ along $\mathbf{i}$ and $\mathbf{j}$, respectively.
   (c) Let $\mathbf{a} = [3, -4]$ and $\mathbf{b} = [5, 12]$. Find the scalar projections of $\mathbf{a}$ along $\mathbf{b}$ and of $\mathbf{b}$ along $\mathbf{a}$. Make a sketch.

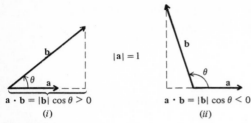

$\mathbf{a} \cdot \mathbf{b} = |\mathbf{b}| \cos \theta > 0$

(i)

$\mathbf{a} \cdot \mathbf{b} = |\mathbf{b}| \cos \theta < 0$

(ii)

Figure 16

(d) Let **a** and **b** be nonzero vectors; let

$$\mathbf{v} = \frac{\mathbf{a}}{|\mathbf{a}|} + \frac{\mathbf{b}}{|\mathbf{b}|}.$$

Show that **v** bisects the angle between **a** and **b**. [*Hint:* show that the scalar projection of **v** along **a** equals that of **v** along **b**. Why is this sufficient?]

(e) What happens in (d) if **a** and **b** are parallel but have opposite directions?

4. In this exercise we outline a proof of the Cauchy-Schwarz inequality which has greater generality than that given in the text. First we indicate what this greater generality might be.

A useful generalization of the vector concept to *n*-dimensions, for arbitrary positive integer *n*, is to define a vector **a** as an ordered *n*-tuple of real numbers:

$$\mathbf{a} = [a_1, a_2, \ldots, a_n].$$

Also, if $\mathbf{b} = [b_1, \ldots, b_n]$, then, by definition,

$$\mathbf{a} = \mathbf{b} \Leftrightarrow a_1 = b_1, \quad a_2 = b_2, \ldots, a_n = b_n$$
$$\mathbf{a} + \mathbf{b} = [a_1 + b_1, a_2 + b_2, \ldots, a_n + b_n]$$
$$h\mathbf{a} = [ha_1, ha_2, \ldots, ha_n], \quad h \in \mathbf{R}$$
$$\mathbf{a} \cdot \mathbf{b} = a_1b_1 + a_2b_2 + \cdots + a_nb_n$$
$$|\mathbf{a}|^2 = \mathbf{a} \cdot \mathbf{a} = a_1^2 + a_2^2 + \cdots + a_n^2$$

and

$$\cos \theta = \frac{\mathbf{a} \cdot \mathbf{b}}{|\mathbf{a}| \, |\mathbf{b}|}.$$

The properties we have studied so far about vectors in the plane would all apply in "*n*-space," but, because we have *defined* the angle between two vectors by the last equation, we cannot use the proof of the text for the Cauchy-Schwarz inequality. (How do we know that $\cos \theta$, so defined, satisfies $-1 \leqslant \cos \theta \leqslant 1$? Answer: by the Cauchy-Schwarz inequality, provided we can find an alternate proof for it.)

(a) Let $t \in \mathbf{R}$. Then, for all t,

$$(\mathbf{a} - t\mathbf{b}) \cdot (\mathbf{a} - t\mathbf{b}) \geqslant 0.$$

Why?

(b) Expand the left-hand side of the inequality in (a), writing it as a quadratic in t, say, $q(t)$.

(c) Since, by part (a), $q(t) \geqslant 0$ for all t, the discriminant of q must be nonpositive. Why? [*Hint:* what would happen to the equation $q(t) = 0$ if the discriminant were positive?]

(d) Calculate the discriminant, impose the condition of being nonpositive, and obtain [21].

(e) Show that equality holds in [21] if and only if $\mathbf{a} = h\mathbf{b}$ for some number h.

(f) Write the detailed expression for [21] in case $\mathbf{a}$ and $\mathbf{b}$ are ordered n-tuples as described at the beginning of this exercise.

C. **1.** See Exercise A16. Let $\mathbf{a}$ and $\mathbf{b}$ be fixed nonzero, nonparallel vectors. Let $\mathbf{v}$ be an arbitrary vector.

(a) Find scalars h and k such that $\mathbf{v} = h\mathbf{a} + k\mathbf{b}$. [*Hint:* solve the system of equations obtained from $\mathbf{v} \cdot \mathbf{a}$ and $\mathbf{v} \cdot \mathbf{b}$.]

(b) Show that if $\mathbf{a}$ and $\mathbf{b}$ are perpendicular, the h and k obtained in part (a) reduce to

$$h = \frac{\mathbf{v} \cdot \mathbf{a}}{\mathbf{a} \cdot \mathbf{a}}, \quad k = \frac{\mathbf{v} \cdot \mathbf{b}}{\mathbf{b} \cdot \mathbf{b}}.$$

(c) Find the h and k of part (a) on the assumption that $\mathbf{a}$ and $\mathbf{b}$ are unit vectors, but not necessarily perpendicular.

(d) Show that if $\mathbf{a}$ and $\mathbf{b}$ are unit vectors and perpendicular, then

$$h = \mathbf{v} \cdot \mathbf{a} \quad \text{and} \quad k = \mathbf{v} \cdot \mathbf{b}. \tag{23}$$

2. See Exercise C1. Let $\mathbf{a}$ be a unit vector that makes an angle α with the positive x-axis, and let $\mathbf{b}$ be a unit vector that makes an angle of $\pi/2$ with $\mathbf{a}$. See Figure 17. The terminal points of $\mathbf{a}$ and $\mathbf{b}$ are then, respectively,

$$(\cos \alpha, \sin \alpha)$$

and

$$\left(\cos\left(\alpha + \frac{\pi}{2}\right), \sin\left(\alpha + \frac{\pi}{2}\right)\right) = (-\sin \alpha, \cos \alpha).$$

Thus

$$\mathbf{a} = [\cos \alpha, \sin \alpha]$$
$$\mathbf{b} = [-\sin \alpha, \cos \alpha].$$

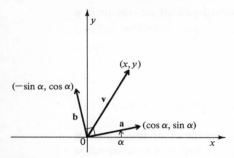

Figure 17

Let $\mathbf{v} = [x, y]$ be an arbitrary vector. Use [23] to express $\mathbf{v}$ in terms of $\mathbf{a}$ and $\mathbf{b}$.

7.4 Vector Functions and Parametric Equations

In this section we shall introduce the concept of a vector function (more exactly, a vector-valued function—the precise definition will be given shortly) and exploit its geometric implications. We shall make use in what follows of a nonempty set $T \subset \mathbf{R}$; it will usually be satisfactory to think of T as an interval—finite, infinite, open, closed, possibly $T = \mathbf{R}$.

DEFINITION 7. *By a vector function* $\mathbf{r}$, *we mean a function that maps a nonempty set* $T \subset \mathbf{R}$ *into* $\mathbf{R}^2$. *In symbols,*

$$\mathbf{r} : T \to \mathbf{R}^2, \qquad T \subset \mathbf{R}, \quad T \neq \varnothing.$$

As each $t_0 \in T$ determines a vector in $\mathbf{R}^2$, we can write

$$\mathbf{r}(t_0) = x_0\mathbf{i} + y_0\mathbf{j};$$

this statement holding true for every $t \in T$, we can write more generally that

$$\mathbf{r}(t) = x(t)\mathbf{i} + y(t)\mathbf{j},$$

where x and y are scalar functions (i.e., the functional values are in $\mathbf{R}$) determined by $\mathbf{r}$. Conversely, given a pair of functions f and g,

$$f : T \to \mathbf{R}$$
$$g : T \to \mathbf{R},$$

we can define a vector function $\mathbf{r}$ by

$$\mathbf{r}(t) = f(t)\mathbf{i} + g(t)\mathbf{j},$$

valid for all $t \in T$.

Thus we see that, just as a vector is an ordered pair of scalars so is a vector function with domain T an ordered pair of scalar functions defined on T.

We now look at some examples.

Example 7. Suppose $\mathbf{r}$ is defined by

$$\mathbf{r}(t) = (2t - 1)\mathbf{i} + (4 - t)\mathbf{j}.$$

In this case $T = \mathbf{R}$. We obtain a geometric interpretation of this function by considering, for every $t \in T$, $\mathbf{r}(t)$ as the vector from the origin to the point $(2t - 1, 4 - t)$. The set of these terminal points then describes a curve in the plane. As a crude method of determining the nature of this curve it is possible to assign values to t and calculate corresponding values of x and y. Thus

$$\mathbf{r}(0) = -\mathbf{i} + 4\mathbf{j}$$
$$\mathbf{r}(1) = \mathbf{i} + 3\mathbf{j}$$
$$\mathbf{r}(2) = 3\mathbf{i} + 2\mathbf{j}, \quad \text{etc.}$$

See Figure 18.

It would appear—and it is true—that the geometric interpretation of $\mathbf{r}$ is in this case a straight line. In fact, if we consider the two scalar functions determined by $\mathbf{r}$:

$$x = 2t - 1$$
$$y = 4 - t,$$

we see that we can solve the first of these for t and substitute into the second, thereby obtaining

$$y = 4 - \frac{x + 1}{2} = -\frac{1}{2}x + \frac{7}{2},$$

the graph of which is clearly the line of Figure 18.

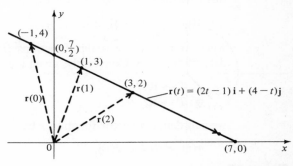

Figure 18

However, we must quickly point out that this straight line is not the *graph* of **r**, but the *range*. According to the obvious generalization of Definition 2.4, the graph of the function **r** is the set

$$G = \{(x, y, t) \mid t \in T, (y, z) = \mathbf{r}(t)\},$$

a subset of $\mathbf{R}^3$. Our interest will continue to focus on the range, not the graph, of vector functions.

Example 8.   Consider the function **r** defined by

$$\mathbf{r}(t) = \cos t\mathbf{i} + \sin t\mathbf{j}. \qquad\qquad [24]$$

Clearly one can take $T = \mathbf{R}$. To discern the geometric description of the range of **r** we note that

$$x(t) = \cos t, \quad y(t) = \sin t.$$

Thus, for all $t \in \mathbf{R}$,

$$x^2(t) + y^2(t) = 1,$$

and we see that the curve described is the unit circle. Notice, however, that the circle is described completely for $0 \leqslant t < 2\pi$, and we could take $T = \{t \mid 0 \leqslant t < 2\pi\}$. Choosing $T = \{t \mid 0 \leqslant t < 4\pi\}$ would give the circle described twice. See Figure 19.

Example 9.   Let

$$\mathbf{r}(t) = \frac{1 - t^2}{1 + t^2}\mathbf{i} + \frac{2t}{1 + t^2}\mathbf{j}. \qquad\qquad [25]$$

To determine the geometric nature of the range of **r**, we observe that

$$x(t) = \frac{1 - t^2}{1 + t^2}, \quad y(t) = \frac{2t}{1 + t^2},$$

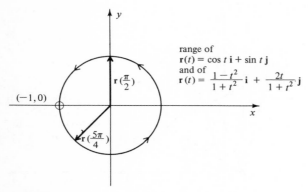

range of
$\mathbf{r}(t) = \cos t\,\mathbf{i} + \sin t\,\mathbf{j}$
and of
$\mathbf{r}(t) = \dfrac{1-t^2}{1+t^2}\,\mathbf{i} + \dfrac{2t}{1+t^2}\,\mathbf{j}$

Figure 19

from which it follows—after a brief computation—that

$$x^2(t) + y^2(t) = 1.$$

Thus it would appear that the set of points determined by [25] is the same as that determined by [24]. A more complete description is this: every point determined by [25] is also determined by [24], but not conversely. In particular, the point $(-1, 0)$ cannot be obtained from [25]; moreover, if t is not restricted, i.e., if t runs through all of **R**, [24] gives every point of the circle infinitely many times, whereas the points of [25] trace out the circle [minus $(-1, 0)$] exactly once for $-\infty < t < \infty$ (see Exercise A15).

Example 10. Consider the function **r** defined by

$$\mathbf{r}(t) = \cos^2\left(\frac{\pi}{2}t\right)\mathbf{i} + \sin^2\left(\frac{\pi}{2}t\right)\mathbf{j}.$$

Letting

$$\left.\begin{aligned} x &= \cos^2 \frac{\pi}{2}t \\ y &= \sin^2 \frac{\pi}{2}t \end{aligned}\right\} \tag{26}$$

we can see that for all t it is true that $x + y = 1$, $x \geqslant 0$, $y \geqslant 0$. Thus the range of this function is the line segment shown in Figure 20. Note, however, that the entire segment is obtained for $0 \leqslant t \leqslant 1$; the t interval, $1 \leqslant t \leqslant 2$, gives the same segment described in the opposite direction.

We call attention to the fact that the range of a vector function gives us more than a set of points; the *more* is an orientation or direction, the positive direction being that of increasing t. We have shown the positive direction by means of arrows in Figures 18 and 19.

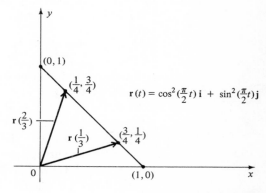

Figure 20

Equations [26] are called *parametric equations* for the curve of Figure 20; the variable *t* is called the *parameter*. In three-dimensional geometry parametric equations are important for representing curves. As we point out in the exercises which follow, and as we have already suggested, a given curve may have many different parametric representations, or *parametrizations*. In Section 7.5 we shall illustrate how a parameter, or auxiliary variable, may be of considerable help in getting an analytic representation for a curve defined by some geometric property.

Exercises

A. In Exercises 1–14 determine the nature of the curve determined by the range of **r**. In each case sketch the curve and indicate the positive direction (that of increasing *t*) along the curve.

1. $\mathbf{r}(t) = (t + 1)\mathbf{i} + (t - 1)\mathbf{j}$, $T = \{t \mid 0 \leqslant t \leqslant 1\}$.
2. $\mathbf{r}(t) = (t + 1)\mathbf{i} + (t - 1)\mathbf{j}$, $T = \{t \mid 1 \leqslant t < \infty\}$.
3. $\mathbf{r}(t) = (t + 1)\mathbf{i} + (t - 1)\mathbf{j}$, $T = \mathbf{R}$.
4. $\mathbf{r}(r) = t\mathbf{i} + \sqrt{4 - t^2}\,\mathbf{j}$, $T = \{t \mid -2 \leqslant t \leqslant 2\}$.
5. $\mathbf{r}(t) = t\mathbf{i} - \sqrt{4 - t^2}\,\mathbf{j}$, $T = \{t \mid -2 \leqslant t \leqslant 2\}$.
6. $\mathbf{r}(t) = (1 - t^2)\mathbf{i} + t^2\mathbf{j}$, $T = \{t \mid 0 \leqslant t \leqslant 1\}$.
7. $\mathbf{r}(t) = [(1 - t), t]$, $T = \{t \mid 0 \leqslant t \leqslant 1\}$.
8. $\mathbf{r}(t) = [t, t^2]$, $T = \mathbf{R}$.
9. $\mathbf{r}(t) = [t^2, t^3]$, $T = \mathbf{R}$
10. $\mathbf{r}(t) = [t^3, t^2]$, $T = \mathbf{R}$.
11. $\mathbf{r}(t) = [a\cos^4(\pi/2)t, a\sin^4(\pi/2)t]$, $a > 0$, $T = \{t \mid 0 \leqslant t \leqslant 1\}$.
12. Same as Exercise A11, except $T = \{t \mid 1 \leqslant t \leqslant 2\}$.
13. $\mathbf{r}(t) = [a\cos^3(\pi/2)t, a\sin^3(\pi/2)t]$, $a > 0$, $T = \{t \mid 0 \leqslant t \leqslant 1\}$.
14. Same as Exercise A13, except $T = \{t \mid 0 \leqslant t \leqslant 4\}$.
15. This refers to Example 9. Describe the portion of the circle determined by each of the following intervals:
    (a) $T = \{t \mid -\infty < t \leqslant -1\}$.
    (b) $T = \{t \mid -1 \leqslant t \leqslant 0\}$.
    (c) $T = \{t \mid 0 \leqslant t \leqslant 1\}$.
    (d) $T = \{t \mid 1 \leqslant t < \infty\}$.
16. What is the relation between the curves described below?
    (a) $\mathbf{r}(t) = [t, t^2]$, $T = \mathbf{R}$.
    (b) $\mathbf{r}(t) = [t^3, t^6]$, $T = \mathbf{R}$.
    (c) $\mathbf{r}(t) = [t^5, t^{10}]$, $T = \mathbf{R}$.
    (d) $\mathbf{r}(t) = [\cos t, 1 - \sin^2 t]$, $T = \{t \mid 0 \leqslant t \leqslant \pi\}$.
17. Compare the curves determined by the following functions:
    (a) $\mathbf{r}(t) = t\mathbf{i} + t^3\mathbf{j}$, $T = \mathbf{R}$.
    (b) $\mathbf{r}(t) = t^3\mathbf{i} + t^9\mathbf{j}$, $T = \mathbf{R}$.
    (c) $\mathbf{r}(t) = (\cos t)\mathbf{i} + \frac{1}{4}(\cos 3t + 3\cos t)\mathbf{j}$, $T = \{t \mid 0 \leqslant t \leqslant \pi\}$.

18. Consider the point $A(1, 1)$ and the vector $\mathbf{v} = [1, 2]$. Find the vector function that describes the line through A in the direction of $\mathbf{v}$. [*Hint:* let P be a point on the desired line. Then

$$\overrightarrow{OP} = \overrightarrow{OA} + \overrightarrow{AP} = [1, 1] + t\mathbf{v} = [1, 1] + t[1, 2].$$

Let $\mathbf{r}(t) = \overrightarrow{OP}$.]

19. Consider the point $A(-3, 2)$ and the vector $\mathbf{v} = 2\mathbf{i} - \mathbf{j}$. Find a vector function that describes the line through A in the direction determined by $\mathbf{v}$. See the hint for Exercise A18.

B. **1.** Consider the point $A(a, b)$ and the vector $\mathbf{v} = h\mathbf{i} + k\mathbf{j}$. Find a vector function that describes the line through A in the direction of $\mathbf{v}$. See Exercises A18 and 19.

2. Let $\mathbf{r}(t) = [x(t), y(t)]$, where x and y are linear functions of t. Show that $\mathbf{r}$ determines a straight line. [*Hint:* let

$$x(t) = a + ht$$
$$y(t) = b + kt.$$

See Exercise B1.]

C. Given a vector function $\mathbf{r}$ or, equivalently, a pair of scalar functions x and y, it is sometimes desirable to eliminate the parameter t from the scalar equations, obtaining therefrom a relation between x and y, possibly expressing y as a function of x. The latter can always be done, as was illustrated in Example 7, if one can find the function inverse to x and then substitute this result into the formula for y. In other cases an identity, perhaps a trigonometric identity, can be used (see Example 10); e.g., in Example 8, where

$$x(t) = \cos t$$
$$y(t) = \sin t,$$

we find that $x^2 + y^2 = 1$. In still other cases no obvious procedure presents itself and one must conjure up whatever ingenuity he can.

Eliminate the parameter from each of the following:

1. $\begin{cases} x = t + 1 \\ y = t - 1 \end{cases}$ (see Exercise A1).

2. $\begin{cases} x = t \\ y = \sqrt{4 - t^2} \end{cases}$ (see Exercise A4).

3. $\begin{cases} x = t^2 \\ y = t^3 \end{cases}$ (see Exercise A9).

4. $\mathbf{r}(t)$ as given in Exercise A13.
5. $\mathbf{r}(t)$ as given in Exercise A16(a).

6. $\begin{cases} x = 2a \cot \phi \\ y = 2a \sin^2 \phi \end{cases}$.

7. $\begin{cases} x = a \cot \phi \\ y = b \sin \phi \cos \phi \end{cases}$.

7.5 Use of a Parameter in Geometric Problems

In this section we shall devote a little attention to a problem mentioned in the discussion at the end of Section 7.4: obtaining with the aid of a parameter an analytic representation of a curve which has been defined by some geometric condition. Our approach will be through a series of examples.

Example 11.   We consider a curve which is defined in terms of two fixed auxiliary curves: a circle $\mathscr{C}$ of diameter a, center at $(a/2, 0)$, and the line l, $x = a$ (see Figure 21). The desired curve is the set of points P obtained as follows: a line is drawn through the origin making an angle θ, $-(\pi/2) < \theta < \pi/2$, with the positive x-axis, intersecting $\mathscr{C}$ at Q and l at M. The point P, on this variable line, is such that $\overrightarrow{OP} = \overrightarrow{QM}$.

The polar coordinate equation of $\mathscr{C}$ is $r = a \cos \theta$. As $x = r \cos \theta$, $y = r \sin \theta$, the rectangular coordinates of Q are $Q(a \cos^2 \theta, a \sin \theta \cos \theta)$. Thus, taking the angle θ, $\theta \in (-\pi/2, \pi/2)$ as parameter, we have

$$\overrightarrow{OP} = \overrightarrow{QM} = \overrightarrow{OM} - \overrightarrow{OQ}$$
$$= (a\mathbf{i} + a \tan \theta \mathbf{j}) - (a \cos^2 \theta \mathbf{i} + a \sin \theta \cos \theta \mathbf{j})$$
$$= a(1 - \cos^2 \theta)\mathbf{i} + a(\tan \theta - \sin \theta \cos \theta)\mathbf{j}$$
$$\mathbf{r}(\theta) = a \sin^2 \theta \mathbf{i} + a \frac{\sin^3 \theta}{\cos \theta}\mathbf{j},$$

where $\mathbf{r}(\theta) = \overrightarrow{OP}$.

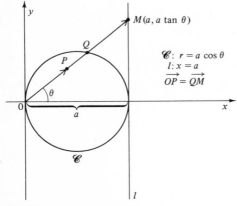

Figure 21

The curve, called the Cissoid of Diocles, has parametric equations

$$\begin{cases} x = a \sin^2 \theta \\ y = a \dfrac{\sin^3 \theta}{\cos \theta} \end{cases}, \qquad -\frac{\pi}{2} < \theta < \frac{\pi}{2}. \tag{27}$$

We leave it as an exercise (A3) to show that if the parameter θ is eliminated one obtains

$$y^2 = \frac{x^3}{a - x}. \tag{28}$$

The curve, the nature of which is reasonably apparent from the original definition, is shown in Figure 22.

Example 12. We consider a curve defined in terms of a circle $\mathscr{C}$, $r = 2a \sin \theta$, and a straight line l, $y = 2a$. A point P on the curve is obtained as follows: a line is drawn through the origin making an angle θ $(0 < \theta < \pi)$ with the positive x-axis, intersecting $\mathscr{C}$ at Q and l at M; the intersection of the horizontal line through Q and the vertical line through M is the point P on the curve (see Figure 23).

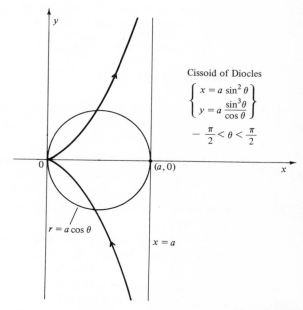

Cissoid of Diocles

$$\begin{cases} x = a \sin^2 \theta \\ y = a \dfrac{\sin^3 \theta}{\cos \theta} \end{cases}$$

$$-\frac{\pi}{2} < \theta < \frac{\pi}{2}$$

$r = a \cos \theta$

$x = a$

Figure 22

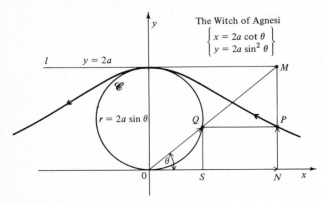

Figure 23

We take as parameter the angle θ. The polar equation of $\mathscr{C}$ being $r = 2a \sin \theta$, we have $\overrightarrow{OQ} = (2a \sin \theta \cos \theta)\mathbf{i} + (2a \sin^2 \theta)\mathbf{j}$. Also, since $|\overrightarrow{NM}| = 2a$, $\overrightarrow{ON} = 2a \cot \theta \mathbf{i}$. Thus

$$\mathbf{r}(\theta) = \overrightarrow{OP} = \overrightarrow{ON} + \overrightarrow{NP} = \overrightarrow{ON} + \overrightarrow{SQ},$$
$$\mathbf{r}(\theta) = (2a \cot \theta)\mathbf{i} + (2a \sin^2 \theta)\mathbf{j}. \tag{29}$$

This curve, shown in Figure 23, called the Witch of Agnesi, has parametric equations

$$\begin{Bmatrix} x = 2a \cot \theta \\ y = 2a \sin^2 \theta \end{Bmatrix}, \quad 0 < \theta < \pi. \tag{30}$$

Its nonparametric equation is

$$y = \frac{8a^3}{x^2 + 4a^2}$$

(see Exercise C6 after Section 7.4).

Example 13. For our next illustration we consider a curve defined by means of a circle of radius a and a straight line. In this case we fix a point on the circle and let the circle roll (without slipping) along the line. We are interested in the path of the specified point on the circle as the circle rolls along the line.

We choose the x-axis as the line along which the circle rolls and take as origin a point where the prescribed point on the circle touches the x-axis. We also assume the circle rolls to the right. See Figure 24.

Again we take as parameter an angle, this time the angle θ through which the circle has rolled from the "starting point" when P was at the origin. The essential fact in finding an analytic representation for the curve is the

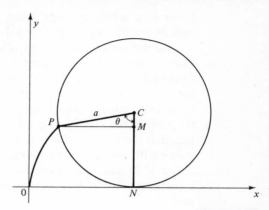

Figure 24

observation that the length of the segment $\overline{ON}$ must equal the length of arc $\overset{\frown}{PN}$. Since $\overset{\frown}{PN} = a\theta$, we have $|\overrightarrow{ON}| = a\theta$. Thus

$$\begin{aligned}\mathbf{r}(\theta) = \overrightarrow{OP} &= \overrightarrow{ON} + \overrightarrow{NM} + \overrightarrow{MP} \\ &= a\theta\mathbf{i} + (a - a\cos\theta)\mathbf{j} + (-a\sin\theta)\mathbf{i},\end{aligned}$$

so

$$\mathbf{r}(\theta) = a(\theta - \sin\theta)\mathbf{i} + a(1 - \cos\theta)\mathbf{j}. \tag{31}$$

This curve, a *cycloid*, has parametric equations

$$\begin{cases} x = a(\theta - \sin\theta) \\ y = a(1 - \cos\theta) \end{cases}. \tag{32}$$

A sketch of one period is given in Figure 25. This is the curve which, as John and James Bernoulli showed, provides a solution to the *brachistochrone problem* first discussed by Galileo: given two points in the same vertical plane, at different heights, although not on the same vertical line, to find a curve along which a bead would slide (without friction) from the upper point to the

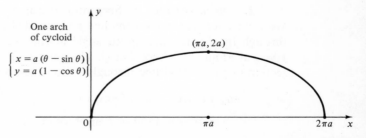

One arch
of cycloid

$$\begin{cases} x = a(\theta - \sin\theta) \\ y = a(1 - \cos\theta) \end{cases}$$

$(\pi a, 2a)$

Figure 25

lower in a minimum time. Euler also solved the brachistochrone problem and, in generalizing it, initiated the calculus of variations.

So far nothing has been said about techniques of sketching a curve from a vector equation or a set of parametric equations. Intercepts can be found from the zeros of the parametric equations, the ranges of the functions for x and y may give useful information about extent of the curve, and in some cases suggestions about symmetry may be available. For example, in the case of the cissoid, it is clear from [27] that $0 \leqslant x \leqslant a$; moreover, the fact that the function for x is even whereas that for y is odd indicates symmetry with respect to the x-axis. Similarly we see from Equations [30] that $0 \leqslant y \leqslant 2a$ and that the curve is symmetric with respect to the y-axis. Equations [32] for the cycloid indicate that $0 \leqslant y \leqslant 2a$ and that the curve is periodic.

Exercises

A. **1.** By a variation of the definition of the Cissoid of Diocles (Example 11) we can obtain another curve, known as the *strophoid*. The same two auxiliary curves are used (see Figure 21); however, for the strophoid we define a point P on the curve by the condition that $\overrightarrow{PQ} = \overrightarrow{QM}$. Thus

$$\overrightarrow{OP} = \overrightarrow{OQ} + \overrightarrow{QP} = \overrightarrow{OQ} - \overrightarrow{QM}.$$

(a) Use the above definition and show that parametric equations for the strophoid are

$$\begin{cases} x = a \cos 2\theta \\ y = a \cos 2\theta \tan \theta \end{cases}, \qquad -\frac{\pi}{2} < \theta < \frac{\pi}{2}.$$

[*Hint:* show that $\overrightarrow{OP} = 2\overrightarrow{OQ} - \overrightarrow{OM}$.]
(b) Sketch the strophoid, indicating its *orientation*, i.e., the direction of the curve as determined by increasing θ.
(c) Eliminate the parameter θ and show that

$$y^2 = x^2 \frac{a - x}{a + x}.$$

2. The curve called the Serpentine is defined as follows (see Figure 26). We use as auxiliary curves the line $y = a$ and the circle $r = b \cos \theta$. A line through the origin, making an angle θ with the positive x-axis, intersects $y = a$ at M and $r = b \cos \theta$ at Q. The point P on the Serpentine is the intersection of the vertical line through M and the horizontal line through Q.

(a) Let $\mathbf{r}(\theta) = \overrightarrow{OP}$. Show that

$$\mathbf{r}(\theta) = a \cot \theta \mathbf{i} + b \sin \theta \cos \theta \mathbf{j}. \qquad [33]$$

[*Hint:* use $\overrightarrow{OP} = \overrightarrow{ON} + \overrightarrow{NP} = \overrightarrow{ON} + \overrightarrow{SQ}$.]

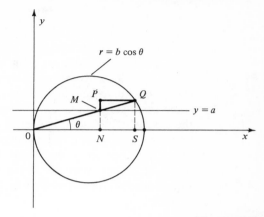

Figure 26

(b) From [33] we obtain as parametric equations of the Serpentine

$$\begin{cases} x = a \cot \theta \\ y = b \sin \theta \cos \theta \end{cases}, \quad -\frac{\pi}{2} \leqslant \theta \leqslant \frac{\pi}{2}, \quad \theta \neq 0. \tag{34}$$

Use these equations to sketch the curve. Note that for $-(\pi/2) \leqslant \theta < 0$ the point P on the curve lies in quadrant III.

(c) Eliminate θ from [34], showing that

$$y = \frac{abx}{a^2 + x^2}$$

3. This refers to Example 11 (the cissoid). Eliminate θ from Equations [27] to obtain

$$y^2 = \frac{x^3}{a - x}.$$

[*Hint:* show that $a - x = a \cos^2 \theta$; use this and the equation for x in the expression for y^2.]

4. A *hypocycloid* is the curve traced out by a point P on a circle of radius b which is rolling (without slipping) on the inside of a fixed circle of radius a, $a > b$. We take the origin at the center of the fixed circle and assume that the specified point on the inner circle touches the fixed circle at a point on the positive x-axis. See Figure 27.

(a) If P has coordinates (x, y), show that

$$\begin{cases} x = (a - b) \cos \theta + b \cos \dfrac{a - b}{b} \theta \\ y = (a - b) \sin \theta - b \sin \dfrac{a - b}{b} \theta \end{cases}. \tag{35}$$

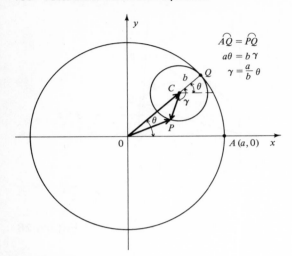

$$\widehat{AQ} = \widehat{PQ}$$
$$a\theta = b\gamma$$
$$\gamma = \frac{a}{b}\theta$$

Figure 27

[*Hint:* let $\mathbf{r}(\theta) = \overrightarrow{OP} = \overrightarrow{OC} + \overrightarrow{CP}$; then show that

$$\overrightarrow{OC} = (a - b)[\cos\theta, \sin\theta]$$
$$\overrightarrow{CP} = b[\cos(2\pi - (\gamma - \theta)), \sin(2\pi - (\gamma - \theta))].]$$

(b) If b/a is irrational, the curve will continue indefinitely, never repeating itself. However, if b/a is rational, the curve will ultimately return to A. Show, in particular, that if $b = \frac{1}{4}a$, the equations in [35] reduce to

$$\left\{ \begin{array}{l} x = a\cos^3\theta \\ y = a\sin^3\theta \end{array} \right\}.$$ [36]

This curve, the *hypocycloid of four cusps*, is traced out completely for $0 \leqslant \theta < 2\pi$.
(c) Sketch the hypocycloid of four cusps.
(d) Eliminate θ from Equations [36] to obtain

$$x^{2/3} + y^{2/3} = a^{2/3}.$$

Geometry and Vectors in Three Dimensions

In this chapter we make a brief study of analytic geometry of three dimensions. We also extend to three dimensions the concept of vector and use it in our consideration of lines and planes in 3-space. Since curves in three dimensions can best be handled by using methods of calculus we bypass this topic and consider a few of the simplest types of surfaces.

8.1 Rectangular Coordinates in Three Dimensions

A rectangular cartesian coordinate system is established in three dimensions by the following procedure. One chooses a point O, the origin; three mutually perpendicular straight lines through O, the x-, y-, and z-axes; a positive direction for each axis; and a unit of length—we shall, unless specific mention is made to the contrary, always use the same unit of length on all three axes.

However, that is not the end of the story, for one more decision must be made. To show why this is so, suppose that the origin O, the three mutually perpendicular lines through O, and the positive direction on each have all been chosen, but that the labels x, y, and z have not yet been assigned. There are, formally, six (3!) different ways in which these assignments can be made; actually, though, these six fall into two groups of three each, the three in each group being essentially the same—and basically different from the three in the other group. We show a representative of each group of three in Figure 1.

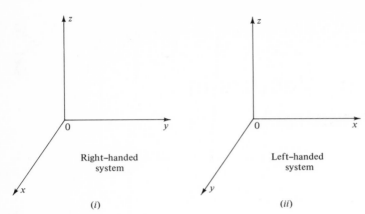

Figure 1

The system in Figure 1(*i*) is known as a *right-handed system* for the reason that a rotation in the direction from positive *x*- to positive *y*-axis is in the same direction that would cause an ordinary right-handed wood screw, positioned with its head at *O*, its pointed end in the direction of the positive *z*-axis, to advance into the wood. The system in Figure 1(*ii*) is *left-handed*. We shall consistently use a right-handed system, although we may use one of the two other possible ways of labeling, e.g., letting *x*- and *y*- be the axes in the plane of the paper in their usual (i.e., two-dimensional) horizontal and vertical positions, and letting the positive *z*-axis be drawn to suggest coming out of the plane of the paper toward the reader.

We strongly recommend that the student draw all six possible ways of assigning labels to the positive axes and pick out the group of three which are right-handed.

The three coordinate axes taken two at a time determine three planes, called the *coordinate planes*. In Figure 1(*i*) the plane of the paper is the *yz*-plane, the horizontal plane perpendicular to the plane of the paper is the *xy*-plane, and the *zx*-plane is the vertical plane perpendicular to the plane of the paper. (For purposes of visualizing, it is often convenient to think of the origin as a corner of a room at the floor; the floor is the *xy*-plane, etc.) The coordinates of a point in space are then directed distances measured from the *coordinate planes*—and perpendicular to these planes. For example, the *z*-coordinate is the directed distance from the *xy*-plane, etc. See Figure 2, where several points are shown with their coordinates (x, y, z).

The three coordinate planes divide space into eight parts, called *octants*. In contrast to the practice of plane geometry, only one of the octants is assigned a number: the octant in which all three coordinates of a point are positive is called the *first octant*.

Each of the equations $x = c$, $y = c$, or $z = c$ determines a set of points

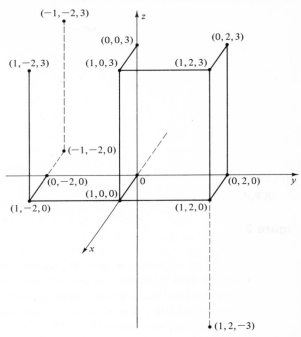

Figure 2

known as a *coordinate surface*. In every case these coordinate surfaces are planes parallel to the coordinate planes. Thus $z = 1$ determines the plane parallel to the xy-plane and one unit above it. The xy-plane itself is $z = 0$; similarly the yz-plane and the zx-plane are, respectively, $x = 0$ and $y = 0$.

The length of a line segment in three dimensions is given by a natural extension of the formula of Theorem 2.2.

THEOREM 1.　　*Given the points $P_1(x_1, y_1, z_1)$ and $P_2(x_2, y_2, z_2)$, the length of the line segment $\overline{P_1P_2}$ is*

$$|\overline{P_1P_2}| = \sqrt{(x_1 - x_2)^2 + (y_1 - y_2)^2 + (z_1 - z_2)^2}. \qquad [1]$$

PROOF.　　See Figure 3. We use the rectangular parallelepiped (box) with sides parallel to the coordinate axes, which has $\overline{P_1P_2}$ as a diagonal. We also use the vertex $Q(x_2, y_2, z_1)$ in the same horizontal plane as P_1. We have, using the Pythagorean Theorem and Theorems 2.1 and 2.2,

$$\begin{aligned} |\overline{P_1P_2}|^2 &= |\overline{P_1Q}|^2 + |\overline{QP_2}|^2 \\ &= [(x_1 - x_2)^2 + (y_1 - y_2)^2] + (z_1 - z_2)^2. \quad \blacksquare \end{aligned}$$

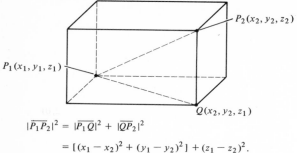

$$|\overline{P_1 P_2}|^2 = |\overline{P_1 Q}|^2 + |\overline{Q P_2}|^2$$

$$= [(x_1 - x_2)^2 + (y_1 - y_2)^2] + (z_1 - z_2)^2.$$

Figure 3

It follows from Theorem 1 that the equation $x^2 + y^2 + z^2 = 1$ determines the set of points which are 1 unit from the origin: a sphere of radius 1 with center at the origin. We shall refer to this as the *unit sphere*.

The examples of the unit sphere and the coordinate surfaces serve to illustrate a fact that occasionally causes trouble for the 3-space novitiate. We refer to the fact that, in general, a single equation in three-dimensional geometry determines a *surface*, a two-dimensional set of points. As we shall see, the analytic description of lines and curves in general is best achieved by means of parametric equations. However, the coordinate axes provide a mild exception to this statement. For example, the z-axis is represented by

$$\left\{ \begin{matrix} x = 0 \\ y = 0 \end{matrix} \right\}.$$

The first of these equations is, of course, the yz-plane, the second the zx-plane; together they represent the intersection of these planes, i.e., the z-axis.

As an illustration of the important point of the preceding paragraph—and as a preview of a topic we look at later in more detail—consider the equation $x^2 + y^2 = 1$. In the xy-plane this equation determines the unit circle. To see that in three dimensions it represents something more, recall that the equation imposes a *condition that must be satisfied* by the coordinates of the points on the graph. But the equation $x^2 + y^2 = 1$, with z absent, imposes no condition, i.e., no restriction, on z. Thus if x_0, y_0 are such that $x_0^2 + y_0^2 = 1$, then (x_0, y_0, z) is on the graph of $x^2 + y^2 = 1$ *for every value* of z. The resulting set of points is the right circular cylinder of radius 1, symmetric with respect to the z-axis. See Figure 4.

In a similar way the equation $y + z = 1$, when restricted to the yz-plane, describes a straight line. But when interpreted as defining a set of points in space it imposes no condition on x; thus, if y_0 and z_0 satisfy $y_0 + z_0 = 1$, the point (x, y_0, z_0) is on the surface for *every* x. As seems evident and as we shall see later is true, this equation defines a plane, shown in part in Figure 5.

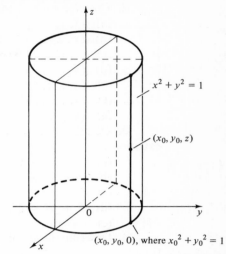

Figure 4

Exercises

A.   **1.** Describe each of the following sets of points in space.

     (a) $\{(x, y, z) \mid z > 0\}$.

     (b) $\{(x, y, z) \mid xy \geqslant 0\}$.

     (c) $\{(x, y, z) \mid x > 0, y = 0, z = 0\}$.

     (d) $\{(x, y, z) \mid x^2 + y^2 = 0\}$.

     (e) $\{(x, y, z) \mid x^2 + y^2 = 1, z = 1\}$ (see Figure 4).

     (f) $\{(x, y, z) \mid y + z = 1, x = 2\}$ (see Figure 5).

     (g) $\{(x, y, z) \mid x = 2, y = 1\}$.

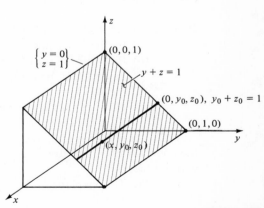

Figure 5

2. Describe each of the following sets of points in space.

(a) $\{(x, y, z) \mid x^2 + y^2 + z^2 \leqslant 1\}$.

(b) $\{(x, y, z) \mid z \geqslant 2\}$.

(c) $\{(x, y, z) \mid 1 \leqslant x^2 + y^2 \leqslant 4\}$.

(d) $\{(x, y, z) \mid x^2 + y^2 = 1, y = 0\}$.

(e) $\{(x, y, z) \mid y = 1, z = 0\}$.

(f) $\{(x, y, z) \mid x^2 + y^2 + z^2 = 4, z = 1\}$.

(g) $\{(x, y, z) \mid x^2 + y^2 = 3\}$.

3. Describe the set of points determined by each of the following equations.

(a) $x^2 + y^2 + z^2 = 2x$. [*Hint:* complete the square in x.]

(b) $x^2 + y^2 + z^2 = 2x + 2y$.

(c) $x^2 + y^2 + z^2 - 2x + 4y - 8z + 17 = 0$.

(d) $x^2 + y^2 = 2x$.

(e) $x = y$.

4. Describe the set of points determined by each of the following equations.

(a) $y^2 + z^2 = 2y$.

(b) $z^2 = 2z$.

(c) $y = z$.

(d) $y^2 + z^2 = 0$.

(e) $x = y = z$.

5. Find the equation satisfied by the coordinates of all points $P(x, y, z)$ that are equidistant from $A(0, 1, 2)$ and $B(2, 1, 0)$. Sketch.

6. Find the equation satisfied by the coordinates of all points $P(x, y, z)$ that are equidistant from $A(1, 1, 1)$ and $B(0, 0, 1)$. Sketch.

7. Find the equation satisfied by the set of all points $P(x, y, z)$ whose perpendicular distance from the y-axis is 2 units.

8. Find the equation satisfied by the set of all points $P(x, y, z)$ whose perpendicular distance from the z-axis is 3 units.

B.   **1.** (a) Reproduce Figure 1 and also draw the four figures obtainable by the other possible assignments of axes.

(b) Pick out the set of three right-handed systems and observe that any one can be transformed into any other of this set by a rigid motion.

(c) Now convince yourself that no rigid motion will convert a right-handed to a left-handed system.

2. Let $a > 0$, $b > 0$, and $c > 0$. Sketch the point $P(a, b, c)$. Now give the coordinates of and draw on your figure the point that is symmetric to P with respect to

(a) The xy-plane.

(b) $x = 0$.

(c) The x-axis.

(d) The *zx*-plane.

(e) The *y*-axis.

(f) The origin.

3. (a) Refer to Equation [2.7]. Develop a formula for the coordinates of the point $P_0(x_0, y_0, z_0)$ that divides the segment $\overline{P_1P_2}$ such that $|\overline{P_1P_0}| = \lambda|\overline{P_1P_2}|$, where P_1 and P_2 have coordinates (x_1, y_1, z_1) and (x_2, y_2, z_2), respectively.

(b) Find the coordinates of the midpoint of $\overline{P_1P_2}$.

(c) Find the midpoint of the segment determined by $P_1(1, -1, 3)$ and $P_2(5, 3, -1)$.

4. Give an analytic description of

(a) The *x*-axis.

(b) The *y*-axis.

8.2 Vectors in Three Dimensions

The definitions and properties of vectors in two dimensions, as formulated in Sections 7.1–7.3, all carry over in the obvious way to vectors in three dimensions.

In particular, a vector $\mathbf{a} \in \mathbf{R}^3$ is, geometrically, a directed line segment, its analytic representation being an ordered triple of numbers. Since we are working with free vectors, we can interpret $\mathbf{a} = [a_1, a_2, a_3]$ either as the line segment directed from the origin to the point (a_1, a_2, a_3); or, if $P_0(x_0, y_0, z_0)$ is an arbitrary point, $\mathbf{a}$ can be interpreted as the line segment directed from P_0 to P_1, where P_1 has coordinates $(x_0 + a_1, y_0 + a_2, z_0 + a_3)$. See Figure 6.

Conversely, if $P_0(x_0, y_0, z_0)$ and $P_1(x_1, y_1, z_1)$ are two points, then the vector from P_0 to P_1 is

$$\overrightarrow{P_0P_1} = [x_1 - x_0, y_1 - y_0, z_1 - z_0].$$

The length or magnitude of the vector $\mathbf{a} = [a_1, a_2, a_3]$ is

$$|\mathbf{a}| = \sqrt{a_1^2 + a_2^2 + a_3^2}. \tag{2}$$

The direction of $\mathbf{a}$ is described by the direction angles α, β, and γ, the angles between the positive direction of the *x*-, *y*-, and *z*-axes, respectively,

Figure 6

and **a**. We agree that α, β, and γ lie between 0 and π, inclusive. The direction cosines are the cosines of the direction angles and are given by

$$\cos \alpha = \frac{a_1}{|\mathbf{a}|}, \quad \cos \beta = \frac{a_2}{|\mathbf{a}|}, \quad \cos \gamma = \frac{a_3}{|\mathbf{a}|} \qquad [3]$$

(see Figure 7).

A *unit vector* **u** is a vector of length 1, $|\mathbf{u}| = 1$. It follows from [3] that the components of a unit vector are its direction cosines, and, in general, it follows from [2] and [3] that, for an arbitrary nonzero vector,

$$\cos^2 \alpha + \cos^2 \beta + \cos^2 \gamma = 1. \qquad [4]$$

Equality of two vectors is defined to mean that they have the same magnitude and same direction. From this we have (cf. Theorem 7.1) that, if $\mathbf{a} = [a_1, a_2, a_3]$ and $\mathbf{b} = [b_1, b_2, b_3]$, then

$$\mathbf{a} = \mathbf{b} \Leftrightarrow a_1 = b_1, \quad a_2 = b_2, \quad a_3 = b_3. \qquad [5]$$

Addition and scalar multiplication are defined as in Definition 7.4: if $\mathbf{a} = [a_1, a_2, a_3]$ and $\mathbf{b} = [b_1, b_2, b_3]$, then

$$\mathbf{a} + \mathbf{b} = [a_1 + b_1, a_2 + b_2, a_3 + b_3] \qquad [6]$$

and

$$c\mathbf{a} = [ca_1, ca_2, ca_3], \qquad c \in \mathbf{R}. \qquad [7]$$

The zero vector is $\mathbf{0} = [0, 0, 0]$.

Then all the algebraic properties as described in Theorem 7.3 are valid, the proof being entirely similar.

The assertion of Theorem 7.4 remains valid (the proof being the same): if A, B, and C are points in 3-space, then

$$\overrightarrow{AB} + \overrightarrow{BC} = \overrightarrow{AC}. \qquad [8]$$

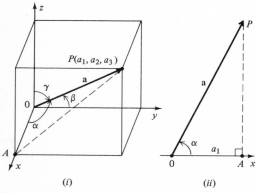

(i)   *(ii)*

Figure 7

Two vectors are parallel if they have the same direction (i.e., the same sets of direction angles). If we define the zero vector to be parallel to every vector, we can assert (cf. Theorem 7.5) that the nonzero vector **a** is parallel to the vector **b** $\Leftrightarrow$ there exists $c \in \mathbf{R}$ such that **b** $= c\mathbf{a}$.

The *inner product* of the vectors **a** $= [a_1, a_2, a_3]$ and **b** $= [b_1, b_2, b_3]$ is defined analogously to Definition 7.5:

$$\mathbf{a} \cdot \mathbf{b} = a_1 b_1 + a_2 b_2 + a_3 b_3. \tag{9}$$

Then the algebraic properties of the inner product, as described in Theorem 7.6, remain valid, as is the geometric interpretation of Theorem 7.7:

$$\mathbf{a} \cdot \mathbf{b} = |\mathbf{a}|\,|\mathbf{b}| \cos \theta, \tag{10}$$

where θ is the angle between **a** and **b**.

As a result of [10] we can assert (see Theorem 7.8) that

$$\mathbf{a} \text{ is perpendicular to } \mathbf{b} \Leftrightarrow \mathbf{a} \cdot \mathbf{b} = 0, \tag{11}$$

the zero vector, by agreement, being perpendicular to every vector.

We observe that the Cauchy-Schwarz Inequality (Theorem 7.9) is valid as well as its corollary, the triangle inequality:

$$(\mathbf{a} \cdot \mathbf{b})^2 \leqslant |\mathbf{a}|^2\,|\mathbf{b}|^2 \tag{12}$$

and

$$|\mathbf{a} + \mathbf{b}| \leqslant |\mathbf{a}| + |\mathbf{b}|. \tag{13}$$

The vectors **i**, **j**, and **k** are the unit vectors in the directions of, respectively, the positive x-, y-, and z-axes. Thus

$$\mathbf{i} = [1, 0, 0], \quad \mathbf{j} = [0, 1, 0], \quad \mathbf{k} = [0, 0, 1]. \tag{14}$$

If **a** $= [a_1, a_2, a_3]$, then we can also write

$$\mathbf{a} = a_1 \mathbf{i} + a_2 \mathbf{j} + a_3 \mathbf{k}, \tag{15}$$

and we note that

$$a_1 = \mathbf{a} \cdot \mathbf{i}, \quad a_2 = \mathbf{a} \cdot \mathbf{j}, \quad a_3 = \mathbf{a} \cdot \mathbf{k}. \tag{16}$$

The *scalar projection* of **b** along **a**, $\text{proj}_a\,\mathbf{b}$, is defined to be $|\mathbf{b}| \cos \theta$, where θ is the angle between **a** and **b**. Thus the scalar projection of **b** along **a** is given by

$$\text{proj}_a\,\mathbf{b} = |\mathbf{b}| \cos \theta = \frac{\mathbf{a} \cdot \mathbf{b}}{|\mathbf{a}|} = \frac{\mathbf{a} \cdot \mathbf{b}}{\sqrt{\mathbf{a} \cdot \mathbf{a}}} = \mathbf{u}_a \cdot \mathbf{b}, \tag{17}$$

where $\mathbf{u}_a$ is the unit vector with the same direction as **a**.

Example 1. Let $\mathbf{a} = 4\mathbf{i} - 3\mathbf{j} + 5\mathbf{k}$. Then $|\mathbf{a}| = \sqrt{50} = 5\sqrt{2}$, and

$$\mathbf{u}_a = \frac{4}{5\sqrt{2}}\mathbf{i} - \frac{3}{5\sqrt{2}}\mathbf{j} + \frac{1}{\sqrt{2}}\mathbf{k}$$

$$= \cos\alpha\mathbf{i} + \cos\beta\mathbf{j} + \cos\gamma\mathbf{k}.$$

Example 2. Find the length of the projection of $\mathbf{b} = -5\mathbf{i} + 3\mathbf{j} + 4\mathbf{k}$ on $\mathbf{a} = \mathbf{i} - 2\mathbf{j} + 2\mathbf{k}$.

We begin by converting $\mathbf{a}$ to a unit vector $\mathbf{u}_a$. Since $|\mathbf{a}| = 3$, we have $\mathbf{u}_a = \frac{1}{3}\mathbf{a} = \frac{1}{3}(\mathbf{i} - 2\mathbf{j} + 2\mathbf{k})$. Now,

$$\mathbf{u}_a \cdot \mathbf{b} = |\mathbf{u}_a| \cdot |\mathbf{b}| \cos\theta = |\mathbf{b}| \cos\theta,$$

the projection of $\mathbf{b}$ on $\mathbf{a}$. The number in this case is

$$\mathbf{u}_a \cdot \mathbf{b} = \tfrac{1}{3}[(1)(-5) + (-2)(3) + (2)(4)] = -1.$$

The negative sign indicates $\pi/2 < \theta < \pi$. See Figure 8. The length of the projection of $\mathbf{b}$ on $\mathbf{a}$ is, therefore, 1.

Exercises

A. In Exercises 1–10 find the vector from P_1 to P_2 and in each case find the direction cosines of the vector.

    1. $P_1(1, 2, -1)$, $P_2(2, 0, 1)$.
    2. $P_1(2, 0, 1)$, $P_2(1, 2, -1)$.
    3. $P_1(0, 0, 0)$, $P_2(1, 1, 1)$.
    4. $P_1(0, 0, 0)$, $P_2(0, 1, 1)$.
    5. $P_1(0, 0, 0)$, $P_2(1, 0, 1)$.
    6. $P_1(0, 0, 0)$, $P_2(4, 0, 0)$.
    7. $P_1(3, 4, 5)$, $P_2(0, 0, 0)$.
    8. $P_1(1, 2, 1)$, $P_2(4, 6, 1)$.
    9. $P_1(1, 1, 1)$, $P_2(1, -3, 4)$.
    10. $P_1(1, 2, 3)$, $P_2(1, 2, 8)$.

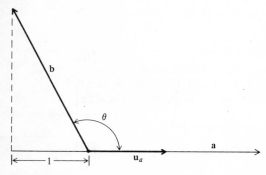

Figure 8

11. Find $\cos \theta$, where θ is the angle between **a** and **b**, for each pair of vectors **a** and **b**.

(a) $\mathbf{a} = 2\mathbf{i} + 2\mathbf{j} - \mathbf{k}$, $\mathbf{b} = 3\mathbf{i} - 4\mathbf{j} + 5\mathbf{k}$.

(b) $\mathbf{a} = \mathbf{i} + \mathbf{j} - \mathbf{k}$, $\mathbf{b} = 3\mathbf{i} + 3\mathbf{k}$.

(c) $\mathbf{a} = 4\mathbf{i} - \mathbf{j} + 2\mathbf{k}$, $\mathbf{b} = -\mathbf{i} + 2\mathbf{j} + 2\mathbf{k}$.

12. For each pair of vectors **a** and **b** of Exercise A11, find the length of the projection of **b** on **a**.

13. Show that the points $P_1(3, 4, -3)$, $P_2(7, 10, -11)$, $P_3(6, 1, 3)$, and $P_4(10, 7, -5)$ are the vertices of a parallelogram. Is the parallelogram a rectangle?

14. Show, without using the length formula, that $P_1(4, 0, 7)$, $P_2(10, -4, 15)$, $P_3(12, 20, 11)$, and $P_4(18, 16, 19)$ are the vertices of a rectangle.

15. Given a vector $\mathbf{v} = a\mathbf{i} + b\mathbf{j} + c\mathbf{k}$. What is the geometric significance of each of the following?

(a) $c = 0$.

(b) $b = c = 0$.

(c) $a = 0$.

(d) $a = b = 0$.

(e) $a = b = c = 0$.

16. The vector $\mathbf{v}_1 = \mathbf{j} - \mathbf{k}$ has its initial point at $P_0(0, 0, 1)$. The vector $\mathbf{v}_2$ also has its initial point at $P_0(0, 0, 1)$, is perpendicular to $\mathbf{v}_1$, lies in the zx-plane, and is $|a|$ units long. Find a such that the vector from the tip of $\mathbf{v}_1$ to the tip of $\mathbf{v}_2$ has length 10 units.

8.3 The Vector Product

In this section we shall define and discuss a binary operation on vectors which, unlike the inner product, produces a vector. We give an analytic definition of this operation, called the *vector product* (other names: *outer product*, *cross product*), and then describe its geometric interpretation.

DEFINITION 1.   *Let* $\mathbf{a} = [a_1, a_2, a_3]$ *and* $\mathbf{b} = [b_1, b_2, b_3]$ *be vectors in* $\mathbf{R}^3$. *Their vector product* $\mathbf{a} \times \mathbf{b}$ *is defined by*

$$\mathbf{a} \times \mathbf{b} = [a_2 b_3 - a_3 b_2, a_3 b_1 - a_1 b_3, a_1 b_2 - a_2 b_1]. \qquad [18]$$

We first describe the algebraic properties of the vector product.

THEOREM 2.   *The vector product satisfies the following relations for arbitrary* $\mathbf{a}, \mathbf{b}, \mathbf{c} \in \mathbf{R}^3$, $k \in \mathbf{R}$.

1. $\mathbf{b} \times \mathbf{a} = -\mathbf{a} \times \mathbf{b}$ *(skew-symmetry or anticommutativity)*.

2. $\mathbf{a} \times \mathbf{a} = \mathbf{0}$.

3. $(k\mathbf{a}) \times \mathbf{b} = \mathbf{a} \times (k\mathbf{b}) = k(\mathbf{a} \times \mathbf{b})$.

4. $\mathbf{a} \times (\mathbf{b} + \mathbf{c}) = \mathbf{a} \times \mathbf{b} + \mathbf{a} \times \mathbf{c}$ $\Big\}$ *(distributivity)*.

5. $(\mathbf{a} + \mathbf{b}) \times \mathbf{c} = \mathbf{a} \times \mathbf{c} + \mathbf{b} \times \mathbf{c}$

PROOF.   The validity of both assertions 1 and 2 comes immediately from the definition of $\mathbf{a} \times \mathbf{b}$. As for assertion 3, it is easy to see from Equation [18] that

$$(k\mathbf{a}) \times \mathbf{b} = \mathbf{a} \times (k\mathbf{b}) = k(\mathbf{a} \times \mathbf{b})$$
$$= [ka_2b_3 - ka_3b_2, ka_3b_1 - ka_1b_3, ka_1b_2 - ka_2b_1].$$

To prove assertion 4, we have

$$\mathbf{a} \times (\mathbf{b} + \mathbf{c}) = [a_2(b_3 + c_3) - a_3(b_2 + c_2), a_3(b_1 + c_1) - a_1(b_3 + c_3),$$
$$a_1(b_2 + c_2) - a_2(b_1 + c_1)]$$
$$= [(a_2b_3 - a_3b_2) + (a_2c_3 - a_3c_2), (a_3b_1 - a_1b_3)$$
$$+ (a_3c_1 - a_1c_3), (a_1b_2 - a_2b_1) + (a_1c_2 - a_2c_1)]$$
$$= [a_2b_3 - a_3b_2, a_3b_1 - a_1b_3, a_1b_2 - a_2b_1]$$
$$+ [a_2c_3 - a_3c_2, a_3c_1 - a_1c_3, a_1c_2 - a_2c_1]$$
$$= \mathbf{a} \times \mathbf{b} + \mathbf{a} \times \mathbf{c}.$$

The proof of assertion 5 follows easily from assertions 1 and 4:

$$(\mathbf{a} + \mathbf{b}) \times \mathbf{c} = -[\mathbf{c} \times (\mathbf{a} + \mathbf{b})] \qquad \text{(1 of this theorem)}$$
$$= -[\mathbf{c} \times \mathbf{a} + \mathbf{c} \times \mathbf{b}] \qquad \text{(4 of this theorem)}$$
$$= -\mathbf{c} \times \mathbf{a} - \mathbf{c} \times \mathbf{b}$$
$$= \mathbf{a} \times \mathbf{c} + \mathbf{b} \times \mathbf{c} \qquad \text{(1 of this theorem).} \quad \blacksquare$$

We next give two of the geometric properties of the vector product.

THEOREM 3.   1. *The vector* $\mathbf{a} \times \mathbf{b}$ *is perpendicular to both* $\mathbf{a}$ *and* $\mathbf{b}$.
2. *The magnitude of* $\mathbf{a} \times \mathbf{b}$ *is given by*

$$|\mathbf{a} \times \mathbf{b}| = |\mathbf{a}| \, |\mathbf{b}| \sin \theta, \qquad\qquad [19]$$

where $\theta, 0 \leqslant \theta \leqslant \pi$, *is the angle between* $\mathbf{a}$ *and* $\mathbf{b}$.

PROOF.   We first show that $\mathbf{a} \times \mathbf{b}$ is perpendicular to $\mathbf{a}$ by showing that the inner product of these vectors is zero;

$$\mathbf{a} \cdot (\mathbf{a} \times \mathbf{b}) = a_1(a_2b_3 - a_3b_2) + a_2(a_3b_1 - a_1b_3) + a_3(a_1b_2 - a_2b_1)$$
$$= a_1a_2b_3 - a_1a_2b_3 + a_2a_3b_1 - a_2a_3b_1 + a_1a_3b_2 - a_1a_3b_2$$
$$= 0.$$

In an exactly similar way one can show that $\mathbf{b} \cdot (\mathbf{a} \times \mathbf{b}) = 0$. Thus, by [11], $\mathbf{a} \times \mathbf{b}$ is perpendicular to $\mathbf{a}$ and to $\mathbf{b}$.

To prove assertion 2, we first prove the following assertion (*lemma* means "auxiliary proposition").

LEMMA 1.   *Let* $\mathbf{a}, \mathbf{b} \in \mathbf{R}^3$; *then*

$$|\mathbf{a} \times \mathbf{b}|^2 = |\mathbf{a}|^2 \, |\mathbf{b}|^2 - (\mathbf{a} \cdot \mathbf{b})^2.$$

PROOF.   We shall in fact show that

$$|\mathbf{a} \times \mathbf{b}|^2 + (\mathbf{a} \cdot \mathbf{b})^2 = |\mathbf{a}|^2 \, |\mathbf{b}|^2.$$

Using [18] and [9], we can write the left-hand side of this equation as

$$\begin{aligned}
|\mathbf{a} \times \mathbf{b}|^2 + (\mathbf{a} \cdot \mathbf{b})^2 &= (a_2 b_3 - a_3 b_2)^2 + (a_3 b_1 - a_1 b_3)^2 + (a_1 b_2 - a_2 b_1)^2 \\
&\quad + (a_1 b_1 + a_2 b_2 + a_3 b_3)^2 \\
&= a_2^2 b_3^2 + a_3^2 b_2^2 + a_3^2 b_1^2 + a_1^2 b_3^2 + a_1^2 b_2^2 + a_2^2 b_1^2 \\
&\quad + a_1^2 b_1^2 + a_2^2 b_2^2 + a_3^2 b_3^2 \\
&= a_1^2 b_1^2 + a_1^2 b_2^2 + a_1^2 b_3^2 + a_2^2 b_1^2 + a_2^2 b_2^2 + a_2^2 b_3^2 \\
&\quad + a_3^2 b_1^2 + a_3^2 b_2^2 + a_3^2 b_3^2 \\
&= a_1^2 (b_1^2 + b_2^2 + b_3^2) + a_2^2 (b_1^2 + b_2^2 + b_3^2) \\
&\quad + a_3^2 (b_1^2 + b_2^2 + b_3^2) \\
&= (a_1^2 + a_2^2 + a_3^2)(b_1^2 + b_2^2 + b_3^2) \\
&= |\mathbf{a}|^2 |\mathbf{b}|^2. \quad \blacksquare
\end{aligned}$$

Now assertion 2 of Theorem 3 follows easily. By [10], $\mathbf{a} \cdot \mathbf{b} = |\mathbf{a}|\,|\mathbf{b}|\,cos\,\theta$; using this in the statement of Lemma 1, we have

$$\begin{aligned}
|\mathbf{a} \times \mathbf{b}|^2 &= |\mathbf{a}|^2 |\mathbf{b}|^2 - |\mathbf{a}|^2 |\mathbf{b}|^2 \cos^2 \theta \\
&= |\mathbf{a}|^2 |\mathbf{b}|^2 (1 - \cos^2 \theta) \\
&= |\mathbf{a}|^2 |\mathbf{b}|^2 \sin^2 \theta. \quad \blacksquare
\end{aligned}$$

COROLLARY 1.   *The magnitude of the vector* $\mathbf{a} \times \mathbf{b}$ *is equal to the area of the parallelogram determined by* $\mathbf{a}$ *and* $\mathbf{b}$.

PROOF.   See Figure 9. The area of the parallelogram determined by $\mathbf{a}$ and $\mathbf{b}$ is the product of the base and the height h. But if the base is taken as the side determined by $\mathbf{a}$, then the height h is given by $h = |\mathbf{b}| \sin \theta$. Thus the area is $|\mathbf{a}|\,|\mathbf{b}| \sin \theta = |\mathbf{a} \times \mathbf{b}|$, by assertion 2 of Theorem 3.   ∎

COROLLARY 2.   *Two vectors* $\mathbf{a}$ *and* $\mathbf{b}$ *are parallel* (*either* $\mathbf{a} = k\mathbf{b}$ *or* $\mathbf{b} = k\mathbf{a}$) $\Leftrightarrow \mathbf{a} \times \mathbf{b} = 0$.

PROOF.   Exercise for student.   ∎

Theorem 3 does not give a complete geometric description of $\mathbf{a} \times \mathbf{b}$; it specifies the magnitude of this vector and it says that $\mathbf{a} \times \mathbf{b}$ is perpendicular to the plane of $\mathbf{a}$ and $\mathbf{b}$. What is lacking is the *sense* of $\mathbf{a} \times \mathbf{b}$. For example, if $\mathbf{a}$ and $\mathbf{b}$ lie in a horizontal plane, is $\mathbf{a} \times \mathbf{b}$ directed upward or downward? We shall provide an answer shortly, but first we make a few observations about the relation between the unit vectors $\mathbf{i}$, $\mathbf{j}$, and $\mathbf{k}$ and the vector product.

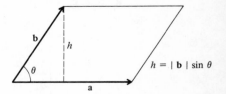

$h = |\mathbf{b}| \sin \theta$

Figure 9

THEOREM 4.   *For the vectors* $\mathbf{i} = [1, 0, 0]$, $\mathbf{j} = [0, 1, 0]$, *and* $\mathbf{k} = [0, 0, 1]$ *the following are true*:

1. $\mathbf{i} \times \mathbf{i} = \mathbf{j} \times \mathbf{j} = \mathbf{k} \times \mathbf{k} = \mathbf{0}$.
2. $\mathbf{i} \times \mathbf{j} = \mathbf{k}$, $\mathbf{j} \times \mathbf{k} = \mathbf{i}$, $\mathbf{k} \times \mathbf{i} = \mathbf{j}$.
3. $\mathbf{j} \times \mathbf{i} = -\mathbf{k}$, $\mathbf{k} \times \mathbf{j} = -\mathbf{i}$, $\mathbf{i} \times \mathbf{k} = -\mathbf{j}$.

PROOF.   Exercise for student.   ∎

Next we remark that the components of the vector product are 2×2 determinants. In fact, using $\mathbf{b}$ and $\mathbf{c}$ (for reasons which will soon be apparent), we can write

$$\mathbf{b} \times \mathbf{c} = \left[\left|\begin{matrix} b_2 & b_3 \\ c_2 & c_3 \end{matrix}\right|, \; \left|\begin{matrix} b_3 & b_1 \\ c_3 & c_1 \end{matrix}\right|, \; \left|\begin{matrix} b_1 & b_2 \\ c_1 & c_2 \end{matrix}\right|\right]$$

$$= \left|\begin{matrix} b_2 & b_3 \\ c_2 & c_3 \end{matrix}\right|\mathbf{i} + \left|\begin{matrix} b_3 & b_1 \\ c_3 & c_1 \end{matrix}\right|\mathbf{j} + \left|\begin{matrix} b_1 & b_2 \\ c_1 & c_2 \end{matrix}\right|\mathbf{k},$$

or

$$\mathbf{b} \times \mathbf{c} = \left|\begin{matrix} \mathbf{i} & \mathbf{j} & \mathbf{k} \\ b_1 & b_2 & b_3 \\ c_1 & c_2 & c_3 \end{matrix}\right|, \tag{20}$$

a *pseudo*determinant in the senses that the elements of the first row are vectors and that the expansion *must* be by the elements of the first row.

Now we introduce the *triple scalar product*.

DEFINITION 2.   *Given three vectors* $\mathbf{a}$, $\mathbf{b}$, *and* $\mathbf{c}$, *their triple scalar product is the number* $\mathbf{a} \cdot \mathbf{b} \times \mathbf{c}$.

Notice that parentheses are not needed for the triple scalar product: $\mathbf{a} \cdot \mathbf{b} \times \mathbf{c}$ must mean $\mathbf{a} \cdot (\mathbf{b} \times \mathbf{c})$, since $(\mathbf{a} \cdot \mathbf{b}) \times \mathbf{c}$ is not meaningful.

THEOREM 5.   *Given the vectors* $\mathbf{a} = [a_1, a_2, a_3]$, $\mathbf{b} = [b_1, b_2, b_3]$, *and* $\mathbf{c} = [c_1, c_2, c_3]$, *the value of their triple scalar product is*

$$\mathbf{a} \cdot \mathbf{b} \times \mathbf{c} = \left|\begin{matrix} a_1 & a_2 & a_3 \\ b_1 & b_2 & b_3 \\ c_1 & c_2 & c_3 \end{matrix}\right|. \tag{21}$$

PROOF.   By Definition 2, the triple scalar product is

$$\mathbf{a} \cdot \mathbf{b} \times \mathbf{c} = a_1(b_2 c_3 - b_3 c_2) + a_2(b_3 c_1 - b_1 c_3) + a_3(b_1 c_2 - b_2 c_1)$$

$$= a_1 \left|\begin{matrix} b_2 & b_3 \\ c_2 & c_3 \end{matrix}\right| + a_2 \left|\begin{matrix} b_3 & b_1 \\ c_3 & c_1 \end{matrix}\right| + a_3 \left|\begin{matrix} b_1 & b_2 \\ c_1 & c_2 \end{matrix}\right|$$

$$= \left|\begin{matrix} a_1 & a_2 & a_3 \\ b_1 & b_2 & b_3 \\ c_1 & c_2 & c_3 \end{matrix}\right|. \quad ∎$$

By means of Theorem 5 we can show an extremely important property of the triple scalar product: the dot and cross can be interchanged.

THEOREM 6.   *For any three vectors* **a**, **b**, *and* **c**,

$$\mathbf{a} \times \mathbf{b} \cdot \mathbf{c} = \mathbf{a} \cdot \mathbf{b} \times \mathbf{c}. \tag{22}$$

PROOF.   We have

$$\mathbf{a} \times \mathbf{b} \cdot \mathbf{c} = \mathbf{c} \cdot \mathbf{a} \times \mathbf{b} \qquad \text{(commutativity of inner product)}$$

$$= \begin{vmatrix} c_1 & c_2 & c_3 \\ a_1 & a_2 & a_3 \\ b_1 & b_2 & b_3 \end{vmatrix} \qquad \text{(Theorem 5)}$$

$$= - \begin{vmatrix} a_1 & a_2 & a_3 \\ c_1 & c_2 & c_3 \\ b_1 & b_2 & b_3 \end{vmatrix}$$

$$= \begin{vmatrix} a_1 & a_2 & a_3 \\ b_1 & b_2 & b_3 \\ c_1 & c_2 & c_3 \end{vmatrix}$$

$$= \mathbf{a} \cdot \mathbf{b} \times \mathbf{c}. \quad \blacksquare$$

Given three vectors **a**, **b**, and **c** and the two symbols $\cdot$ and $\times$, there are, formally, twelve distinct ways of writing triple scalar products. Because of the commutativity of the inner product and because of Theorem 6, the following assertion is true.

THEOREM 7.   *Given vectors* **a**, **b**, *and* **c**, *let* $\mathbf{a} \cdot \mathbf{b} \times \mathbf{c} = q$. *Then*

$$\mathbf{a} \times \mathbf{b} \cdot \mathbf{c} = \mathbf{b} \cdot \mathbf{c} \times \mathbf{a} = \mathbf{b} \times \mathbf{c} \cdot \mathbf{a} = \mathbf{c} \cdot \mathbf{a} \times \mathbf{b} = \mathbf{c} \times \mathbf{a} \cdot \mathbf{b} = q$$

and

$$\mathbf{a} \cdot \mathbf{c} \times \mathbf{b} = \mathbf{a} \times \mathbf{c} \cdot \mathbf{b} = \mathbf{b} \cdot \mathbf{a} \times \mathbf{c} = \mathbf{b} \times \mathbf{a} \cdot \mathbf{c} = \mathbf{c} \cdot \mathbf{b} \times \mathbf{a}$$
$$= \mathbf{c} \times \mathbf{b} \cdot \mathbf{a} = -q.$$

PROOF.   Exercise for student. $\blacksquare$

Notice that the essential property is the *cyclic* order: counterclockwise produces one sign, clockwise the opposite. See Figure 10.

We return to the question of the direction of $\mathbf{a} \times \mathbf{b}$.

DEFINITION 3.   1. *The ordered set of vectors* **a**, **b**, **c** *forms a* right-handed triple $\Leftrightarrow \mathbf{a} \times \mathbf{b} \cdot \mathbf{c} > 0$.

2. *The ordered set of vectors* **a**, **b**, **c** *forms a* left-handed triple $\Leftrightarrow \mathbf{a} \times \mathbf{b} \cdot \mathbf{c} < 0$.

As a result of Theorem 7, we see that if **a**, **b**, **c** form a right-handed triple, then so will **b**, **c**, **a** and **c**, **a**, **b**, whereas changing the cyclic order will produce a left-handed triple.

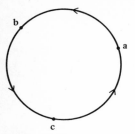

Figure 10

The geometric significance of Definition 3 is simply this: Since

$$\mathbf{a} \times \mathbf{b} \cdot \mathbf{c} = |\mathbf{a} \times \mathbf{b}| \, |\mathbf{c}| \cos \phi, \qquad\qquad\qquad [23]$$

where ϕ is the angle between $\mathbf{a} \times \mathbf{b}$ and $\mathbf{c}$, and since $|\mathbf{a} \times \mathbf{b}| > 0$, $|\mathbf{c}| > 0$
for nonzero $\mathbf{a} \times \mathbf{b}$ and $\mathbf{c}$, the requirement that $\mathbf{a} \times \mathbf{b} \cdot \mathbf{c} > 0 \Rightarrow \cos \phi > 0$,
i.e., that ϕ lies between 0 and $\pi/2$. This means that the vectors $\mathbf{a} \times \mathbf{b}$ and $\mathbf{c}$
lie on the same side of the plane determined by $\mathbf{a}$ and $\mathbf{b}$. For a specific frame
of reference we make the reassuring observation that the positive axes of a
right-handed coordinate system in the usual order form a right-handed
triple, for

$$\mathbf{i} \times \mathbf{j} \cdot \mathbf{k} = \mathbf{k} \cdot \mathbf{k} = 1 > 0,$$

since $\mathbf{i} \times \mathbf{j} = \mathbf{k}$ (Theorem 4).

The following assertion, which completes the geometric description of
the vector $\mathbf{a} \times \mathbf{b}$, is now a triviality.

THEOREM 8.   *If* $\mathbf{a}$ *and* $\mathbf{b}$ *are not parallel, then the vectors* $\mathbf{a}$, $\mathbf{b}$, *and* $\mathbf{a} \times \mathbf{b}$,
in that order, form a right-handed triple.

PROOF.   We have, applying Definition 3 to $\mathbf{a}$, $\mathbf{b}$, $\mathbf{a} \times \mathbf{b}$,

$$\mathbf{a} \times \mathbf{b} \cdot (\mathbf{a} \times \mathbf{b}) = |\mathbf{a} \times \mathbf{b}|^2 > 0,$$

since the hypothesis that $\mathbf{a}$ and $\mathbf{b}$ are not parallel implies that $\mathbf{a} \times \mathbf{b} \neq \mathbf{0}$.
(Note that the discussion preceding the statement of Theorem 8 indicates
that all we have to show is that $\mathbf{a} \times \mathbf{b}$ and $\mathbf{a} \times \mathbf{b}$ lie on the same side of the
plane determined by $\mathbf{a}$ and $\mathbf{b}$, truly trivial.) ∎

Roughly, what Theorem 8 says is that the vectors $\mathbf{a}$, $\mathbf{b}$, and $\mathbf{a} \times \mathbf{b}$ are
oriented like the positive axes of a right-handed coordinate system; in general,
though, $\mathbf{a}$ and $\mathbf{b}$ will not be perpendicular.

There is a useful geometric interpretation of the triple scalar product.

THEOREM 9.   *If the vectors* $\mathbf{a}$, $\mathbf{b}$, *and* $\mathbf{c}$ *form a right-handed triple, then*
$\mathbf{a} \times \mathbf{b} \cdot \mathbf{c}$ *represents the volume of the parallelepiped which they determine.*

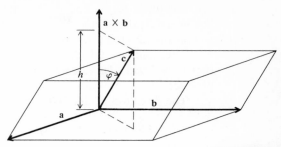

Figure 11

PROOF.   See Figure 11. We have, as in Equation [23],

$$\mathbf{a} \times \mathbf{b} \cdot \mathbf{c} = |\mathbf{a} \times \mathbf{b}| \cdot |\mathbf{c}| \cos \phi,$$

where ϕ is the angle between $\mathbf{a} \times \mathbf{b}$ and $\mathbf{c}$. But $|\mathbf{c}| \cos \phi = h$, the height of the parallelepiped, and $|\mathbf{a} \times \mathbf{b}|$ is the area of the base. Thus, their product gives the volume. ∎

Example 3.   We find the area of the triangle with vertices $A(2, 1, 3)$, $B(-1, 2, 2)$, and $C(3, 0, 2)$.

The sketch in Figure 12 is schematic and can be thought of as being in the plane determined by A, B, and C. The area of the triangle $\triangle ABC$ is half the area of the parallelogram determined by the vectors $\overrightarrow{AB} = \mathbf{b}$ and $\overrightarrow{AC} = \mathbf{c}$. In turn, this area is equal to $|\mathbf{b} \times \mathbf{c}|$. Thus our first step is to find, $\mathbf{b}$, $\mathbf{c}$, and $\mathbf{b} \times \mathbf{c}$:

$$\mathbf{b} = \overrightarrow{AB} = -3\mathbf{i} + \mathbf{j} - \mathbf{k}$$
$$\mathbf{c} = \overrightarrow{AC} = \mathbf{i} - \mathbf{j} - \mathbf{k}.$$

Then

$$\mathbf{b} \times \mathbf{c} = -2\mathbf{i} - 4\mathbf{j} + 2\mathbf{k} = 2(-\mathbf{i} - 2\mathbf{j} + \mathbf{k}).$$

From this we find $|\mathbf{b} \times \mathbf{c}| = 2\sqrt{6}$, and the area of $\triangle ABC$ is $\sqrt{6}$ square units.

The next illustration shows how the vector product can be used to find a vector perpendicular to each of two given vectors.

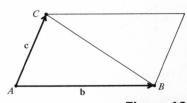

Figure 12

Example 4.   The points $A(1, 2, -1)$ and $B(3, -1, 2)$ determine a line in space; the points $C(1, 0, 2)$ and $D(2, 1, 3)$ determine another. We want to find the minimum distance between these two lines.

The fundamental idea is that the shortest distance will lie along a line that is *perpendicular to each of the given lines*—hence the use of the vector product.

The direction of line AB is given by

$$\mathbf{v}_1 = \overrightarrow{AB} = 2\mathbf{i} - 3\mathbf{j} + 3\mathbf{k};$$

that of line CD by

$$\mathbf{v}_2 = \overrightarrow{CD} = \mathbf{i} + \mathbf{j} + \mathbf{k}.$$

Hence, the mutually perpendicular direction is that of

$$\mathbf{n} = \mathbf{v}_1 \times \mathbf{v}_2 = -6\mathbf{i} + \mathbf{j} + 5\mathbf{k}.$$

Because we are primarily interested in the information $\mathbf{n}$ has for us about *direction*, we convert it to a unit vector:

$$\mathbf{u}_n = \frac{1}{|\mathbf{n}|}\mathbf{n} = \frac{1}{\sqrt{62}}(-6\mathbf{i} + \mathbf{j} + 5\mathbf{k}).$$

In Figure 13 we show a schematic sketch which, necessarily inaccurate because it is drawn in a plane, suggests how to obtain the desired distance.

As $\mathbf{u}_n$ is perpendicular to both lines, if we take any vector from one line to the other, say $\overrightarrow{AD}$, and project it on $\mathbf{u}_n$ drawn with its initial point at A, the length of the projection obtained will be the desired minimum distance. Now $\overrightarrow{AD} = \mathbf{i} - \mathbf{j} + 4\mathbf{k}$; the projection is found from the inner product (remember: $\mathbf{u}_n$ is a unit vector):

$$\overrightarrow{AD} \cdot \mathbf{u}_n = \frac{1}{\sqrt{62}}(-6 - 1 + 20) = \frac{13}{\sqrt{62}} \approx 1.65 \text{ units.}$$

A different choice of vector between line AB and line CD, say $\overrightarrow{CB}$, may make the inner product negative, but its absolute value in any case would be $13/\sqrt{62}$.

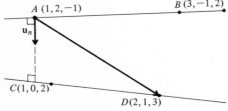

Figure 13

Exercises

A.   **1.** Find $\mathbf{a} \times \mathbf{b}$:
   (a) $\mathbf{a} = [1, 3, -2]$, $\mathbf{b} = [2, 0, 1]$.
   (b) $\mathbf{a} = [-3, 1, 4]$, $\mathbf{b} = [4, -2, 1]$.
   (c) $\mathbf{a} = 2\mathbf{i} + \mathbf{j} - 3\mathbf{k}$, $\mathbf{b} = -4\mathbf{i} + 3\mathbf{j} + 5\mathbf{k}$.
   (d) $\mathbf{a} = -\mathbf{i} + 4\mathbf{j} - \mathbf{k}$, $\mathbf{b} = 6\mathbf{i} - 3\mathbf{j} + 2\mathbf{k}$.
   (e) $\mathbf{a} = [1, 1, 1]$, $\mathbf{b} = [1, -1, 0]$.
   2. Find a unit vector perpendicular to both of the given vectors.
   (a) $\mathbf{a} = [1, 0, 1]$, $\mathbf{b} = [0, 1, -1]$.
   (b) $\mathbf{a} = \mathbf{i} + 2\mathbf{j} - \mathbf{k}$, $\mathbf{b} = 2\mathbf{i} + \mathbf{j} + 4\mathbf{k}$.
   (c) $\mathbf{a} = \mathbf{i} - \mathbf{j} + 3\mathbf{k}$, $\mathbf{b} = -\mathbf{i} + \mathbf{j}$.
   (d) $\mathbf{a} = [2, -3, 1]$, $\mathbf{b} = [-3, 0, 2]$.
   (e) $\mathbf{a} = \mathbf{i} - \mathbf{k}$, $\mathbf{b} = \mathbf{j} + \mathbf{k}$.
   3. Find the volume of the parallelepiped determined by each of the
following triples of vectors.
   (a) $\mathbf{a} = [1, 1, 0]$, $\mathbf{b} = [3, -2, 1]$, $\mathbf{c} = [0, 2, -1]$.
   (b) $\mathbf{a} = -\mathbf{i} + 2\mathbf{j} - 5\mathbf{k}$, $\mathbf{b} = 3\mathbf{i} + \mathbf{j}$, $\mathbf{c} = \mathbf{i} - \mathbf{k}$.
   (c) $\mathbf{a} = [1, -1, 2]$, $\mathbf{b} = [2, 1, -1]$, $\mathbf{c} = [1, 5, -8]$.
   (d) $\mathbf{a} = [1, 3, -2]$, $\mathbf{b} = [0, 2, -1]$, $\mathbf{c} = [3, 5, -4]$.
   4. Consider the three points $A(1, 2, -1)$, $B(3, 0, 1)$, and $C(2, -1, 0)$.
   (a) Find a unit vector perpendicular to the plane determined by
       A, B, and C.
   (b) Find the area of the triangle $\triangle ABC$.
   (c) Find the distance between the origin and the plane of A, B, C.
   5. Find the shortest distance between the lines determined by A, B
and C, D, where:
   (a) $A(1, 0, 0)$, $B(2, 1, 2)$, $C(3, -1, 4)$, $D(1, 0, 2)$.
   (b) $A(0, 1, 2)$, $B(1, 0, 3)$, $C(2, 1, 0)$, $D(-1, -1, 1)$.
   (c) $A(1, 2, 3)$, $B(-3, 0, -3)$, $C(-5, 4, 1)$, $D(7, 0, 5)$.
   6. Let

$$\mathbf{a} = 2\mathbf{i} + \mathbf{j} + \mathbf{k}$$
$$\mathbf{b} = \mathbf{i} - \mathbf{j} - 2\mathbf{k}$$
$$\mathbf{c} = \mathbf{i} + 3\mathbf{j} + 2\mathbf{k}.$$

   (a) Find $(\mathbf{a} \times \mathbf{b}) \times \mathbf{c}$.
   (b) Find $\mathbf{a} \times (\mathbf{b} \times \mathbf{c})$.
   (c) Does the associative law hold for vector multiplication?
   7. Which of the triples $\mathbf{a}$, $\mathbf{b}$, $\mathbf{c}$ of Exercise A3 are right-handed?
   8. Find the area of the triangles with the given vertices.
   (a) $A(2, -3, 7)$, $B(1, 0, 2)$, $C(3, -4, 1)$.
   (b) $A(1, 0, -2)$, $B(3, 1, 1)$, $C(2, -3, -1)$.
   (c) $A(2, -2, 0)$, $B(1, -3, 1)$, $C(3, -4, 0)$.

B.   **1.** The second assertion of Theorem 3 is that $|\mathbf{a} \times \mathbf{b}| = |\mathbf{a}|\,|\mathbf{b}|\sin\theta$; the proof concludes with $|\mathbf{a} \times \mathbf{b}|^2 = |\mathbf{a}|^2\,|\mathbf{b}|^2\sin^2\theta$. Why does the assertion itself follow from this equation?

2. Prove Corollary 2 to Theorem 3: $\mathbf{a}$ and $\mathbf{b}$ are parallel $\Leftrightarrow \mathbf{a} \times \mathbf{b} = \mathbf{0}$. [*Hint:* for the $\Leftarrow$ part use assertion 2 of Theorem 3.]

3. Prove Theorem 4.

4. Prove Theorem 7.

5. This exercise fills a gap in the discussion of right- and left-handed triples. Prove

THEOREM 10.   **a, b, c** *are coplanar* $\Leftrightarrow \mathbf{a} \times \mathbf{b} \cdot \mathbf{c} = 0$.

[Hint for $\Rightarrow$: if $\mathbf{a}$ and $\mathbf{b}$ are not parallel and $\mathbf{c}$ lies in the plane of $\mathbf{a}$ and $\mathbf{b}$, then $\mathbf{c} = h\mathbf{a} + k\mathbf{b}$, for some $h, k \in \mathbf{R}$.]

C.   **1.** (a) Show that $(\mathbf{a} \times \mathbf{b}) \times \mathbf{c}$ must lie in the plane of $\mathbf{a}$ and $\mathbf{b}$.

(b) Show that $\mathbf{a} \times (\mathbf{b} \times \mathbf{c})$ must lie in the plane of $\mathbf{b}$ and $\mathbf{c}$.

2. Let $\mathbf{v}_1$ and $\mathbf{v}_2$ be vectors with the property that

$$\mathbf{a} \cdot \mathbf{v}_1 = \mathbf{a} \cdot \mathbf{v}_2$$

for every possible choice of $\mathbf{a}$. Show that $\mathbf{v}_1 = \mathbf{v}_2$. [*Hint:* suppose $\mathbf{v}_1 \neq \mathbf{v}_2$, i.e., $\mathbf{v}_1 - \mathbf{v}_2 \neq \mathbf{0}$; try $\mathbf{a} = \mathbf{v}_1 - \mathbf{v}_2$.]

8.4 Planes

In plane analytic geometry we know that the equations of first degree in x and y represent straight lines. In three-dimensional geometry the first-degree equations represent planes (recall that a single equation in 3-space geometry represents a surface).

The essential geometric property of lines is that they are curves of constant direction. Similarly, for our purposes a plane is a surface of constant direction. One way of making this more explicit is as follows: a surface is a plane if and only if normal vectors (vectors perpendicular to the surface) drawn at any two points are parallel. With this as our working definition we can obtain an analytic description of a plane.

Suppose a plane has a normal vector $\mathbf{n} = a\mathbf{i} + b\mathbf{j} + c\mathbf{k}$. Suppose also the plane goes through the point $P_0(x_0, y_0, z_0)$. We seek conditions for $P(x, y, z)$ to be an arbitrary point on the plane. See Figure 14.

If $P \neq P_0$ is any point of the plane, then the vector $\overrightarrow{P_0P}$ must be perpendicular to $\mathbf{n}$. Or, since $\overrightarrow{P_0P} = (x - x_0)\mathbf{i} + (y - y_0)\mathbf{j} + (z - z_0)\mathbf{k}$,

$$a(x - x_0) + b(y - y_0) + c(z - z_0) = 0, \qquad [24]$$

which is the desired equation of the plane.

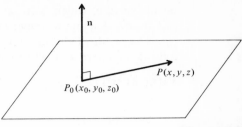

Figure 14

Equation [24] can be put in the form

$$ax + by + cz = ax_0 + by_0 + cz_0,$$

or

$$ax + by + cz = d. \qquad [25]$$

Thus we see that a plane does have an equation of the first degree in x, y, and z. Notice that the coefficients of x, y, and z are precisely the components of the normal vector to the plane. Information about the *position* of the plane is contained in the constant d.

Example 5. One plane goes through the origin and has normal $\mathbf{n} = 2\mathbf{i} + \mathbf{j} + \mathbf{k}$. A second plane has the same normal and goes through $P_0(-3, 1 - 7)$. Find their equations.

Using [14] and the given information, we have

first plane: $2x + y + z = 0$
second plane: $2(x + 3) + (y - 1) + (z + 7) = 0$ or
$$2x + y + z = -12.$$

The two planes are distinct but parallel.

If we agree that not all of a, b, c are zero, then the equation in [25] is one way of writing the most general linear (i.e., first-degree) equation in x, y, and z. Will such an equation always represent a plane? The answer is easily seen to be in the affirmative. For, suppose $c \neq 0$; if we set $x = y = 0$, we can easily solve for z_0: $z_0 = d/c$, thereby obtaining a point $P_0(0, 0, d/c)$ on the surface determined by [25]. But now we can write the equation in the form

$$a(x - 0) + b(y - 0) + c(z - (d/c)) = 0,$$

or

$$\mathbf{n} \cdot \overrightarrow{P_0P} = 0,$$

where $\mathbf{n} = a\mathbf{i} + b\mathbf{j} + c\mathbf{k}$ and $P(x, y, z)$ is an arbitrary point on the surface. This shows that $\mathbf{n}$ is perpendicular to the vector from P_0 to any other point on the surface, which is to say the surface is a plane. If $c = 0$, then either $a \neq 0$ or $b \neq 0$ and a similar argument applies.

The result of the preceding discussion can be summarized formally as follows (compare with Theorem 3.5).

THEOREM 11. *A surface in 3-space is a plane $\Leftrightarrow$ it has an equation of the form*

$$ax + by + cz = d,$$

where a, b, c are not all zero. When this is so the vector $\mathbf{n} = a\mathbf{i} + b\mathbf{j} + c\mathbf{k}$ is normal to the plane.

Example 6.   Consider the equation

$$4x + y + 2z = 8.$$

From Theorem 11 we know the equation represents (is) a plane, with normal vector $\mathbf{n} = 4\mathbf{i} + \mathbf{j} + 2\mathbf{k}$. We can easily find some points on the plane by looking for the intercepts with the axes. Thus, $y = z = 0 \Rightarrow x = 2$; $x = z = 0 \Rightarrow y = 8$; $x = y = 0 \Rightarrow z = 4$. We sketch in Figure 15 the portion of this plane which cuts across the first octant.

Example 7.   In general, three points determine a plane. We find the plane determined by $A(1, 2, 1)$, $B(2, 0, 3)$, and $C(1, -2, 0)$.

First Method.   We can start with the equation $ax + by + cz = d$ and substitute in the coordinates of A, B, and C, obtaining a linear system for a, b, c, and d:

$$\left\{ \begin{array}{l} a + 2b + c\ \ \ = d \\ 2a \ \ \ \ \ \ \ + 3c = d \\ a - 2b \ \ \ \ \ \ = d \end{array} \right\}.$$

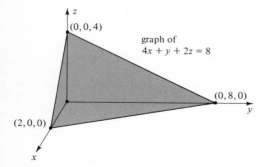

graph of
$4x + y + 2z = 8$

$(0,0,4)$

$(0,8,0)$

$(2,0,0)$

Figure 15

We can solve for a, b, and c in terms of d:

$$a = \frac{5d}{4}, \quad b = \frac{d}{8}, \quad c = -\frac{d}{2}.$$

Taking $d = 8$ gives $a = 10$, $b = 1$, $c = -4$, and the desired equation is $10x + y - 4z = 8$. It is routine to check that coordinates of A, B, and C all satisfy this equation.

Second Method.   The vectors

$$\mathbf{b} = \overrightarrow{AB} = \mathbf{i} - 2\mathbf{j} + 2\mathbf{k}$$

and

$$\mathbf{c} = \overrightarrow{AC} = -4\mathbf{j} - \mathbf{k}$$

lie in the desired plane (see Figure 16). Their vector product will be a normal to the plane. This normal is

$$\mathbf{n} = \mathbf{b} \times \mathbf{c} = 10\mathbf{i} + \mathbf{j} - 4\mathbf{k}.$$

Using the expression for $\mathbf{n}$ and the coordinates of A in [24] gives immediately

$$10x + y - 4z = 8,$$

as before.

Example 8.   Find the equation of a plane that is parallel to

$$3x - 5y + 2z = 7$$

and that contains the point $P_0(2, -1, -4)$.

If the two planes are parallel, they share the same normal $\mathbf{n} = 3\mathbf{i} - 5\mathbf{j} + 2\mathbf{k}$, and the equation of the plane sought is

$$3x - 5y + 2z = d.$$

To find d we merely substitute in the coordinates of P_0:

$$3(2) + (-5)(-1) + 2(-4) = d,$$

or $d = 3$. Thus the required equation is

$$3x - 5y + 2z = 3.$$

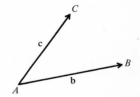

Figure 16

Exercises

A. **1.** Find the equation of the plane through P_0 with normal vector $\mathbf{n}$.

(a) $P_0(0, 0, 0)$, $\mathbf{n} = a\mathbf{i} + b\mathbf{j} + c\mathbf{k}$.

(b) $P_0(-1, 3, 7)$, $\mathbf{n} = -2\mathbf{i} + 4\mathbf{j} - \mathbf{k}$.

(c) $P_0(1, 1, 0)$, $\mathbf{n} = \mathbf{i} + \mathbf{j}$.

(d) $P_0(1, 2, 3)$, $\mathbf{n} = \mathbf{k}$.

(e) $P_0(0, 1, 0)$, $\mathbf{n} = \mathbf{i}$.

(f) $P_0(1, 1, 1)$, $\mathbf{n} = \mathbf{j} - \mathbf{k}$.

2. Find the equation of the plane determined by the following points.

(a) $A(3, -4, 2)$, $B(2, -1, 1)$, $C(0, 1, 2)$.

(b) $A(1, 0, 1)$, $B(0, -1, 2)$, $C(3, -4, 1)$.

(c) $A(2, 3, 1)$, $B(1, -1, 1)$, $C(4, 0, 1)$.

3. A plane through $(5, -1, 6)$ is parallel to $3x - 7y + z = 4$. Find its equation.

4. Find the equation of the plane that is parallel to $2x - 5y + 7z = 3$ and that contains the point $(3, -4, -6)$.

5. Find the equation satisfied by the points $P(x, y, z)$ which are equidistant from $(3, 0, 5)$ and $(1, -2, -1)$. Identify the set of points thus determined.

6. The vector normal to a plane is $\mathbf{n} = [4, 2, 7]$. The point $(-1, 5, 8)$ lies in the plane. Find the equation of the plane.

7. A plane contains the points $(3, 8, 5)$ and $(2, 4, 6)$ and does not intersect the x-axis. Find its equation.

8. Find the equation of the plane that does not intersect the y-axis and that contains the points $(1, 3, 2)$ and $(7, 1, -3)$.

9. A plane through the origin has the z-component of its normal vector equal to 0. If the point $(1, 1, 1)$ lies in the plane, find the equation of the plane.

10. Two planes are perpendicular if their normal vectors are perpendicular. Find the equation of the plane that is perpendicular to $3x - 2y + z = 4$ and that contains $P_1(2, 0, 3)$ and $P_2(1, 4, -2)$.

11. Find the equation of the plane that is perpendicular to the xy-plane and that contains the points $P_1(2, 0, 0)$ and $P_2(0, 2, 0)$.

12. Find the equation of the plane that is perpendicular to $x - 3y + z - 6 = 0$ and that contains the points $(1, 2, 1)$ and $(3, -1, 0)$.

C. **1.** Give a necessary and sufficient condition for the plane $ax + by + cz = d$ to have no intersection with the y-axis.

2. Give a necessary and sufficient condition for the plane $ax + by + cz = d$ to intersect all three coordinate axes.

3. Find the distance from the origin to the plane $ax + by + cz = d$.

Hints: (i) Adjust the coefficients so that $d > 0$. (ii) Divide both sides by $|\mathbf{n}| = \sqrt{a^2 + b^2 + c^2}$, so that the equation can be written as

$$(\cos \alpha)x + (\cos \beta)y + (\cos \gamma)z = p,$$

where $\cos \alpha$, etc., are the direction cosines of the normal vector $\mathbf{n}$ and $p = d/|\mathbf{n}|$. (iii) Observe that the left-hand side of the last equation is an inner product, i.e., the equation can be written as

$$\mathbf{u}_n \cdot \overrightarrow{OP} = p.$$

(iv) What if $d = 0$?

8.5 Lines

As we did when we studied lines in the plane, we begin by assuming that a line is described by its direction and by a particular point on the line. A natural way to give the direction of the line is in terms of a vector $\mathbf{v} = [a, b, c]$; suppose, further, that the line contains the point $P_0(x_0, y_0, z_0)$. Then, if $P(x, y, z)$ is an arbitrary point on the line, we have (see Figure 17)

$$\overrightarrow{OP} = \overrightarrow{OP_0} + t\mathbf{v},$$

or, letting $\mathbf{r}(t) = [x, y, z] = \overrightarrow{OP}$,

$$\mathbf{r}(t) = [x_0, y_0, z_0] + t[a, b, c],$$

or

$$\mathbf{r}(t) = [x_0 + at, y_0 + bt, z_0 + ct]. \tag{26}$$

The function $\mathbf{r}$ is a *linear vector function*, i.e., $\mathbf{r} : \mathbf{R} \to \mathbf{R}^3$ and its three component functions $x(t) = x_0 + at$, $y(t) = y_0 + bt$, and $z(t) = z_0 + ct$ are first-degree functions of t.

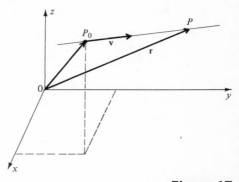

Figure 17

Conversely, if we start with a function such as described by [26], we can easily reverse the steps to see that **r** is the position vector from the origin to a point *P* on the line through $P_0(x_0, y_0, z_0)$ in the direction of the vector **v** = [*a, b, c*]. Thus, we have proved the following assertion.

THEOREM 12.   *A vector function* **r** : **R** → **R**³ *of the variable t represents a straight line ⇔* **r** *is linear, i.e.,* **r** *has the form of Equation* [26]. *When this is the case the line contains the point* $P_0(x_0, y_0, z_0)$ *and has the direction of* **v** = [*a, b, c*].

Example 9.   Find the equation of the line through $P_0(1, 2, 3)$ in the direction **v** = [−2, 3, −1].

Letting **r**(*t*) be the position vector from the origin to an arbitrary point on the line, we have, by Theorem 12,

$$\mathbf{r}(t) = [1 - 2t, 2 + 3t, 3 - t]$$
$$= (1 - 2t)\mathbf{i} + (2 + 3t)\mathbf{j} + (3 - t)\mathbf{k}.$$

If we recall that **r**(*t*) = [*x, y, z*], where *P*(*x, y, z*) is an arbitrary point on the line, we can write [26] in the form

$$\begin{cases} x = x_0 + at \\ y = y_0 + bt \\ z = z_0 + ct \end{cases}.$$ [27]

These are the *parametric equations* of the line through P_0 in the direction of [*a, b, c*].

Example 10.   Find the equations of the line through $P_0(2, -1, 3)$ and $P_1(4, 2, 5)$.

We can take **v** as $\overrightarrow{P_0P_1}$; thus **v** = [2, 3, 2]. The vector equation for the line is

$$\mathbf{r}(t) = [2 + 2t, -1 + 3t, 3 + 2t],$$

and the corresponding parametric equations are

$$\begin{cases} x = 2 + 2t \\ y = -1 + 3t \\ z = 3 + 2t \end{cases}.$$

In case *abc* ≠ 0 we can solve each of the equations in [27] for *t*; equating these common values gives us the *symmetric form of the equations of a straight line*:

$$\frac{x - x_0}{a} = \frac{y - y_0}{b} = \frac{z - z_0}{c}.$$ [28]

It is even customary to use [28] if one or two of *a, b, c* equals zero; the understanding in this case is that the corresponding numerator(s) also be zero.

Example 11. Find the parametric and symmetric forms for the equations of the $\overrightarrow{\text{line}}$ through $P_0(4, 1, 2)$ and $P_1(5, 3, 2)$.

The vector $\overrightarrow{P_0 P_1} = \mathbf{i} + 2\mathbf{j} = \mathbf{v}$. Thus the vector form of the equations is $\mathbf{r}(t) = [4 + t, 1 + 2t, 2]$ and the parametric form is

$$\begin{cases} x = 4 + t \\ y = 1 + 2t \\ z = 2 \end{cases}.$$

Clearly this line lies entirely in the plane $z = 2$. We can eliminate t from the first two equations and write

$$\begin{cases} \dfrac{x - 4}{1} = \dfrac{y - 1}{2} \\ z = 2 \end{cases}.$$

Of course a line can be represented as the intersection of two planes, but only in especially simple cases (example: $x = 0$, $z = 2$) is such an analytic description at all informative. We illustrate a technique for converting this type of representation to parametric form.

Example 12. Find parametric equations for the line of intersection of the planes

$$\begin{cases} x + 4y - z = 7 \\ 3x - y + 2z = 4 \end{cases}.$$

The normal $\mathbf{n}_1 = \mathbf{i} + 4\mathbf{j} - \mathbf{k}$ to the first plane is perpendicular to every line in that plane; similarly the normal $\mathbf{n}_2 = 3\mathbf{i} - \mathbf{j} + 2\mathbf{k}$ is perpendicular to every line in the second plane. The line of intersection of the two planes will then be perpendicular to both normals; thus its direction will be given by the vector product

$$\mathbf{n}_1 \times \mathbf{n}_2 = 7\mathbf{i} - 5\mathbf{j} - 13\mathbf{k}.$$

All we need now is a point on the line, i.e., a point on both planes. There are many ways to extract one point from the above pair of equations. One such is to set one of the coordinates—we shall use y—equal to zero and solve for the other two:

$$\begin{cases} x - z = 7 \\ 3x + 2z = 4 \end{cases}.$$

The solution of this system is readily found to be $x_0 = \frac{18}{5}$, $z_0 = -\frac{17}{5}$; we already have $y_0 = 0$. Thus a parametric form for the equations is

$$\begin{cases} x = \frac{18}{5} + 7t \\ y = -5t \\ z = -\frac{17}{5} - 13t \end{cases}.$$

Example 13. Determine whether or not the two lines

$$\begin{cases} x = -2 + 4t \\ y = -2 + t \\ z = 5 - 2t \end{cases} \text{ and } \begin{cases} x = -4 - 3s \\ y = 3 + 2s \\ z = 11 + 4s \end{cases}$$

intersect. If they do, find the point of intersection. [*Note:* These lines are not parallel. Even so, they might not intersect.]

For a point of intersection there would have to exist a value t_0 and a value s_0 that produce the same triple (x_0, y_0, z_0) in both sets of equations. Thus we equate the right-hand sides of the respective equations and seek a common solution:

$$\begin{cases} -2 + 4t = -4 - 3s \\ -2 + t = 3 + 2s \\ 5 - 2t = 11 + 4s \end{cases}.$$

Rewritten, the system is

$$\begin{cases} 4t + 3s = -2 \\ t - 2s = 5 \\ -2t - 4s = 6 \end{cases}.$$

It is routine to find that the system is consistent, the unique solution being $t_0 = 1$, $s_0 = -2$. Using either of these values in its parametric system, we find the coordinates of the point of intersection to be $(2, -1, 3)$.

Exercises

A. **1.** Find vector, parametric, and symmetric forms for the equations of the lines determined by the following pairs of points.

(a) $P_0(4, -5, 2)$, $P_1(2, 7, -3)$.
(b) $P_0(3, -3, 6)$, $P_1(5, -3, 2)$.
(c) $P_0(-1, 0, 8)$, $P_1(2, 5, -4)$.
(d) $P_0(3, 5, 2)$, $P_1(6, 5, 2)$.
(e) $P_0(4, -1, 7)$, $P_1(4, 2, 5)$.

2. Write vector and parametric equations for each of the following lines.

(a) $x = 0$, $z = 2$. (Ans.: $\mathbf{r}(t) = [0, t, 2]$; $x = 0$, $y = t$, $z = 2$.)
(b) $y = 3$, $z = 1$.
(c) $x = 1$, $y = 2$.
(d) $x = 0$, $y = 0$.
(e) $x = 4$, $z = -1$.

3. Write parametric equations for the lines of intersection of the following pairs of planes.

(a) $3x + y + z = 2$, $x + 3y + 4z = 7$.
(b) $2x - y - 3z = 4$, $3x + y + 5z = 8$.

(c) $x + y - 6z = 0, 2x - 3y + 4z = 1$.

(d) $x - 2y + 3z = 6, 2x - 3y + 4z = 11$.

4. Find the point of intersection of the line $\mathbf{r}(t) = [2 + t, -1 + 2t, 3 - t]$ and the plane $x - 2y + 4z = 2$.

5. By definition, a line is *parallel* to a plane $\Leftrightarrow$ the line is perpendicular to the normal to the plane. Find the parametric equations for each of the following lines.

(a) Parallel to $2x - y + 3z = 6$ and to $x + 4y - 3z = 8$ and contains $P_0(5, -4, 2)$.

(b) Parallel to $x - 4y = 5$ and to $3y + z = 4$ and contains $P_0(1, 1, 1)$.

6. A line has the direction of $\mathbf{v} = 2\mathbf{i} - 7\mathbf{j} + 4\mathbf{k}$ and goes through the point of intersection of the line

$$\frac{x}{1} = \frac{y - 2}{-3} = \frac{z - 1}{2}$$

and the plane $3x + y + 6z + 4 = 0$. Find its vector equation.

7. Determine whether or not the following pairs of lines intersect. If they do, find the point of intersection.

(a) $\mathbf{r}(t) = [1 + 2t, 3 + t, -4 - 3t]$
$\mathbf{r}(s) = [-3s, -1 + 2s, -2 + 4s]$.

(b) $\begin{cases} x = 1 - t \\ y = 2 + 4t \\ z = -3 + 2t \end{cases}$, $\begin{cases} x = 5 + 3s \\ y = -1 + s \\ z = 2 - 4s \end{cases}$.

C. **1.** Give a necessary and sufficient condition for the parameter t in

$$\begin{cases} x = x_0 + at \\ y = y_0 + bt \\ z = z_0 + ct \end{cases}$$

to represent the directed distance along the line.

2. See Exercise C1. Can one always choose the parameter in setting up parametric equations for a line so that it represents directed distance along the line?

8.6 Surfaces

In this section we shall begin a brief study of the analytic geometry of surfaces. Specifically, we shall be interested in methods for extracting geometric information from equations such as $z = x^2 + y^2$, $z = x^2 - y^2$, $x^2 + y^2 - z^2 = 1$, and $z = (1 - \frac{1}{4}x) \cos^2 y$. In general, such equations will correspond to a two-dimensional set of points, a surface. The types of information we look for are, for the most part, analogous to the sort of things we investigate in the study of curves in the plane: extent, intercepts, symmetry, and so on. There is, however, an additional and very considerable complication in the present problem. We refer to the difficulty of drawing in two dimensions (on paper or on a blackboard) a configuration that exists in three dimensions. At this point our only words of wisdom are that practice helps. We shall try to give some more explicit aid in what follows.

   Intercepts with the coordinate axes can be found—if they exist—by setting two of the variables equal to zero. For example, with

$$x^2 + y^2 - z^2 = 1$$

we find $x = \pm 1$, $y = z = 0$; $x = 0$, $y = \pm 1$, $z = 0$; but putting $x = y = 0$ gives $-z^2 = 1$, which has no solution, indicating no intersection with the z-axis.

   However, far more useful than the set of points obtained in this way is knowledge of the *traces* on the coordinate planes. These are the curves of intersection of the surface with the coordinate planes; they are found by setting one of the variables equal to zero. Using the above equation as an example, we have

$z = 0$ (xy-plane), $x^2 + y^2 = 1$, circle
$y = 0$ (zx-plane), $x^2 - z^2 = 1$, hyperbola
$x = 0$ (yz-plane), $y^2 - z^2 = 1$, hyperbola.

   Related to the traces on the coordinate planes are traces in planes parallel to the coordinate planes. For example, with the equation $z = x^2 + y^2$, we find from $z = 0$, $x^2 + y^2 = 0$, that the surface intersects the xy-plane only in a point, the origin. But if we consider planes parallel to and above the xy-plane, planes $z = c$, $c > 0$, we find $z = c$, $x^2 + y^2 = c$, a circle with center on the z-axis, radius $= \sqrt{c}$. Clearly, the circles enlarge as c, the distance above the xy-plane, increases.

   Similarly, with $z = x^2 - y^2$, the trace in the xy-plane, $z = 0$, $x^2 - y^2 = 0$, is simply a pair of straight lines; but in the plane $z = c$, $c \neq 0$, we find $z = c$, $x^2 - y^2 = c$, a hyperbola, the nature of the transverse axis depending on whether c is positive or negative.

   Symmetry with respect to the coordinate axes can be found, if it exists, by checking whether or not *pairs* of the variables can be replaced by their negatives without changing the nature of the relation (see Exercise B2). For example, $z = x^2 + y^2$ is unchanged if x and y are replaced by $-x$ and $-y$, respectively, indicating that the surface is symmetric with respect to the z-axis. But there is no symmetry with respect to the other axes. However, as with intercepts, symmetry with respect to the coordinate *planes* can be more helpful than with respect to axes. With this same example, $z = x^2 + y^2$, we see that replacing x by $-x$ leaves the equation unchanged, indicating symmetry with respect to the yz-plane (see Exercise B1). Similarly, there is symmetry with respect to the zx-plane (why?), but there is none with respect to the xy-plane (why?).

The equation $x^2 + y^2 - z^2 = 1$ immediately reveals symmetry with respect to all coordinate planes—and axes—whereas the equation $z = (x - 1)y$ reveals no symmetry.

Obtaining information about *extent* of the surface depends very much, as regards ease or difficulty, on the nature of the equation. With the equation $z = y(x^2 + 1)$, for example, we see that all pairs $(x, y) \in \mathbf{R}^2$ can be used on the right-hand side, the sign of z depending on the sign of y: the surface is above the xy-plane for $y > 0$, below for $y < 0$.

With the equation $z = x^2 + y^2$ it is easy to see that all pairs $(x, y) \in \mathbf{R}^2$ can be used; in this case, clearly, $z \geqslant 0$: the entire surface lies above the xy-plane except for the origin, the vertex of this paraboloid.

If we write $x^2 + y^2 - z^2 = 1$ as $z^2 = x^2 + y^2 - 1$, we see that only (x, y) such that $x^2 + y^2 \geqslant 1$ (points on and outside the unit circle) can be used; also, *all* values of z can be obtained.

In contrast to the surfaces of these examples, the surface corresponding to

$$\frac{x^2}{a^2} + \frac{y^2}{b^2} + \frac{z^2}{c^2} = 1$$

lies entirely in a bounded region of space. For example, we can write the equation in the form

$$z^2 = c^2\left[1 - \frac{x^2}{a^2} - \frac{y^2}{b^2}\right],$$

which shows at once that only pairs (x, y) such that $(x^2/a^2) + (y^2/b^2) \leqslant 1$ can be used and that, in any case, z must satisfy $-c \leqslant z \leqslant c$. In fact, this surface, having all kinds of symmetry, lies entirely within the box $\{(x, y, z) \mid |x| \leqslant a, |y| \leqslant b, |z| \leqslant c\}$. It is an ellipsoid.

Example 14.   We illustrate some of the preceding ideas by obtaining a sketch of the surface represented analytically by $z = x^2 + y^2$.

We summarize the information already found, plus a little more, as follows.

TRACES.

xy-plane	zx-plane	yz-plane	planes $z = c$, $c > 0$
$\left\{\begin{array}{l} z = 0 \\ x^2 + y^2 = 0 \end{array}\right\}$	$\left\{\begin{array}{l} y = 0 \\ z = x^2 \end{array}\right\}$	$\left\{\begin{array}{l} x = 0 \\ z = y^2 \end{array}\right\}$	$\left\{\begin{array}{l} z = c \\ x^2 + y^2 = c \end{array}\right\}$

SYMMETRY.   With respect to yz- and zx-planes. With respect to z-axis.

EXTENT: All $(x, y) \in \mathbf{R}^2$ are admissible. $z \geqslant 0$ (surface lies on and above xy-plane).

As regards the sketching, the *order* in which the various traces are drawn may make a difference. A suggestion which may help is to draw first the trace, if any, in the plane of the paper (*yz*-plane); then draw in traces in the *xy*-plane and in planes parallel to the *xy*-plane. (With regard to the latter, if the surface is of infinite extent, chop it off somewhere with planes $z = c$.) Finally, draw in the trace in the *zx*-plane. We illustrate this suggestion (this *one* time) with a sequence of drawings for $z = x^2 + y^2$. See Figure 18. This surface is a *circular paraboloid* or *paraboloid of revolution*, for it can be generated by revolving the parabola $z = y^2$ about the *z*-axis.

Example 15. For an illustration of a different sort we sketch a part of the graph of $z = (1 - \frac{1}{4}x)\cos^2 y$. In particular, we concern ourselves with that part that lies above the rectangle $S = \{(x, y) \mid 0 \leqslant x \leqslant 2, 0 \leqslant y \leqslant \pi\}$. The analysis provides the following information.

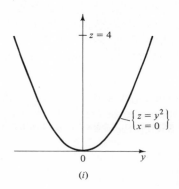

(*i*)

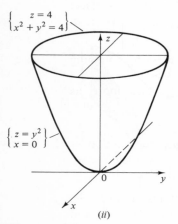

(*ii*)

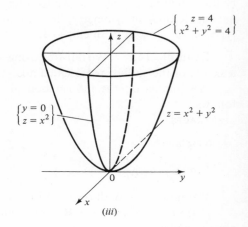

(*iii*)

Figure 18

TRACES:

xy-plane	zx-plane	yz-plane	plane $y = \pi$
$\left\{\begin{matrix} z = 0 \\ y = \pi/2 \end{matrix}\right\}$	$\left\{\begin{matrix} y = 0 \\ z = 1 - \frac{1}{4}x \end{matrix}\right\}$	$\left\{\begin{matrix} x = 0 \\ z = \cos^2 y \end{matrix}\right\}$	$\left\{\begin{matrix} y = \pi \\ z = 1 - \frac{1}{4}x \end{matrix}\right\}$

plane $x = 2$

$$\left\{\begin{matrix} x = 2 \\ z = \frac{1}{2}\cos^2 y \end{matrix}\right\}$$

SYMMETRY.   With respect to zx-plane, since $\cos^2(-y) = \cos^2 y$.

EXTENT.   All $(x, y) \in \mathbf{R}^2$ are admissible.

NOTE: The information just listed about symmetry and extent is not relevant to our present purposes, since we are sketching only that part of the surface lying above the rectangle S; these facts were given for the sake of completeness.

Since $\cos^2 y$ satisfies $0 \leqslant \cos^2 y \leqslant 1$, and since $0 \leqslant x \leqslant 2 \Rightarrow \frac{1}{2} \leqslant 1 - \frac{1}{4}x \leqslant 1$, we observe that the portion of the surface we are sketching lies entirely on and between the planes $z = 0$ and $z = 1$.

The sketch is shown in Figure 19.

Exercises

A. In Exercises 1–20 perform a systematic analysis on the equation, extract as much geometric information as possible, and make a sketch.

    1. $z = 4 - x^2 - y^2$. Sketch the part for which $x^2 + y^2 \leqslant 4$.

    2. $z = x^4 + y^4$.

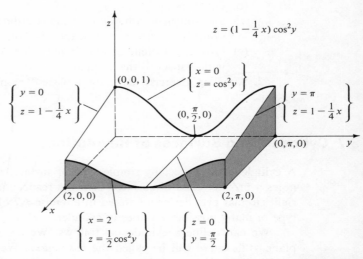

Figure 19

3. $z = x + y$.

4. $z = y^2$. (This is a surface.)

5. $z = \cos^2 \pi x$. Sketch the portion above the rectangle $S = \{(x, y) \mid 0 \leqslant x \leqslant 1, 0 \leqslant y \leqslant 2\}$.

6. $z^2 = x^2 + y^2$.

7. $x^2 + y^2 = 4$. (This is a surface.)

8. $z = 1/(4 - x^2 - y^2)$. How is the surface of Exercise A7 related to that of this exercise?

9. $z = 1 + \sin y$.

10. $z = y^2 + 1$.

11. $z = (1 - \frac{1}{2}x)(1 - \frac{1}{3}y)$. Sketch only the portion above the rectangle $S = \{(x, y) \mid 0 \leqslant x \leqslant 2, 0 \leqslant y \leqslant 3\}$.

12. $x^2 + y^2 + z^2 = 4$ (first octant only).

13. $x^2 + y^2 + 4z^2 = 4$ (first octant only).

14. $x^2 + 4y^2 + 9z^2 = 36$.

15. $x^2 + y^2 - z^2 = 1$.

16. $z = 4 - x^2 - 4y^2$.

17. $z = 1/(x^2 + y^2)$.

18. $x = y^2 + z^2$. [*Hint:* *one* way would be to draw the axes so that the positive x-axis has the position usually occupied by the positive z-axis. Be sure the system is right-handed.]

19. $y = 1 - z^2 - x^2$. See hint for Exercise A18.

20. $z = xy$. [*Hint:* consider traces in the planes $y = x$ and $y = -x$.]

B. **1.** (a) Define the following property. Points P_1 and P_2 are symmetric with respect to the xy-plane.

(b) Given points $P_1(x_1, y_1, z_1)$ and $P_2(x_2, y_2, z_2)$. Find a necessary and sufficient condition on the coordinates for P_1 and P_2 to be symmetric with respect to the xy-plane.

(c) Give a sufficient condition for a set $S \subset \mathbf{R}^3$ to be symmetric with respect to the xy-plane.

2. Same as Exercise B1 only replace "xy-plane" throughout with "z-axis."

8.7 Cylinders and Surfaces of Revolution

A cylinder is an especially simple type of surface. However, the term connotes a broader class of surfaces than the reader may suspect. The familiar right circular cylinder encountered in Exercise A7 of Section 8.6 is only one type of many possible varieties of cylinder.

We can define a cylinder as follows. We consider a curve lying in a plane—this curve will be called the *base curve*. We let a straight line, perpendicular to the plane of the base curve, trace out the base curve. The set of points generated in this way constitutes the cylinder. If the base curve is a circle, then the cylinder is a right circular cylinder. (The word *right* refers to the fact that the generating line is perpendicular to the plane of the base curve. One could consider cylinders other than right, but we shall not here.) We can, though, also have parabolic or elliptic or logarithmic cylinders.

If the base curve lies in a plane parallel to one of the coordinate planes, which implies that the generating line will be parallel to one of the coordinate axes, then the equation of the cylinder assumes a rather simple and easily recognizable form. Suppose, to be definite about it, we have a curve lying in the *yz*-plane; it could be represented analytically as

$$\begin{cases} f(y, z) = 0 \\ x = 0 \end{cases},$$

where f is some function of two variables [e.g., $f(y, z) = y^2 + z^2 - 4$]. If $(0, y_0, z_0)$ is a point on the base curve, i.e., y_0, z_0 satisfy the condition imposed by f, then (x, y_0, z_0) will be on the generating line—a fixed position of the generating line is called a *generator*—for *every* $x \in \mathbf{R}$. See Figure 20. Thus (x, y_0, z_0) is on the cylinder for every $x \in \mathbf{R}$. Conversely, given any point (x_0, y_0, z_0) on the cylinder, $(0, y_0, z_0)$ must be on the base curve, which implies $f(y_0, z_0) = 0$ describes exactly the set of points on the cylinder with base curve $f(y, z) = 0$, $x = 0$, and with generators parallel to the *x*-axis. A similar argument applies to an equation with y or z missing.

In summary, *if an equation in the geometry of 3-space has a variable missing, it represents a cylinder with generators parallel to the axis of the missing variable.*

It follows that the surfaces in Exercises A4, 5, 9, and 10 in Section 8.6 are all cylinders.

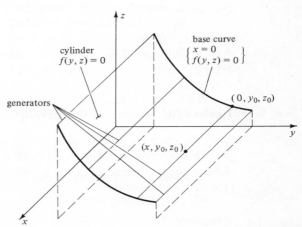

Figure 20

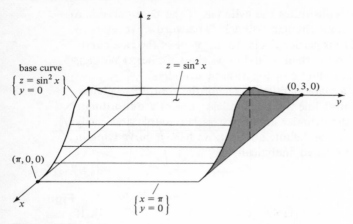

Figure 21

Example 16.   We consider the surface determined by

$$z = \sin^2 x.$$

It is clear from the preceding discussion that the surface is a cylinder with base curve in the zx-plane and with generators parallel to the y-axis. We show a portion of the cylinder in Figure 21.

Surfaces of Revolution.   A right circular cylinder, in addition to being the most familiar example of a cylinder, is also an example of a *surface of revolution*. For example, the cylinder $x^2 + y^2 = 4$ can be thought of as generated by revolving the straight line $x = 0$, $y = 2$ about the z-axis.

A special case of the most general situation will now be discussed. We consider a curve $\mathscr{C}$ in the yz-plane, the equation of which, *in the yz-plane*, is $z = f(y)$, where f is a function. We revolve $\mathscr{C}$ about the y-axis, thus generating a surface. We are interested in an analytic representation of the surface. Let $P_0(0, y_0, z_0 = f(y_0))$ be a point on the curve, and let $P_1(x_1, y_1, z_1)$ be an arbitrary point on the circle—hence on the surface—generated as P_0 is revolved about the y-axis. See Figure 22.

Referring to Figure 22, we can now obtain the following relations between the coordinates of P_0 and P_1:

$$y_1 = y_0$$
$$x_1^2 + z_1^2 = z_0^2 = [f(y_0)]^2 = [f(y_1)]^2.$$

As there was nothing special about P_1, we can drop the subscript:

$$x^2 + z^2 = [f(y)]^2. \qquad [29]$$

Reversing the steps shows that every point whose coordinates satisfy [29] will lie on the surface generated by revolving $\mathscr{C}$ about the y-axis. [Notice that

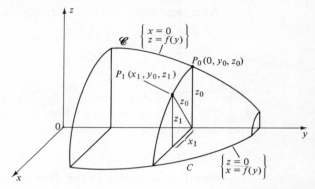

Figure 22

the trace of the surface on the yz-plane is $x = 0$, $z = \pm f(y)$; also the trace on the xy-plane is $z = 0$, $x = \pm f(y)$.]

The transition from the equation of the plane curve $\mathscr{C}$ to the equation of the surface of revolution can be symbolized as

$$z = f(y) \rightarrow z^2 = [f(y)]^2 \rightarrow x^2 + z^2 = [f(y)]^2.$$

Verbally this says: square both sides, then replace z^2 by $x^2 + z^2$.

Similar remarks apply to surfaces generated by revolving curves about other axes.

Example 17. Find the equation of the surface generated by revolving the parabola $z = y^2$ about the z-axis.

Because the curve in question is to be revolved about the z-axis, we solve the equation for y, limiting ourselves to half of the parabola: $y = \sqrt{z} = f(z)$. See Figure 23.

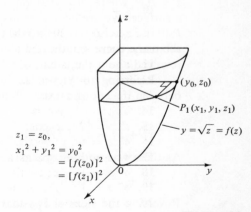

Figure 23

As is clear from Figure 23, the equation of the surface is

$$x^2 + y^2 = [f(z)]^2 = (\sqrt{z})^2,$$

or

$$z = x^2 + y^2, \tag{30}$$

which was discussed in detail in Example 14.

The transition from the equation of the plane curve to the equation of the surface can be symbolized in this case as follows:

$$y = f(z) = \sqrt{z} \rightarrow y^2 = [f(z)]^2 = z \rightarrow x^2 + y^2 = z.$$

Similarly, returning to the right circular cylinder with which we began this discussion, if we start with the line $y = 2$ in the yz-plane and consider $y = 2$ as a constant function of z, then a transition identical in form with that just displayed shows how to find the equation of the surface generated when this line is revolved about the z-axis.

$$y = f(z) = 2 \rightarrow y^2 = [f(z)]^2 = 4 \rightarrow x^2 + y^2 = 4.$$

Exercises

A.   In Exercises 1–10 sketch the cylinder determined by the equation.

   1. $\sqrt{z} = y.$
   2. $x + y = 1.$
   3. $z = \cos y.$
   4. $z = \sin y + 1.$
   5. $z = x^2 + 1.$
   6. $x^2 + 4y^2 = 4.$
   7. $xy = 1.$
   8. $y = x.$
   9. $x^2 y = 1.$
   10. $z = 1 - y^2.$

In Exercises 11–20 find the equation of the surface generated by revolving the plane curve $\mathscr{C}$ indicated about the prescribed axis. Sketch.

   11. $\mathscr{C}: z^2 = y;$ z-axis.
   12. $\mathscr{C}: \sqrt{z} = y;$ y-axis.
   13. $\mathscr{C}: z = y;$ z-axis.
   14. $\mathscr{C}: yz = 1;$ y-axis.
   15. $\mathscr{C}: x = 2y;$ x-axis.
   16. $\mathscr{C}: z = \sin y;$ y-axis.
   17. $\mathscr{C}: z = 1 - x;$ x-axis.
   18. $\mathscr{C}: z = 1 - x;$ z-axis.
   19. $\mathscr{C}: z = 1 - y^2;$ z-axis.
   20. $\mathscr{C}: y^2 - z^2 = 1;$ y-axis.
   21. Is every plane a cylinder? Explain.

8.8 Quadric Surfaces

We conclude this study of surfaces with a description of the quadric surfaces—the three-dimensional analog of the conic section curves considered in Chapter 5.

From an analytic point of view the relation between the conic section curves and the quadric surfaces is very strong: the former are the curves obtained from the general equation of second degree in x and y; the latter are the surfaces represented by the general equation of second degree in x, y, and z. As we shall see, there are close geometric ties between the two families. In particular—and quite naturally—the traces of the quadric surfaces in the coordinate planes are conic section curves.

The equations we consider are all special cases of the following:

$$Ax^2 + By^2 + Cz^2 + Dyz + Ezx + Fxy + Gx + Hy + Iz + J = 0,$$
[31]

where not all of A, B, C, D, E, F are zero.

We shall look at several different classes of these surfaces. We begin with the only class, the *ellipsoids*, which lies in a bounded region of space. With a coordinate system suitably chosen, the equation takes the form

$$\frac{x^2}{a^2} + \frac{y^2}{b^2} + \frac{z^2}{c^2} = 1.$$
[32]

It is easy to see that the ellipsoid lies entirely within the box $S = \{(x, y, z) \mid x \leqslant |a|, y \leqslant |b|, z \leqslant |c|\}$. The analysis in terms of the procedures set forth in Section 8.6 is simple, straightforward, and fruitful. The traces in coordinate planes and in planes parallel to them are ellipses; and there is symmetry with respect to all coordinate planes and axes. A sketch is shown in Figure 24.

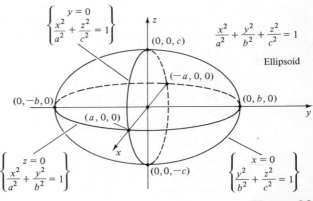

Figure 24

If two (but not three) of the numbers a, b, c are equal, the ellipsoid is called a *spheroid*; the spheroid is a surface of revolution. If all three of a, b, c are equal, the ellipsoid is, of course, a sphere.

If the center of the ellipsoid is not at the origin but the axes of symmetry are parallel to the coordinate axes, the equation of the ellipsoid will have terms of the first degree. The coordinates of the center and other essential information can easily be found by completing the squares in x, y, and z.

Another class of the family of quadric surfaces is called the *hyperboloids*. There are, as it turns out, two groups of these. The first ones we consider are called *hyperboloids of one sheet*, the simplest form of the equation being of the type

$$\frac{x^2}{a^2} + \frac{y^2}{b^2} - \frac{z^2}{c^2} = 1. \tag{33}$$

The systematic analysis is again routine. Traces in the xy- and parallel planes are ellipses; traces in the zx- and yz-planes are hyperbolas. There is symmetry to all coordinate planes and axes. By writing [33] in the form

$$z^2 = c^2 \left[\frac{x^2}{a^2} + \frac{y^2}{b^2} - 1 \right]$$

we see that (x, y) must satisfy $(x^2/a^2) + (y^2/b^2) \geq 1$. The hyperboloid of one sheet is unbounded. A sketch of one is shown in Figure 25.

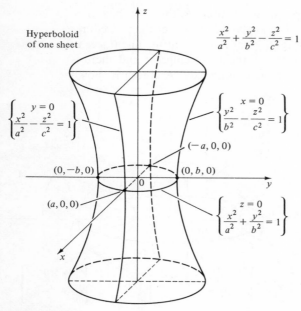

Figure 25

The other group of hyperboloids are those of *two sheets*, the standard form of the equation having *two* minus signs on the left-hand side, such as

$$-\frac{x^2}{a^2} + \frac{y^2}{b^2} - \frac{z^2}{c^2} = 1.$$ [34]

This surface has hyperbolas as traces in the *xy*- and *yz*-planes. There is no trace in the *zx*-plane ($y = 0$), but if $|k| > b$, the traces in the planes $y = k$ are ellipses. There is symmetry with respect to all coordinate planes and axes. If the equation in [34] is written as

$$y^2 = b^2\left[1 + \frac{x^2}{a^2} + \frac{z^2}{c^2}\right],$$

it becomes clear that we must have $|y| \geqslant b$. A sketch of a hyperboloid of two sheets is shown in Figure 26.

The preceding surfaces have all had centers; they are like the ellipses and hyperbolas in this respect. There are two types of *paraboloids*, neither of which is a central quadric surface.

The first of these is the *elliptic paraboloid*, the general form of the equation being

$$cz = \frac{x^2}{a^2} + \frac{y^2}{b^2}.$$ [35]

We have already, in Example 14 (Figure 18) in Section 8.6 given a complete analysis of this surface for $a = b = c = 1$, so no further discussion is necessary here. See, also, Example 17 in Section 8.7.

The *hyperbolic paraboloid* is in some ways the most interesting of the quadric surfaces. The form of the equation with which we shall work is

$$cz = -\frac{x^2}{a^2} + \frac{y^2}{b^2},$$ [36]

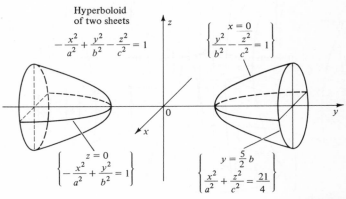

Figure 26

The trace of this surface on the xy-plane is simply a pair of lines: $z = 0$, $b^2x^2 = a^2y^2$. However, traces in planes $z = k$ parallel to the xy-plane are hyperbolas, a shift in transverse axis occurring as k changes from positive to negative values. The trace in the yz-plane is the parabola $cz = y^2/b^2$, whereas that in the zx-plane is the parabola $cz = -(x^2/a^2)$.

There is symmetry with respect to the yz- and zx-planes, but not with respect to the xy-plane (see the preceding paragraph). There is also symmetry with respect to the z-axis.

The hyperbolic paraboloid is a saddle-shaped figure with a "minimax" point at the origin. Traveling in the yz-plane, one experiences a minimum at the origin, but one restricted to live in the zx-plane would look on the origin as a maximum point. See Figure 27 for a sketch.

The final class of quadric surfaces we take up should perhaps have been included earlier, among the other surfaces that have a center. We refer to the *cones*, which, with suitable choice of coordinate system, can be represented by equations such as

$$\frac{x^2}{a^2} + \frac{y^2}{b^2} - \frac{z^2}{c^2} = 0.$$ [37]

For this surface the traces are especially simple. In the xy-plane the trace is a point; in planes parallel to the xy-plane the traces are ellipses. In both the yz- and zx-planes the traces are pairs of line intersecting at the origin. (What are the traces in planes parallel to the yz- and zx-planes?)

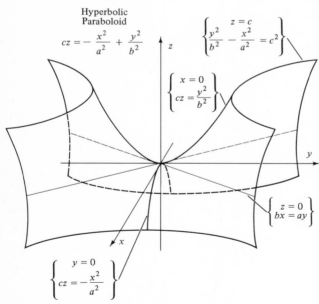

Figure 27

It is easy to see that the surface in [37] has symmetry with respect to all coordinate planes and axes. A sketch appears in Figure 28.

Notice that the equation of the cone is homogeneous in x, y, z: every term is of the same degree. This algebraic property is characteristic of cones in this position: if an equation of degree two in x, y, and z is homogeneous, the corresponding surface is a cone with its vertex at the origin.

It is easy to see that if $a = b$ in Equation [37], the cone is then a surface of revolution: traces in planes parallel to the xy-plane will be circles rather than, as in the general case, ellipses.

We should point out that in discussing the different classes of quadric surfaces we have in each case used only one of several possible positions of the surface with respect to the coordinate system. Thus a paraboloid of revolution could have an equation such as $4x = y^2 + z^2$, its axis of symmetry then being the x-axis. Or a hyperboloid of one sheet could have an equation such as $-x^2 + 4y^2 + 4z^2 = 4$. This surface would then surround the x-axis. As we remarked when discussing the ellipsoids, the presence of terms of first degree for the central quadric surfaces or of additional terms of first degree for the paraboloids would indicate a translation parallel to the axes. By completing the squares and, if desired, introducing new coordinates, one can identify and describe the surface. Finally, if any of the crossproduct terms, such as xy or zx, is present, the identification of the surface would be difficult in terms of the limited discussion we have had. A suitable rotation of axes will eliminate these crossproduct terms. The theory which most

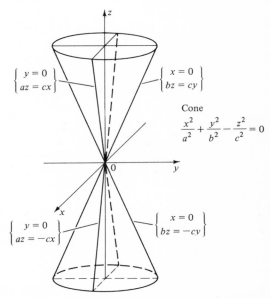

$$\begin{cases} y = 0 \\ az = cx \end{cases}$$

$$\begin{cases} x = 0 \\ bz = cy \end{cases}$$

Cone

$$\frac{x^2}{a^2} + \frac{y^2}{b^2} - \frac{z^2}{c^2} = 0$$

$$\begin{cases} y = 0 \\ az = -cx \end{cases}$$

$$\begin{cases} x = 0 \\ bz = -cy \end{cases}$$

Figure 28

efficiently describes this process lies in the part of linear algebra concerned
with quadratic forms. See Section 9.4.

Exercises

A. In Exercises 1–15 identify and sketch each of the surfaces.
  1. $2x^2 + y^2 + z^2 = 2.$
  2. $-2x^2 + y^2 + z^2 = 2.$
  3. $2x^2 - y^2 - z^2 = 2.$
  4. $x^2 + y^2 + z^2 = 2.$
  5. $-2x + y^2 + z^2 = 2.$
  6. $-2x + y^2 + z^2 = 0.$
  7. $z = y^2 - x^2.$
  8. $-2x^2 + y^2 + z^2 = 0.$
  9. $-2x^2 + y^2 = 0.$
  10. $-2x^2 + y = 0.$
  11. $x^2 - y^2 - z^2 = 0.$
  12. $3z = x^2 - 4y^2.$
  13. $4y = x^2 + z^2.$
  14. $x^2 - y^2 = 0.$
  15. $z = xy.$

In Exercises 16–26 find the equation of the surface generated when the
plane curve given is revolved about the axis indicated. Name and sketch the
surface.
  16. $z = 2y$; z-axis.
  17. $z = 2y$; y-axis.
  18. $4y^2 - z^2 = 4$; y-axis.
  19. $4y^2 - z^2 = 4$; z-axis.
  20. $y^2 + 4z^2 = 4$; z-axis.
  21. $y^2 + 4z^2 = 4$; y-axis.
  22. $z = 3x$; x-axis.
  23. $x^2 + y^2 = 1$; y-axis.
  24. $x^2 + y^2 = 1$; x-axis.
  25. $x^2 - 4y^2 = 4$; y-axis.
  26. $x^2 - 4y^2 = 4$; x-axis.

C. **1.** The hyperboloid of one sheet contains two complete families of
straight lines. Show that this is so for the particular hyperboloid $x^2 + y^2 -
z^2 = 1.$

Hints: (i) Write the equation as $x^2 - z^2 = 1 - y^2$; now factor
both sides. (ii) Divide both sides by $(1 - y)(x + z)$. (iii) Set each fraction

equal to t; in each case multiply both sides of the equation by the denominator. This should give you

$$\begin{cases} x - z = t(1 - y) \\ 1 + y = t(x + z) \end{cases}.$$

For each value of t this system is a straight line, every point of which lies on the hyperboloid. (iv) Return to the factored equation found in hint (i) and divide both sides by $(1 + y)(x + z)$. Set each fraction equal to s and follow through the procedure of hint (iii). A surface of this sort is called a *ruled* surface.

    2. See Exercise C1. Show that the hyperbolic paraboloid $z = y^2 - x^2$ is a ruled surface.

9
Matrices

In this chapter we shall be concerned with algebra, more specifically, linear algebra. The early parts of the chapter will be strictly algebraic; we shall introduce and develop some of the fundamental notions and theory of linear algebra. We then turn to a few geometric applications.

Although we shall continue to work with the geometry of the plane and 3-space, many of the ideas of this chapter can be extended to n-space, i.e., $\mathbf{R}^n$.

9.1 Linear Systems

We shall develop in this section a systematic procedure for finding—if it exists—a solution to a set of simultaneous linear equations, or a *linear system*. As examples of what we shall be dealing with we cite

$$\left\{\begin{matrix} 3x - 2y + z = 2 \\ x + 3y - 2z = 1 \\ 4x + 2y - 5z = -7 \end{matrix}\right\} \tag{1}$$

and

$$\left\{\begin{matrix} 3x + 3y + 2z = 1 \\ 2x + 2y + z = 2 \end{matrix}\right\}. \tag{2}$$

For the general definition we use subscripts to distinguish the different unknowns and coefficients.

DEFINITION 1. *By a* linear system *L we mean a system of m linear equations in the n unknowns* $x_1, x_2, \ldots, x_n$ *with coefficients* $a_{11}, \ldots, a_{mn}, b_1, \ldots, b_m \in \mathbf{R}$:

$$L = \left\{ \begin{array}{l} a_{11}x_1 + a_{12}x_2 + \cdots + a_{1n}x_n = b_1 \\ \vdots \qquad \vdots \qquad \qquad \vdots \qquad \vdots \\ a_{m1}x_1 + a_{m2}x_2 + \cdots + a_{mn}x_n = b_m \end{array} \right\}. \qquad [3]$$

We also write this as

$$L = \left\{ \sum_{j=1}^{n} a_{ij}x_j = b_i, i = 1, \ldots, m \right\}.$$

(See Appendix 3 on the sigma notation.)

In [1] we have $m = n = 3$, whereas in [2] $m = 2, n = 3$.

DEFINITION 2. *A* solution *of a linear system L is an n-tuple* $[x_1^\circ, \ldots, x_n^\circ]$ *of numbers in* $\mathbf{R}$ *(a vector* $\mathbf{x}^\circ \in \mathbf{R}^n$*) satisfying all m equations of L, i.e.,*

$$\sum_{j=1}^{n} a_{ij}x_j^\circ = b_i, \qquad i = 1, \ldots, m.$$

The set S of all solutions is the solution set *of L:*

$$S = \{\mathbf{x}^\circ \mid \mathbf{x}^\circ = [x_1^\circ, \ldots, x_n^\circ] \text{ is a solution of } L\}.$$

If $S = \varnothing$ *we say L is* inconsistent; *if* $S \neq \varnothing$, *L is* consistent.

Our method of solution will be to use operations on L which preserve S (see Exercise C1 for a formal discussion); i.e., the operations will transform L into a system L_1, say, which has the same solution set S as does L. As we shall see, an L_1 can often be found for which S is obtainable by inspection.

There are three operations that we shall use. To describe them we denote the first equation by E_1, etc. If an operation involves multiplying the second equation by 3, we indicate this as $E_2 \rightarrow 3E_2$ (the arrow can be verbalized as "gazinta").

DEFINITION 3. *The* elementary operations *on a linear system L are*

Type I: *interchange* E_i *and* E_k; $E_i \leftrightarrow E_k$.
Type II: *multiply* E_i *by* $c \neq 0$; $E_i \rightarrow cE_i$, $c \neq 0$.
Type III: *add c times* E_k *to* E_i; $E_i \rightarrow E_i + cE_k$.

THEOREM 1. *If a system* L_1 *is obtained from a system L by a finite sequence of elementary operations, then* L_1 *has the same solution set as L.*

PROOF. Exercise for student (Exercise B1). ∎

We now illustrate these ideas.

Example 1. We use the system [1]. The symbol $\sim$ may be verbalized as "is equivalent to" (see Exercise C1). The object will be to obtain a system in which each unknown appears in one equation with a coefficient of one, all other unknowns having coefficients of zero in that equation. Watch.

$$L = \begin{cases} 3x - 2y + z = 2 \\ x + 3y - 2z = 1 \\ 4x + 2y - 5z = -7 \end{cases}$$

$$\sim \begin{cases} x + 3y - 2z = 1 \\ 3x - 2y + z = 2 \\ 4x + 2y - 5z = -7 \end{cases} \qquad (E_1 \leftrightarrow E_2; \text{I})$$

$$\sim \begin{cases} x + 3y - 2z = 1 \\ 0x - 11y + 7z = -1 \\ 0x - 10y + 3z = -11 \end{cases} \qquad \begin{pmatrix} E_2 \to E_2 - 3E_1; \text{III} \\ E_3 \to E_3 - 4E_1; \text{III} \end{pmatrix}$$

$$\sim \begin{cases} x + 3y - 2z = 1 \\ 0x - y + 4z = 10 \\ 0x - 10y + 3z = -11 \end{cases} \qquad (E_2 \to E_2 - E_3; \text{III})$$

$$\sim \begin{cases} x + 3y - 2z = 1 \\ 0x + y - 4z = -10 \\ 0x - 10y + 3z = -11 \end{cases} \qquad (E_2 \to (-1)E_2; \text{II})$$

$$\sim \begin{cases} 1x + 0y + 10z = 31 \\ 0x + y - 4z = -10 \\ 0x + 0y - 37z = -111 \end{cases} \qquad \begin{pmatrix} E_1 \to E_1 - 3E_2; \text{III} \\ E_3 \to E_3 + 10E_2; \text{III} \end{pmatrix}$$

$$\sim \begin{cases} 1x + 0y + 10z = 31 \\ 0x + 1y - 4z = -10 \\ 0x + 0y + 1z = 3 \end{cases} \qquad \left(E_3 \to \left(\frac{-1}{37}\right)E_3; \text{II}\right)$$

$$\sim \begin{cases} 1x + 0y + 0z = 1 \\ 0x + 1y + 0z = 2 \\ 0x + 0y + 1z = 3 \end{cases} \qquad \begin{pmatrix} E_1 \to E_1 - 10E_3; \text{III} \\ E_2 \to E_2 + 4E_3; \text{III} \end{pmatrix}$$

$$= L_1.$$

It is truly obvious that there is one solution to L_1: $x = 1$, $y = 2$, $z = 3$, i.e., $S = \{[1, 2, 3]\}$, and Theorem 1 guarantees that this is the solution set for the original system L. This is easily checked.

As an indication of what might happen if $m \neq n$ we consider the system [2].

Example 2. We proceed as in Example 1. Here

$$L = \begin{Bmatrix} 3x + 3y + 2z = 1 \\ 2x + 2y + z = 2 \end{Bmatrix}$$

$$\sim \begin{Bmatrix} x + y + z = -1 \\ 2x + 2y + z = 2 \end{Bmatrix} \qquad (E_1 \to E_1 - E_2; \text{III})$$

$$\sim \begin{Bmatrix} x + y + z = -1 \\ 0x + 0y - z = 4 \end{Bmatrix} \qquad (E_2 \to E_2 - 2E_1; \text{III})$$

$$\sim \begin{Bmatrix} x + y + z = -1 \\ 0x + 0y + 1z = -4 \end{Bmatrix} \qquad (E_2 \to (-1)E_2; \text{II})$$

$$\sim \begin{Bmatrix} 1x + 1y + 0z = 3 \\ 0x + 0y + 1z = -4 \end{Bmatrix} \qquad (E_1 \to E_1 - E_2; \text{III})$$

$$= L_1.$$

The system L_1 gives $z = -4$ and enables us to solve for x in terms of y (or for y in terms of x): $x = 3 - y$. Thus the solution is $x = 3 - y, y = y, z = -4$, or

$$S = \{[3 - y, y, -4] \mid y \in \mathbf{R}\};$$

there are infinitely many solutions.

Here is another possible outcome.

Example 3. We have

$$L = \begin{Bmatrix} x - 2y = 4 \\ -2x + 4y = -8 \end{Bmatrix}$$

$$\sim \begin{Bmatrix} x - 2y = 4 \\ 0x + 0y = 0 \end{Bmatrix} \qquad (E_2 \to E_2 + 2E_1; \text{III})$$

$$= L_1.$$

The second equation of L_1 makes no contribution (makes no demands on x and y); any solution of the first equation is a solution of the system. Thus, letting $x = 2y + 4$, we can write $S = \{[2y + 4, y] \mid y \in \mathbf{R}\}$.

We can save a considerable amount of writing in solving a linear system if we recognize that the letters for the unknowns serve no purpose except marking the places for the coefficients. This place-keeping can be done without the letters. To this end we introduce the concept of matrix.

DEFINITION 4. *An $m \times n$ matrix A is a rectangular array of numbers $a_{ij} \in \mathbf{R}, i = 1, 2, \ldots, m, j = 1, 2, \ldots, n$, usually displayed as*

$$A = \begin{bmatrix} a_{11} & a_{12} & \cdots & a_{1n} \\ a_{21} & a_{22} & \cdots & a_{2n} \\ \vdots & \vdots & & \vdots \\ a_{m1} & a_{m2} & \cdots & a_{mn} \end{bmatrix}. \qquad [4]$$

For the sake of brevity we may write this as $A = [a_{ij}]$. The individual numbers a_{ij} are called the elements of A. The n-tuples $[a_{i1}, a_{i2}, \ldots, a_{in}]$, $i = 1, \ldots, m$, are called the rows; and the m-tuples.

$$\begin{bmatrix} a_{1j} \\ a_{2j} \\ \vdots \\ a_{mj} \end{bmatrix} \quad j = 1, 2, \ldots, n,$$

are the columns of A. If $m = n$, A is called a square matrix. If $m = 1$, we may speak of A as a row vector; if $n = 1$, we may call A a column vector. The numbers m and n are the dimensions of A.

Associated with every linear system L, as defined in [3] is the *matrix of the coefficients*, [4]. Thus, the matrix of the coefficients for the system [1] is the 3×3 matrix

$$A = \begin{bmatrix} 3 & -2 & 1 \\ 1 & 3 & -2 \\ 4 & 2 & -5 \end{bmatrix}.$$

However, to use matrices in the solution of linear systems we must include the constants b_i in the right-hand sides of the equations in [3]. These m numbers constitute an $m \times 1$ matrix or column vector B. We adjoin this matrix to A, creating an $m \times (n + 1)$ matrix, which is called the *augmented matrix* of the system:

$$[A, B] = \begin{bmatrix} a_{11} & \cdots & a_{1n} & b_1 \\ a_{21} & \cdots & a_{2n} & b_2 \\ \vdots & & \vdots & \vdots \\ a_{m1} & \cdots & a_{mn} & b_m \end{bmatrix}. \tag{5}$$

The technique of solving a linear system L is then as follows: translate L to its corresponding augmented matrix $[A, B]$, transform this matrix, using the elementary operations of Definition 3 on the rows R_i of $[A, B]$ to obtain a "simpler" (precise definition to appear shortly) matrix, translate back to its system L_1, and read off the solution. (See Exercise C2 for a formal discussion of part of this technique.)

We give an illustration.

Example 4.   We solve the system

$$L = \left\{ \begin{array}{l} x_1 - 2x_2 \quad - \quad x_4 = 0 \\ 3x_1 + x_2 - 2x_3 + 5x_4 = 0 \\ -2x_1 - 10x_2 + 4x_3 - 14x_4 = 0 \end{array} \right\}.$$

We see that $b_1 = b_2 = b_3 = 0$—the column vector $B = 0$. A system of this type, where $B = 0$, is called a *homogeneous* system. Obviously every homogeneous system has the solution $x_1^\circ = x_2^\circ = \cdots = x_n^\circ = 0$, $\mathbf{x}^\circ = \mathbf{0}$. This is called the *trivial solution*. We are usually interested in finding, if they exist, *nontrivial solutions*, i.e., solutions for which at least one $x_i \neq 0$.

As B is in this case a column of zeros, we consider only the coefficient matrix

$$A = \begin{bmatrix} 1 & -2 & 0 & -1 \\ 3 & 1 & -2 & 5 \\ -2 & -10 & 4 & -14 \end{bmatrix}$$

$$\sim \begin{bmatrix} 1 & -2 & 0 & -1 \\ 0 & 7 & -2 & 8 \\ 0 & -14 & 4 & -16 \end{bmatrix} \quad \begin{pmatrix} R_2 \to R_2 - 3R_1; \text{III} \\ R_3 \to R_3 + 2R_1; \text{III} \end{pmatrix}$$

$$\sim \begin{bmatrix} 1 & -2 & 0 & -1 \\ 0 & 1 & -\frac{2}{7} & \frac{8}{7} \\ 0 & -14 & 4 & -16 \end{bmatrix} \quad (R_2 \to \tfrac{1}{7}R_2; \text{II})$$

$$\sim \begin{bmatrix} 1 & 0 & -\frac{4}{7} & \frac{9}{7} \\ 0 & 1 & -\frac{2}{7} & \frac{8}{7} \\ 0 & 0 & 0 & 0 \end{bmatrix}. \quad \begin{pmatrix} R_1 \to R_1 + 2R_2; \text{III} \\ R_3 \to R_3 + 14R_2; \text{III} \end{pmatrix}$$

This is as far as we can profitably go; translating back to the associated linear system we have

$$\begin{cases} x_1 \quad\quad - \tfrac{4}{7}x_3 + \tfrac{9}{7}x_4 = 0 \\ \quad\quad x_2 - \tfrac{2}{7}x_3 + \tfrac{8}{7}x_4 = 0 \\ 0x_1 + 0x_2 + 0x_3 + 0x_4 = 0 \end{cases}.$$

We can solve this system for x_1 and x_2 in terms of x_3 and x_4:

$$\begin{cases} x_1 = \tfrac{4}{7}x_3 - \tfrac{9}{7}x_4 \\ x_2 = \tfrac{2}{7}x_3 - \tfrac{8}{7}x_4 \\ x_3 = \quad x_3 \\ x_4 = \quad\quad x_4 \end{cases}.$$

A slightly better way of writing the solution is to introduce parameters s and t for x_3 and x_4, respectively. Then we can write the solution set as

$$S = \left\{ \left[\frac{4s - 9t}{7}, \frac{2s - 8t}{7}, s, t \right] \mid s, t \in \mathbf{R} \right\}.$$

Clearly there exist nontrivial solutions; one such, letting $s = 1$, $t = 2$, is $[-2, -2, 1, 2]$.

We now indicate the type of matrix toward which we work with the elementary row operations. The last matrix in Example 4 has the desired *echelon form*, which we describe.

DEFINITION 5.   *An m × n matrix is an* echelon matrix ⇔

1. *The first r rows, $0 \leqslant r \leqslant m$, are nonzero; the last $m - r$ rows are zero rows (i.e., all elements are zero).*
2. *In each nonzero row the leading (i.e., leftmost) nonzero element is equal to 1. All other elements in the column of this 1 are zero.*
3. *The column numbers of these leading 1's increase as the row numbers increase. In symbols, if the leading 1 of row R_i is in column C_{j_i}, then $j_1 < j_2 < j_3 < \cdots < j_r$.*

A few comments about an echelon matrix are in order. If $r = 0$, then all elements of the matrix are zero—we call this the $m \times n$ zero matrix 0; if $r = m$ then there are no zero rows. The number r is called the *row rank* of the matrix. Obviously $r \leqslant m$; but also $r \leqslant n$, for there is a one-to-one correspondence between the nonzero rows and the columns in which their leading 1's occur. (Thus, a 12×2 matrix can have a row rank of at most 2.)

It is a theorem, which we shall not prove, that every matrix can be transformed by elementary row operations into an echelon matrix.

From the point of view of solving linear systems, the essential fact is that the system L_1 that corresponds to the echelon matrix can be solved for the r unknowns $x_{j_1}, x_{j_2}, \ldots, x_{j_r}$ in terms of the remaining $n - r$ x's.

In particular, if the system is homogeneous and if $m < n$, then we have $r \leqslant m < n$, which implies that $n - r > 0$. In other words, it will be possible to express all n unknowns in terms of $n - r$ parameters (as illustrated in Example 4). This proves the following assertion.

THEOREM 2.   *A homogeneous system $\sum_{j=1}^{n} a_{ij} x_j = 0$, $i = i, \ldots, m$, with $m < n$, always has nontrivial solutions.*

There are two other theorems about the existence of solutions, which we state without proof.

THEOREM 3.   *Let L be the system $\sum_{j=1}^{n} a_{ij} x_j = b_i$, $i = 1, \ldots, m$. Let r and r' be the ranks of the echelon matrices obtainable from A and [A, B], respectively. Then*

$$\left. \begin{array}{l} \text{a solution exists for L} \\ (S \neq \varnothing) \end{array} \right\} \Leftrightarrow r' = r.$$

The next theorem concerns the case where $m = n$.

THEOREM 4.   *Let L be the system $\sum_{j=1}^{n} a_{ij} x_j = b_i$, where $i = 1, \ldots, n$. Let r and r' be the ranks of the echelon matrices obtainable from A and [A, B], respectively. Then*

1. *$r' = r = n \Rightarrow$ there exists a unique solution.*

2. $r' = r < n \Rightarrow$ *there are infinitely many solutions.*
3. $r' = r + 1 \leqslant n \Rightarrow$ *there are no solutions.*

We conclude this section with an illustration of case 3 of Theorem 4.

Example 5.   Consider the system

$$L = \begin{cases} x_1 + 3x_2 + 5x_3 = 9 \\ 2x_1 + 7x_2 + 11x_3 = 20 \\ 3x_1 + 11x_2 + 17x_3 = 35 \end{cases}.$$

The augmented matrix is

$$[A, B] = \begin{bmatrix} 1 & 3 & 5 & 9 \\ 2 & 7 & 11 & 20 \\ 3 & 11 & 17 & 35 \end{bmatrix}$$

$$\sim \begin{bmatrix} 1 & 3 & 5 & 9 \\ 0 & 1 & 1 & 2 \\ 0 & 2 & 2 & 8 \end{bmatrix} \quad \begin{pmatrix} R_2 \rightarrow R_2 - 2R_1; \text{III} \\ R_3 \rightarrow R_3 - 3R_1; \text{III} \end{pmatrix}$$

$$\sim \begin{bmatrix} 1 & 0 & 2 & 3 \\ 0 & 1 & 1 & 2 \\ 0 & 0 & 0 & 4 \end{bmatrix} \quad \begin{pmatrix} R_1 \rightarrow R_1 - 3R_2; \text{III} \\ R_3 \rightarrow R_3 - 2R_2; \text{III} \end{pmatrix}$$

$$\sim \begin{bmatrix} 1 & 0 & 2 & 3 \\ 0 & 1 & 1 & 2 \\ 0 & 0 & 0 & 1 \end{bmatrix} \quad (R_3 \rightarrow \tfrac{1}{4}R_3; \text{II})$$

$$\sim \begin{bmatrix} 1 & 0 & 2 & 0 \\ 0 & 1 & 1 & 0 \\ 0 & 0 & 0 & 1 \end{bmatrix} \quad \begin{pmatrix} R_1 \rightarrow R_1 - 3R_3; \text{III} \\ R_2 \rightarrow R_2 - 2R_3; \text{III} \end{pmatrix}.$$

Clearly the rank r' of this matrix is 3, whereas if the last column is dropped the resulting matrix has rank $r = 2$. Notice that the equation obtained from the last row of the above echelon matrix is $0x_1 + 0x_2 + 0x_3 = 1$, which obviously has no solution; thus neither L_1 nor L has a solution.

Exercises

A. In Exercises 1–16 solve the system by the technique described in this section.

1. $\begin{cases} x - 3y = 1 \\ 3x - 8y = 4 \end{cases}.$

2. $\begin{cases} 4x + 2y = -1 \\ 2x - 3y = 5 \end{cases}$.

3. $\begin{cases} 2x + y - z = 3 \\ x - 2y + 3z = 4 \end{cases}$.

4. $\begin{cases} x + 2y = 3 \\ 3x - y = 2 \end{cases}$.

5. $\begin{cases} x - 3y = -2 \\ -3x + 9y = 6 \end{cases}$.

6. $\begin{cases} x - 3y = -2 \\ -4x + 12y = 7 \end{cases}$.

7. $\{x + 5y = 3\}$.

8. $\begin{cases} 5x - y + 2z = 6 \\ x + 2y - 4z = 5 \end{cases}$

9. $\begin{cases} x + y + z = 5 \\ 2x - 3y + 2z = 20 \\ -3x + 2y + 3z = -1 \end{cases}$.

10. $\begin{cases} 2x - y - 3z = 4 \\ x + 3y + 2z = -5 \\ 2x - 15y - 17z = 32 \end{cases}$.

11. $\begin{cases} 3x + y - 4z = 2 \\ x - 2y + 3z = -1 \\ x + 5y - 10z = 5 \end{cases}$.

12. $\begin{cases} 3x + y - 4z = 0 \\ x - 2y + 3z = 0 \\ x + 5y - 10z = 0 \end{cases}$.

13. $\begin{cases} x + 3y - 5z = 2 \\ 3x - y + 4z = 7 \\ x + 13y - 24z = 1 \end{cases}$.

14. $\begin{cases} 2x + 3y - 4z = 0 \\ x - 2y + 5z = 0 \end{cases}$.

15. $\begin{cases} x - 2y = 4 \\ 2x + 3y = 1 \\ 3x - 2y = 2 \end{cases}$.

16. $\begin{cases} x_1 + 3x_2 - 5x_3 = 0 \\ x_1 + 4x_2 + 2x_3 = 0 \\ 4x_1 - 2x_2 - x_3 = 0 \\ x_1 + 19x_2 - 10x_3 = 0 \end{cases}$.

17. Give the maximum rank of an echelon matrix with the following dimensions.

(a) 1×10.   (e) 4×100.
(b) 3×5.   (f) 100×4.
(c) 2×4.   (g) 6×6.
(d) 5×2.

B.   1. Prove Theorem 1.

Hints: (i) It is sufficient to show that an operation of each type does not change the solution set. (ii) This is obvious for a Type I operation. (iii) For Type II only equation E_i is altered. Since $c \neq 0$,

$$ca_{i1}x_1^\circ + \cdots + ca_{in}x_n^\circ = cb_i \Leftrightarrow a_{i1}x_1^\circ + \cdots + a_{in}x_n^\circ = b_i.$$

(iv) For Type III, consider E_k, E_i, and $E_i + cE_k$. Show that any solution of E_k and E_i is a solution of $E_i + cE_k$ and that any solution of E_k and $E_i + cE_k$ is a solution of E_i.

2. An echelon matrix is $m \times r$ and has rank r. Describe it completely.

3. (a) Write the echelon matrix which is 3×3 and has rank 3.

(b) Same as part (a), but for an $n \times n$ matrix with rank n.

C.   1. In this exercise we begin a formal description of the theory behind the technique illustrated in this section for solving a linear system.

For $m, n \in \mathbf{N}$, we let $\mathscr{L} = \mathscr{L}(m, n)$ be the set of all linear systems with m equations in n unknowns. Two systems $L_1, L_2 \in \mathscr{L}$ with solution sets S_1 and S_2, respectively, are defined to be *equivalent* provided S_1 and S_2 are equal. In symbols,

$$L_1 \sim L_2 \Leftrightarrow S_1 = S_2.$$

Prove that this relation on $\mathscr{L}$ is an *equivalence relation*, i.e., that it has the following properties:

(a) $L \sim L$ (reflexivity).
(b) $L_1 \sim L_2 \Rightarrow L_2 \sim L_1$ (symmetry).
(c) $\left.\begin{array}{l} L_1 \sim L_2 \\ L_2 \sim L_3 \end{array}\right\} \Rightarrow L_1 \sim L_3$ (transitivity).

[The relation $\sim$ divides $\mathscr{L}$ into classes, called *equivalence classes* characterized as follows. Two systems are in the same class $\Leftrightarrow$ they are equivalent (have the same solution set); distinct classes are disjoint; and the union of all the classes is $\mathscr{L}$. Theorem 1 guarantees that the elementary operations keep a system in the same equivalence class.]

2. We continue with the theory begun in Exercise C1, concentrating here on matrices. We begin with two definitions.

DEFINITION 6. *Let A be an arbitrary matrix with rows R_1, R_2 ..., R_m. The* elementary row operations *on A are*

Type I: *interchange R_i and R_k; $\mathcal{O}_1(i, k)$.*
Type II: *multiply R_i by $c \neq 0$; $\mathcal{O}_2(i; c)$.*
Type III: *add c times R_k to R_i; $\mathcal{O}_3(i; k, c)$.*

DEFINITION 7. *Two matrices A and A_1, of the same dimensions, are* row equivalent, *$A \sim A_1$, if A_1 can be obtained from A by a finite sequence of elementary row operations.*

We now, by analogy with the discussion in Exercise C1, let $\mathscr{A} = \mathscr{A}(m, n)$ be the set of all $m \times n$ matrices. Your part of the exercise is to prove that the relation $\sim$ on $\mathscr{A}$ is an equivalence relation, i.e., that the following properties hold:

(a) $A \sim A$.
(b) $A_1 \sim A_2 \Rightarrow A_2 \sim A_1$.
(c) $\left.\begin{array}{c} A_1 \sim A_2 \\ A_2 \sim A_3 \end{array}\right\} \Rightarrow A_1 \sim A_3.$

Hints: (i) For (a), consider $\mathcal{O}_2(1; 1)$. Or, alternatively, consider $\mathcal{O}_1(1, 1)$, used twice.

(ii) The essential fact for proving (b) and (c) is the observation that each of the three operations is reversible, i.e., has an inverse, and that the inverse of each operation is one of the same type. Thus, using $\mathcal{O}^{-1}$ for the inverse of $\mathcal{O}$,

$$\mathcal{O}_1^{-1}(i, k) = \mathcal{O}_1(i, k) \qquad (\mathcal{O}_1 \text{ is its own inverse})$$
$$\mathcal{O}_2^{-1}(i, c) = \mathcal{O}_2(i, c^{-1})$$
$$\mathcal{O}_3^{-1}(i; k, c) = \mathcal{O}_3(i; k, -c).$$

To prove (b), note that $A_1 \sim A_2 \Rightarrow$

$$A_2 = \mathcal{O}_{i_k} \cdots \mathcal{O}_{i_1} A_1, \tag{6}$$

where the $\mathcal{O}_{i_j}$ are elementary row operations. Now operate on both sides of [6] with the inverses of the $\mathcal{O}$'s but in the reverse order.

(iii) To prove (c), use the fact that $A_1 \sim A_2$ and $A_2 \sim A_3$ give two equations such as [6]. Simply put them together.

The formal technique of solving a linear system in $\mathscr{L}(m, n)$ is to translate to the associated augmented matrix $[A, B]$ in $\mathscr{A}(m, n + 1)$ (there is a one-to-one correspondence between these two sets), reduce $[A, B]$ to its equivalent echelon matrix, and translate from this matrix back to the solution.

3. There are six nonzero 2×3 echelon matrices. Write them.

Hint: One of them can be written as

$$\begin{bmatrix} 1 & a & a \\ 0 & 0 & 0 \end{bmatrix},$$

where the a's could be any numbers, not necessarily the same.

9.2 The Algebra of Matrices

Although we have encountered matrices as labor-saving devices in solving linear systems, we shall see that they prove to be useful in a number of other contexts. Some of these other uses involve the performing of arithmetic operations on matrices. We begin our study of these operations in this section.

First we need a definition of equality for matrices. This amounts to strict identity.

DEFINITION 8. Let $A = [a_{ij}]$, $B = [b_{ij}]$ be matrices. Then $A = B \Leftrightarrow A$ and B have the same dimensions, $m \times n$, say, and, for every $i = 1, \ldots, m$, and every $j = 1, \ldots, n$, $a_{ij} = b_{ij}$.

Addition of matrices is element-wise, similar to addition of vectors.

DEFINITION 9. Let $A = [a_{ij}]$ and $B = [b_{ij}]$ be $m \times n$ matrices. The sum $A + B$ of A and B is the $m \times n$ matrix $C = [c_{ij}]$, where $c_{ij} = a_{ij} + b_{ij}$, $i = 1, \ldots, m, j = 1, \ldots, n$. Thus

$$A + B = [a_{ij} + b_{ij}].$$

If A and B are not of like dimensions the sum is not defined.

There is another operation analogous to one for vectors.

DEFINITION 10. Let $A = [a_{ij}]$ be an $m \times n$ matrix, and let $c \in \mathbf{R}$. By cA we mean the $m \times n$ matrix

$$cA = [ca_{ij}].$$

Example 6. Let

$$A = \begin{bmatrix} 2 & 3 & 1 \\ 1 & 0 & -1 \end{bmatrix}, \quad B = \begin{bmatrix} 4 & -8 & 0 \\ 2 & 5 & 9 \end{bmatrix}, \quad c = 3.$$

Then

$$A + B = \begin{bmatrix} 2+4 & 3-8 & 1+0 \\ 1+2 & 0+5 & -1+9 \end{bmatrix} = \begin{bmatrix} 6 & -5 & 1 \\ 3 & 5 & 8 \end{bmatrix}$$

$$3A = \begin{bmatrix} 6 & 9 & 3 \\ 3 & 0 & -3 \end{bmatrix},$$

and

$$-B = (-1)B = \begin{bmatrix} -4 & 8 & 0 \\ -2 & -5 & -9 \end{bmatrix}.$$

As a result of the form of Definitions 9 and 10, the following assertions are immediate (cf. Theorem 7.3).

THEOREM 5. *Let A, B, and C, be m × n matrices, and let r and s be numbers in* **R**. *Then the following are true.*

1. *$A + B$ is an $m \times n$ matrix.*
2. *$A + B = B + A$.*
3. *$A + (B + C) = (A + B) + C$.*
4. *There exists an $m \times n$ matrix 0 such that $A + 0 = A$.*
5. *For every A there exists $-A$ such that $A + (-A) = 0$.*
6. *rA is an $m \times n$ matrix.*
7. *$r(A + B) = rA + rB$.*
8. *$(r + s)A = rA + sA$.*
9. *$(rs)A = r(sA)$.*
10. *$1A = A$.*

PROOF. Exercise for student. ∎

Before defining the product of two matrices, we return briefly to the subject of linear systems. The simplest linear equation in one unknown is

$$ax = b,$$

where a and b are numbers and x is the unknown. For the systems we have been considering an analogous form can be obtained in terms of matrices. Suppose we illustrate for the case of a system with two equations and three unknowns. We have already introduced the matrices

$$A = \begin{bmatrix} a_{11} & a_{12} & a_{13} \\ a_{21} & a_{22} & a_{23} \end{bmatrix} \quad \text{and} \quad B = \begin{bmatrix} b_1 \\ b_2 \end{bmatrix}.$$

It remains to introduce the matrix

$$X = \begin{bmatrix} x_1 \\ x_2 \\ x_3 \end{bmatrix}$$

and a method of multiplying so that the matrix equation

$$AX = B,$$

or

$$\begin{bmatrix} a_{11} & a_{12} & a_{12} \\ a_{21} & a_{22} & a_{23} \end{bmatrix}_{2 \times 3} \begin{bmatrix} x_1 \\ x_2 \\ x_3 \end{bmatrix}_{3 \times 1} = \begin{bmatrix} b_1 \\ b_2 \end{bmatrix}_{2 \times 1,} \tag{7}$$

is equivalent to the system

$$\begin{Bmatrix} a_{11}x_1 + a_{12}x_2 + a_{13}x_3 = b_1 \\ a_{21}x_1 + a_{22}x_2 + a_{23}x_3 = b_2 \end{Bmatrix}. \tag{8}$$

Now, a comparison of [7] and [8] and consideration of Definition 8 for equality of matrices indicate that the product of $A_{2 \times 3}$ and $X_{3 \times 1}$ must be a 2×1 matrix. Notice also that the left-hand sides of the equations in [8] are in fact inner products of the respective rows of the matrix A and the column vector X. Thus the first row of AX should be the inner product of the first row of A and X, and the second row of AX should be the inner product of the second row of A and X. That is, we should have

$$\underbrace{A}_{2 \times 3} X_{3 \times 1} = \begin{bmatrix} a_{11}x_1 + a_{12}x_2 + a_{13}x_3 \\ a_{21}x_1 + a_{22}x_2 + a_{23}x_3 \end{bmatrix}_{2 \times 1}. \tag{9}$$

If the right-hand factor in the product has more than one column, we simply repeat the same process to obtain the other columns of the product matrix. In this way the product matrix inherits its row dimension from the left-hand factor and its column dimension from the right-hand factor. The crucial condition is the equality of the column dimension of the left-hand factor and the row dimension of the right, the "inner" dimensions on the left-hand side of [9].

The formal description follows.

DEFINITION 11. *Let $A = [a_{ik}]_{m \times n}$, $B = [b_{kj}]_{n \times p}$. Then the product AB is the matrix $C = [c_{ij}]_{m \times p}$, where*

$$c_{ij} = \sum_{k=1}^{n} a_{ik}b_{kj}, \qquad i = 1, \ldots, m, \quad j = 1, \ldots, p.$$

Thus

$$\underbrace{A}_{m \times n} B_{n \times p} = \left[\sum_{k=1}^{n} a_{ik}b_{kj} \right]_{m \times p}.$$

In other words, the element in row i and column j of the product is the inner product of the ith row vector of A and the jth column vector of B. Clearly this is meaningful only if the column dimension of A equals the row dimension of B.

Some illustrations are in order.

Example 7. Let

$$A = \begin{bmatrix} a_{11} & a_{12} \\ a_{21} & a_{22} \end{bmatrix}_{2 \times 2}, \qquad B = \begin{bmatrix} b_{11} & b_{12} \\ b_{21} & b_{22} \end{bmatrix}_{2 \times 2}.$$

Then

$$AB = \begin{bmatrix} a_{11}b_{11} + a_{12}b_{21} & a_{11}b_{12} + a_{12}b_{22} \\ a_{21}b_{11} + a_{22}b_{21} & a_{21}b_{12} + a_{22}b_{22} \end{bmatrix}.$$

Example 8. Let

$$A = \begin{bmatrix} 2 & 3 & 1 \\ 1 & 0 & -1 \end{bmatrix}, \quad B = \begin{bmatrix} 1 & 2 \\ 0 & 1 \\ 2 & -1 \end{bmatrix}.$$

Then

$$_{2 \times 3}AB_{3 \times 2} = \begin{bmatrix} 2 \cdot 1 + 3 \cdot 0 + 1 \cdot 2 & 2 \cdot 2 + 3 \cdot 1 + 1(-1) \\ 1 \cdot 1 + 0 \cdot 0 + (-1)2 & 1 \cdot 2 + 0 \cdot 1 + (-1)(-1) \end{bmatrix}$$

$$= \begin{bmatrix} 4 & 6 \\ -1 & 3 \end{bmatrix}_{2 \times 2}.$$

Also

$$_{3 \times 2}BA_{2 \times 3} = \begin{bmatrix} 4 & 3 & -1 \\ 1 & 0 & -1 \\ 3 & 6 & 3 \end{bmatrix}_{3 \times 3}.$$

Example 9. Let

$$A = \begin{bmatrix} 0 & 0 \\ 1 & 0 \end{bmatrix}, \quad B = \begin{bmatrix} 0 & 0 \\ 0 & 1 \end{bmatrix}.$$

Then

$$AB = \begin{bmatrix} 0 & 0 \\ 0 & 0 \end{bmatrix}, \quad BA = \begin{bmatrix} 0 & 0 \\ 1 & 0 \end{bmatrix}.$$

Obviously matrix multiplication is not commutative; in fact, AB may exist and BA may not. Moreover, note that in Example 9 neither $A = 0$ nor $B = 0$, yet $AB = 0$.

The properties that do hold for matrix multiplication are listed in the following assertion. With regard to the statement about dimensions, see Exercise B1. The proof, using matrix techniques, is messy and we omit it here. See, however, Exercises C2–4.

THEOREM 6.   *Let A, B, C, and D be matrices with dimensions so that the operations indicated are meaningful. Let $c \in \mathbf{R}$. Then*

1. $(AB)D = A(BD)$ *(associativity).*
2. $A(B + C) = AB + AC$ ⎱
3. $(B + C)D = BD + CD$ ⎰   *(distributivity).*
4. $(cA)B = A(cB) = c(AB)$.

We conclude this section with mention of one other matrix operation (unary, in that it involves only one matrix).

DEFINITION 12. *Let $A = [a_{ij}]$ be an $m \times n$ matrix. The* transpose *of A, A^t, is the $n \times m$ matrix obtained by interchanging the rows and columns of A. In terms of elements,*

$$A^t = [a'_{ij}]_{n \times m}, \quad \text{where } a'_{ij} = a_{ji}, \qquad \begin{cases} j = 1, \ldots, m \\ i = 1, \ldots, n. \end{cases}$$

The notation involving subscripts gets a bit sticky in working with transposes, but that is inevitable.

Example 10. Let

$$A = \begin{bmatrix} 2 & 0 & 3 \\ 1 & 4 & 5 \end{bmatrix}, \quad B = [1 \quad 4 \quad 7], \quad C = \begin{bmatrix} 3 & 1 & -2 \\ 0 & 2 & 5 \\ 1 & 1 & 4 \end{bmatrix}.$$

Then

$$A^t = \begin{bmatrix} 2 & 1 \\ 0 & 4 \\ 3 & 5 \end{bmatrix}, \quad B^t = \begin{bmatrix} 1 \\ 4 \\ 7 \end{bmatrix}, \quad C^t = \begin{bmatrix} 3 & 0 & 1 \\ 1 & 2 & 1 \\ -2 & 5 & 4 \end{bmatrix}.$$

As is illustrated with B in this example, the transpose of a 1-row matrix (row vector) is a 1-column matrix (column vector).

The properties of the transpose and its relations with the other matrix operations are given in the following theorem.

THEOREM 7. *Let $A_{m \times n}$, $B_{m \times n}$, and $C_{n \times p}$ be matrices with dimensions as indicated; let $c \in \mathbf{R}$. Then*

1. $(A^t)^t = A$.
2. $(A + B)^t = A^t + B^t$.
3. $(cA)^t = cA^t$.
4. $(AC)^t = C^t A^t$.

PROOF. Parts 1 and 3 are obvious. The proof of 2, not difficult, is left for the student (Exercise B2). We consider 4. Let

$$A = [a_{ij}], \quad C = [c_{ij}], \quad AC = [p_{ij}] = \left[\sum_{k=1}^{n} a_{ik} c_{kj} \right];$$

then

$$A^t = [a'_{ij}], \quad C^t = [c'_{ij}], \quad (AC)^t = [p'_{ij}],$$

where $a'_{ij} = a_{ji}$, $c'_{ij} = c_{ji}$, $p'_{ij} = p_{ji}$. Then

$$(AC)^t = [p'_{ij}] = [p_{ji}] = \left[\sum_{k=1}^{n} a_{jk} c_{ki} \right]$$

$$= \left[\sum_{k=1}^{n} c_{ki} a_{jk} \right] = \left[\sum_{k=1}^{n} c'_{ik} a'_{kj} \right]$$

$$= C^t A^t. \quad \blacksquare$$

Some matrices have the property of being invariant with respect to transposition. Clearly a necessary condition for this is that the dimensions be equal, i.e., that the matrix be *square*.

DEFINITION 13. *A square matrix A is* symmetric $\Leftrightarrow A^t = A$. *A square matrix B is* skew-symmetric $\Leftrightarrow B^t = -B$.

For example, let

$$A = \begin{bmatrix} 1 & 0 & 2 \\ 0 & 3 & -1 \\ 2 & -1 & 4 \end{bmatrix}, \quad B = \begin{bmatrix} 0 & 1 & 2 \\ -1 & 0 & -3 \\ -2 & 3 & 0 \end{bmatrix}.$$

Then $A^t = A$ (A is symmetric) and B is skew-symmetric.

In a square matrix $A = [a_{ij}]$ the elements a_{ii}, $i = 1, \ldots, n$, are called the *main diagonal* elements.

Exercises

A. **1.** Find $A + B$, $-A$, AB, BA, A^t, and B^t:

(a)
$$A = \begin{bmatrix} 2 & 3 \\ -1 & 4 \end{bmatrix}, \quad B = \begin{bmatrix} 1 & 0 \\ 3 & -2 \end{bmatrix}.$$

(b)
$$A = \begin{bmatrix} 1 & 0 & 3 \\ 2 & -1 & 7 \\ 3 & -2 & 2 \end{bmatrix}, \quad B = \begin{bmatrix} 4 & 1 & 0 \\ -1 & 0 & 2 \\ 3 & -1 & 2 \end{bmatrix}.$$

2. Find AB and BA:

(a)
$$A = \begin{bmatrix} 1 & 2 \end{bmatrix}, \quad B = \begin{bmatrix} 3 \\ 5 \end{bmatrix}.$$

(b)
$$A = \begin{bmatrix} 3 & 2 & 0 \\ 1 & 0 & -2 \end{bmatrix}, \quad B = \begin{bmatrix} 1 & -4 \\ -2 & 6 \\ 0 & 1 \end{bmatrix}.$$

(c)
$$A = \begin{bmatrix} 2 & -1 & 0 \end{bmatrix}, \quad B = \begin{bmatrix} 4 \\ 3 \\ -1 \end{bmatrix}.$$

(d) $A = \begin{bmatrix} a_1 & a_2 & \cdots & a_n \end{bmatrix}$, $B^t = \begin{bmatrix} b_1 & b_2 & \cdots & b_n \end{bmatrix}$.

3. Let
$$A = \begin{bmatrix} 0 & 1 & 1 \\ 0 & 0 & 1 \\ 0 & 0 & 0 \end{bmatrix}.$$

  (a) Find $A^2 = AA$.
  (b) Find $A^3 = AA^2$.
  4. Let

$$A = \begin{bmatrix} 1 & 1 & 1 \\ 0 & 1 & 1 \\ 0 & 0 & 1 \end{bmatrix}.$$

  (a) Find $A^2 = AA$.
  (b) Find $A^3 = AA^2$.
  (c) Find $A^4 = AA^3$.
  5. Let

$$A = \begin{bmatrix} 1 & 1 & 1 & 1 \\ 0 & 1 & 1 & 1 \\ 0 & 0 & 1 & 1 \\ 0 & 0 & 0 & 1 \end{bmatrix}.$$

Find A^2, A^3, A^4, A^5, and A^n.
  6. Find the products:

  (a) $\begin{bmatrix} 3 & 1 \\ 2 & 1 \end{bmatrix} \begin{bmatrix} 1 & -1 \\ -2 & 3 \end{bmatrix}.$

  (b) $\begin{bmatrix} 4 & -1 \\ -3 & 1 \end{bmatrix} \begin{bmatrix} 1 & 1 \\ 3 & 4 \end{bmatrix}.$

  (c) $\begin{bmatrix} 1 & 2 \\ 3 & 4 \end{bmatrix} \begin{bmatrix} -2 & 1 \\ \frac{3}{2} & -\frac{1}{2} \end{bmatrix}.$

  (d) $\begin{bmatrix} 1 & 0 \\ 0 & 1 \end{bmatrix} \begin{bmatrix} a & b \\ c & d \end{bmatrix}.$

  (e) $\begin{bmatrix} 1 & 0 & 2 \\ 3 & 1 & 0 \\ 2 & -1 & 1 \end{bmatrix} \begin{bmatrix} -1 & 2 & 2 \\ 3 & 3 & -6 \\ 5 & -1 & -1 \end{bmatrix}.$

B.   **1.** This refers to the statement of Theorem 6. Suppose A is $m \times n$. Give dimensions for B, C, and D so that the expressions of the theorem are meaningful.

  2. Prove assertion 2 of Theorem 7, i.e., show that if A and B are $m \times n$, then

$$(A + B)^t = A^t + B^t.$$

  3. Let A be $m \times n$, and B be $p \times q$.

(a) Find a necessary condition on m, n, p, q so that AB and BA are both defined.

(b) Find a further condition on m, n, p, q so that AB and BA have the same dimensions.

(c) Are the necessary conditions found in (a) and (b) also sufficient?

4. Let $\mathbf{a} = A_{1 \times n}$ and $\mathbf{b} = B_{1 \times n}$ be vectors in $\mathbf{R}^n$.

(a) Show that the inner product is $\mathbf{a} \cdot \mathbf{b} = AB^t$.

(b) What is A^tB?

5. Let A be $m \times n$ and let B be $n \times p$ so that AB is defined. Suppose the columns of B are $B_1, B_2, \ldots, B_p$, so that we can write

$$B = [B_1, \ldots, B_p],$$

where the B_j's are column vectors. Show that

$$AB = [AB_1, AB_2, \ldots, AB_p]. \tag{10}$$

Hint: Let

$$AB_j = C_j = \begin{bmatrix} c_{1j} \\ \vdots \\ c_{mj} \end{bmatrix}.$$

Show that c_{ij} is the ijth element of AB.

6. See Exercise B5. Let A and B be as in that exercise. Let the rows of A be $A_1, \ldots, A_m$. Then

$$AB = \begin{bmatrix} A_1 \\ \vdots \\ A_m \end{bmatrix} B = \begin{bmatrix} A_1B \\ \vdots \\ A_mB \end{bmatrix}. \tag{11}$$

7. Prove that if $A = [a_{ij}]$ is skew-symmetric, then $a_{ii} = 0$ for $i = 1, 2, \ldots, n$.

C. **1.** Let $A = [a_{ij}]_{n \times n}$.

(a) Prove that A symmetric $\Rightarrow A^2$ symmetric.

(b) Prove that A skew-symmetric $\Rightarrow A^2$ symmetric.

2. Consider m numbers $x_1, x_2, \ldots, x_m$ and mn numbers y_{ij} for $i = 1, \ldots, m, j = 1, \ldots, n$. Show that the following equations are valid:

$$\sum_{i=1}^m x_i \sum_{j=1}^n y_{ij} = \sum_{i=1}^m \sum_{j=1}^n x_iy_{ij} = \sum_{j=1}^n \sum_{i=1}^m x_iy_{ij}. \tag{12}$$

[Hint for the equality of the second and third expressions: For each $i = 1, 2, \ldots, m$ write out the terms of the sum; thus for $i = 1$,

$$\sum_{j=1}^n x_1y_{1j} = x_1y_{11} + x_1y_{12} + \cdots + x_1y_{1n}.$$

Then add the rows and the columns of the resulting rectangular array.]

    3. See Theorem 6, assertion 1. Let

$$A = [a_{ij}]_{m \times n}, \quad B = [b_{jk}]_{n \times p}, \quad C = [c_{kl}]_{p \times q}.$$

Prove that $(AB)C = A(BC)$.

    Hints: (i) Let $AB = [g_{ik}]_{m \times p}$. Write the expression for g_{ik} in terms of the elements of A and B. (ii) Let $BC = [h_{jl}]$. Same as in hint (i) except in terms of B and C. (iii) Then

$$(AB)C = \left[\sum_{k=1}^{p} g_{ik} c_{kl} \right]$$

$$= \left[\sum_{k=1}^{p} \left(\sum_{j=1}^{n} a_{ij} b_{jk} \right) c_{kl} \right].$$

Now use Equation [12] of Exercise C2 a few times to show that

$$(AB)C = \left[\sum_{j=1}^{n} a_{ij} h_{jl} \right]$$

$$= A(BC).$$

    4. Prove assertion 2 of Theorem 6. (This is easier than Exercise C3).

9.3 Invertible Matrices

In this section we shall work almost exclusively with square matrices. In the exceptional cases we shall indicate dimensions explicitly.

    We begin by calling attention to the nature of the $n \times n$ echelon matrix with rank n. Clearly the conditions imposed (echelon, rank n) require that every column contain a leading 1, thus forcing the matrix to be

$$I_n = \begin{bmatrix} 1 & 0 & \cdots & 0 \\ 0 & 1 & \cdots & 0 \\ \vdots & \vdots & & \vdots \\ 0 & 0 & \cdots & 1 \end{bmatrix}. \qquad [13]$$

DEFINITION 14.   *The matrix defined by* [13] *is called the* $n \times n$ *identity matrix.*

There is a symbol that is useful in working with the identity matrix—and elsewhere.

DEFINITION 15.   *The* Kronecker δ *is defined by*

$$\begin{Bmatrix} \delta_{ij} = 0 \text{ if } i \neq j \\ \delta_{ii} = 1 \end{Bmatrix}.$$

There is a Kronecker δ for each $n \in \mathbf{N}$; usually there is no confusion if the n is not specified.

In terms of the Kronecker δ, $I = [\delta_{ij}]$.

The significance of the matrix I is that it has the role of multiplicative identity. More exactly, we have the following assertion.

THEOREM 8.   *Let $A = [a_{ij}]$ be $m \times n$. Then*

1. $I_m A = A$.
2. $A I_n = A$.

PROOF.   We prove only assertion 1; the proof of assertion 2 is entirely similar. By Definition 11, we have

$$I_m A = \left[\sum_{k=1}^{m} \delta_{ik} a_{kj} \right].$$

In the summation over k all values of δ are zero except for $k = i$ when $\delta_{ii} = 1$. Thus for every $i = 1, \ldots, m$, and $j = 1, \ldots, n$, we have

$$\sum_{k=1}^{m} \delta_{ik} a_{kj} = a_{ij},$$

so $I_m A = A$.   ∎

Of course, for $n \times n$ matrices A we have $I_n A = A I_n = A$.

We next consider the possibility of the existence of a multiplicative inverse of a square matrix.

DEFINITION 16.   *Let A be an $n \times n$ matrix. If there exists an $n \times n$ matrix B such that $AB = BA = I$, then B is called the* inverse *of A and will be denoted A^{-1}. If A has an inverse, A is said to be* invertible (*sometimes* nonsingular). *If A has no inverse, then A is* singular.

Example 11.   Let

$$A = \begin{bmatrix} 1 & 1 \\ 1 & 2 \end{bmatrix}.$$

It is easy to verify that

$$A^{-1} = \begin{bmatrix} 2 & -1 \\ -1 & 1 \end{bmatrix}$$

satisfies $A A^{-1} = A^{-1} A = I$.

On the other hand, let

$$C = \begin{bmatrix} 0 & 0 \\ 1 & 0 \end{bmatrix}$$

and let

$$B = \begin{bmatrix} b_{11} & b_{12} \\ b_{21} & b_{22} \end{bmatrix}.$$

Then

$$CB = \begin{bmatrix} 0 & 0 \\ b_{11} & b_{12} \end{bmatrix}.$$

Clearly no choice of B can make $CB = I$, so C is singular.

One of our aims will be to find techniques for discerning whether or not a matrix is invertible, and, if so, how to find its inverse. First, however, we mention a few properties of the inverse.

THEOREM 9.   *Let A be invertible with inverse A^{-1}. If B is such that $AB = BA = I$, then $B = A^{-1}$. (In other words, A^{-1} is unique.)*

PROOF.   We have

$$B = BI = B(AA^{-1}) = (BA)A^{-1} \quad \text{(associativity)}$$
$$= IA^{-1}$$
$$= A^{-1}. \quad \blacksquare$$

COROLLARY.   *If A is invertible, then so is A^{-1} and $(A^{-1})^{-1} = A$.*

PROOF.   Since $A^{-1}A = AA^{-1} = I$, A fills the role of the unique inverse of A^{-1}. $\blacksquare$

Invertibility is preserved by multiplication.

THEOREM 10.   *Let A and B be invertible. Then AB is invertible and $(AB)^{-1} = B^{-1}A^{-1}$.*

PROOF.   We show that $B^{-1}A^{-1}$ fulfills the conditions for the inverse of AB:

$$(AB)(B^{-1}A^{-1}) = A(BB^{-1})A^{-1} \quad \text{(associativity)}$$
$$= AIA^{-1} = AA^{-1}$$
$$= I;$$

and

$$(B^{-1}A^{-1})(AB) = B^{-1}(A^{-1}A)B = B^{-1}IB$$
$$= B^{-1}B$$
$$= I.$$

Thus, by Definition 16, AB is invertible and $(AB)^{-1} = B^{-1}A^{-1}$, since, by Theorem 9, the inverse is unique. $\blacksquare$

COROLLARY.   *Let $A_1, \ldots, A_m$ be invertible. Then $A_1A_2 \cdots A_m$ is invertible and $(A_1 \cdots A_m)^{-1} = A_m^{-1} \cdots A_1^{-1}$.*

PROOF.   By induction. Exercise for student. $\blacksquare$

The relation between inverses and transposes is a very satisfactory one.

THEOREM 11.   *If A is invertible, so is A^t and $(A^t)^{-1} = (A^{-1})^t$.*

PROOF.   Since A is invertible

$$AA^{-1} = A^{-1}A = I.$$

Taking transposes, we have

$$(AA^{-1})^t = (A^{-1}A)^t = I^t.$$

Now using Theorem 7, assertion 4, and the fact that I is symmetric, we find

$$(A^{-1})^t A^t = A^t (A^{-1})^t = I.$$

These relations simply say, by Definition 16, that $(A^{-1})^t$ is the inverse of A^t. ∎

We now consider the problem of finding the inverse of a matrix. We begin with a simple illustration.

Example 12.   We let

$$A = \begin{bmatrix} 1 & 2 \\ 3 & 4 \end{bmatrix}$$

and try to find

$$A^{-1} = \begin{bmatrix} x_{11} & x_{12} \\ x_{21} & x_{22} \end{bmatrix}$$

such that $AA^{-1} = I$ (this is, to be sure, only half the condition to be satisfied by A^{-1}—we shall comment on this point later).

Now if we let X_1 and X_2 be the columns of the unknown matrix A^{-1}, then the condition to be satisfied is

$$AA^{-1} = A[X_1 \quad X_2] = I,$$

or, by Equation [10] (Exercise B5 after Section 9.2),

$$[AX_1 \quad AX_2] = \begin{bmatrix} 1 & 0 \\ 0 & 1 \end{bmatrix}.$$

This equation can be decomposed into two linear systems:

$$A\begin{bmatrix} x_{11} \\ x_{21} \end{bmatrix} = \begin{bmatrix} 1 \\ 0 \end{bmatrix} \tag{14}$$

and

$$A\begin{bmatrix} x_{12} \\ x_{22} \end{bmatrix} = \begin{bmatrix} 0 \\ 1 \end{bmatrix}. \tag{15}$$

Each of these systems can be solved by the technique of Section 9.1. Thus, for [14], reducing the augmented matrix to echelon form, we have

$$\begin{bmatrix} 1 & 2 & 1 \\ 3 & 4 & 0 \end{bmatrix} \sim \begin{bmatrix} 1 & 2 & 1 \\ 0 & -2 & -3 \end{bmatrix} \sim \begin{bmatrix} 1 & 2 & 1 \\ 0 & 1 & \frac{3}{2} \end{bmatrix} \sim \begin{bmatrix} 1 & 0 & -2 \\ 0 & 1 & \frac{3}{2} \end{bmatrix} \Rightarrow$$

$$\begin{cases} x_{11} = -2 \\ x_{21} = \frac{3}{2} \end{cases}.$$

Similarly for [15]:

$$\begin{bmatrix} 1 & 2 & 0 \\ 3 & 4 & 1 \end{bmatrix} \sim \begin{bmatrix} 1 & 2 & 0 \\ 0 & -2 & 1 \end{bmatrix} \sim \begin{bmatrix} 1 & 2 & 0 \\ 0 & 1 & -\frac{1}{2} \end{bmatrix} \sim \begin{bmatrix} 1 & 0 & 1 \\ 0 & 1 & -\frac{1}{2} \end{bmatrix} \Rightarrow$$

$$\begin{cases} x_{12} = 1 \\ x_{22} = -\frac{1}{2} \end{cases}.$$

From these calculations we can draw two conclusions, one obvious and immediate and the second more subtle but with long-range significance. The first is that the inverse for A is

$$A^{-1} = \begin{bmatrix} -2 & 1 \\ \frac{3}{2} & -\frac{1}{2} \end{bmatrix}.$$

In fact, it is easily checked (exercise for student) that $AA^{-1} = A^{-1}A = I$.

The second and more important observation is to the effect that there was waste motion in solving separately the two linear systems: the reduction of A to echelon form was the same in each case. Therefore the solutions could be obtained simultaneously by considering, in this case, the 2×4 matrix $[A, I]$ and using elementary operations to reduce A to the 2×2 echelon matrix (which, if there is to be a solution, must be of rank 2 and hence must be the 2×2 identity matrix—see the remarks preceding Definition 14). When this has been done the solutions to the systems appear as the columns of the matrix into which I has been transformed. In symbols, this technique can be described by

$$[A, I] \sim [I, A^{-1}]. \tag{16}$$

This scheme is valid for square matrices of arbitrary dimension. If A is $n \times n$, assume its inverse is $A^{-1} = [x_{ij}] = [X_1 \cdots X_j \cdots X_n]$, where the $X_j, j = 1, \ldots, n$, are the columns of X. Then, by Equation [10],

$$AX = A[X_1 \cdots X_n] = [AX_1 \cdots AX_n],$$

so the equation $AX = I$ is equivalent to the n systems

$$AX_j = \begin{bmatrix} 0 \\ \vdots \\ 0 \\ 1 \\ 0 \\ \vdots \\ 0 \end{bmatrix} \leftarrow j\text{th row}, \qquad j = 1, \dots, n.$$

These n systems can be handled simultaneously by starting with the $n \times 2n$ matrix $[A, I]$, reducing A to its echelon form by elementary operations, and performing the same sequence of operations on I. If it is possible in this way to reduce A to I, then I will have been transformed to A^{-1}, as Equation [16] suggests.

Two further remarks are in order. First of all, what if A is not invertible? Then the n systems of equations will not have n unique solutions; this will be apparent in that it will be impossible to reduce A to an echelon matrix of rank n, the $n \times n$ identity (see Example 13). In other words, this technique produces an inverse if A is invertible and otherwise shows up singularity.

We should also comment on the fact that Definition 16 requires A^{-1} to satisfy $A^{-1}A = I$ as well as $AA^{-1} = I$. The fact is that it is possible to prove, although we shall not do it, that if either $AB = I$ or $BA = I$ for some matrix B, then A is invertible and $B = A^{-1}$.

Example 13.   Let

$$A = \begin{bmatrix} 1 & 0 & 2 \\ 1 & 2 & 4 \\ 3 & -2 & 4 \end{bmatrix}.$$

We use row operations on A, working toward the echelon form, and carry out the same operations on I:

$$[A, I] = \begin{bmatrix} 1 & 0 & 2 & 1 & 0 & 0 \\ 1 & 2 & 4 & 0 & 1 & 0 \\ 3 & -2 & 4 & 0 & 0 & 1 \end{bmatrix} \overset{\text{III}}{\sim} \begin{bmatrix} 1 & 0 & 2 & 1 & 0 & 0 \\ 0 & 2 & 2 & -1 & 1 & 0 \\ 0 & -2 & -2 & -3 & 0 & 1 \end{bmatrix}$$

$$\overset{\text{II}}{\sim} \begin{bmatrix} 1 & 0 & 2 & 1 & 0 & 0 \\ 0 & 1 & 1 & -\frac{1}{2} & \frac{1}{2} & 0 \\ 0 & -2 & -2 & -3 & 0 & 1 \end{bmatrix} \overset{\text{III}}{\sim} \begin{bmatrix} 1 & 0 & 2 & 1 & 0 & 0 \\ 0 & 1 & 1 & -\frac{1}{2} & \frac{1}{2} & 0 \\ 0 & 0 & 0 & -4 & 1 & 1 \end{bmatrix}.$$

We can now see that A is singular, for the echelon matrix to which it has been reduced does not have rank 3. But all of the three augmented matrices have rank 3 and, by assertion 3 of Theorem 4, the three systems all have no solutions. Thus A is singular.

Example 14.   Consider

$$A = \begin{bmatrix} 1 & 0 & 2 \\ 3 & 1 & 5 \\ -2 & 1 & -7 \end{bmatrix}.$$

Using the same technique as in Example 13, we have

$$[A, I] = \begin{bmatrix} 1 & 0 & 2 & \vdots & 1 & 0 & 0 \\ 3 & 1 & 5 & \vdots & 0 & 1 & 0 \\ -2 & 1 & -7 & \vdots & 0 & 0 & 1 \end{bmatrix} \overset{\text{III}}{\sim} \begin{bmatrix} 1 & 0 & 2 & \vdots & 1 & 0 & 0 \\ 0 & 1 & -1 & \vdots & -3 & 1 & 0 \\ 0 & 1 & -3 & \vdots & 2 & 0 & 1 \end{bmatrix}$$

$$\overset{\text{III}}{\sim} \begin{bmatrix} 1 & 0 & 2 & \vdots & 1 & 0 & 0 \\ 0 & 1 & -1 & \vdots & -3 & 1 & 0 \\ 0 & 0 & -2 & \vdots & 5 & -1 & 1 \end{bmatrix} \overset{\text{II}}{\sim} \begin{bmatrix} 1 & 0 & 2 & \vdots & 1 & 0 & 0 \\ 0 & 1 & -1 & \vdots & -3 & 1 & 0 \\ 0 & 0 & 1 & \vdots & -\frac{5}{2} & \frac{1}{2} & -\frac{1}{2} \end{bmatrix}$$

$$\overset{\text{III}}{\sim} \begin{bmatrix} 1 & 0 & 0 & \vdots & 6 & -1 & 1 \\ 0 & 1 & 0 & \vdots & -\frac{11}{2} & \frac{3}{2} & -\frac{1}{2} \\ 0 & 0 & 1 & \vdots & -\frac{5}{2} & \frac{1}{2} & -\frac{1}{2} \end{bmatrix}.$$

Thus

$$A^{-1} = \tfrac{1}{2} \begin{bmatrix} 12 & -2 & 2 \\ -11 & 3 & -1 \\ -5 & 1 & -1 \end{bmatrix}.$$

It is routine to verify that $AA^{-1} = A^{-1}A = I$.

Exercises

A. In Exercises 1–11 determine whether or not the matrix is invertible. If it is, find the inverse.

1. $\begin{bmatrix} 4 & 3 \\ 1 & -5 \end{bmatrix}.$

2. $\begin{bmatrix} 2 & -3 \\ -6 & 9 \end{bmatrix}.$

3. $\begin{bmatrix} 1 & 3 \\ 2 & 5 \end{bmatrix}.$

4. $\begin{bmatrix} 1 & 0 & 4 \\ 2 & 1 & -3 \\ 0 & 2 & -1 \end{bmatrix}.$

5. $\begin{bmatrix} -2 & 1 & 4 \\ 3 & 0 & -1 \\ 2 & 5 & 0 \end{bmatrix}$.

6. $\begin{bmatrix} 1 & -3 & 4 \\ 1 & 9 & -14 \\ 2 & 0 & -1 \end{bmatrix}$.

7. $\begin{bmatrix} 3 & -2 & 1 \\ 5 & 0 & 2 \\ 2 & 1 & 4 \end{bmatrix}$.

8. $\begin{bmatrix} 0 & 1 & 7 \\ 5 & -2 & 3 \\ 5 & -3 & -4 \end{bmatrix}$.

9. $\begin{bmatrix} 2 & 0 & 5 \\ 8 & 1 & 0 \\ 0 & 1 & -1 \end{bmatrix}$.

10. $\begin{bmatrix} 1 & -2 & 3 & 0 \\ -4 & 2 & 0 & -1 \\ 3 & 5 & 2 & 1 \\ 0 & 2 & 1 & 7 \end{bmatrix}$.

11. $\begin{bmatrix} 0 & -1 & 2 & 4 \\ 2 & 3 & 0 & 1 \\ -1 & 4 & 5 & 2 \\ 1 & 2 & 3 & 0 \end{bmatrix}$.

12. Let

$$A = \begin{bmatrix} 1 & 2 \\ 3 & a \end{bmatrix}.$$

For what value(s) of a is this matrix singular? Find the inverse for the values of a for which A is invertible.

B. **1.** One way of looking at Definition 16 for the inverse of a matrix is to say that A^{-1} is both a left ($A^{-1}A = I$) and right ($AA^{-1} = I$) inverse. The following assertion says that left and right inverses cannot be different and that a matrix which has left and right inverses is invertible.

THEOREM 12. *Suppose A, B, and C are matrices such that* $AB = CA = I$. *Then A is invertible and* $B = C = A^{-1}$.

Prove Theorem 12.

Hint: Show first that $B = C$ by considering $C = CI = \cdots$.

As has already been remarked, a stronger statement than that in Theorem 12 is valid: if a matrix has *either* a left or a right inverse it is invertible. This, however, is difficult to prove with the tools now available to us, so we shall make the precise statement and assume its validity.

THEOREM 13. *Let A be a square matrix. Then*

$$A \text{ is invertible} \Leftrightarrow \begin{cases} \text{there exists a square matrix B such that} \\ \text{either (1) } BA = I \\ \quad \text{or (2) } AB = I. \end{cases}$$

In either case (1) *or* (2), $B = A^{-1}$.

2. This exercise relates the invertibility of a matrix to linear systems consisting of n equations in n unknowns.

THEOREM 14. *Let A be an* $n \times n$ *matrix, let* $X = [x_i]$ *be* $n \times 1$, *and let* $B = [b_i]$ *be an arbitrary* $n \times 1$ *matrix. Then*

A is invertible $\Leftrightarrow$ $AX = B$ *has a unique solution.*

Prove Theorem 14.

Hints: (i) For the $\Rightarrow$ step, multiply both sides of $AX = B$ by A^{-1}. (ii) For the $\Leftarrow$ part, use the fact that B can be arbitrary. For $j = 1, \ldots, n$, let

$$B_j = \begin{bmatrix} 0 \\ \vdots \\ 0 \\ 1 \\ 0 \\ \vdots \\ 0 \end{bmatrix} \leftarrow j\text{th row} \qquad [17]$$

and use an argument related to that given in the text just after Equation [16]. Also, it is necessary to use Theorem 13.

3. This exercise relates invertibility to the form of the echelon matrix.

THEOREM 15. *Let A be a square matrix. Then*

$$A \text{ is invertible} \Leftrightarrow \begin{cases} \text{the echelon matrix obtained} \\ \text{from A is the identity matrix} \end{cases}.$$

Prove Theorem 15.

Hints: Supply reasons for the following chain:

$$A \text{ invertible } \Leftrightarrow \left\{ \begin{matrix} \text{there exists unique } X, \\ AX = I \end{matrix} \right\} \Leftrightarrow A[X_1 \ \cdots \ X_n] = I$$

$$\Leftrightarrow [AX_1 \ \cdots \ AX_n] = I$$

$$\Leftrightarrow \left\{ \begin{matrix} \text{there exist unique solutions to } AX_j = B_j \\ \text{(Equation [17])}, j = 1, \ldots, n \end{matrix} \right\}$$

$$\Leftrightarrow \left\{ \begin{matrix} \text{the echelon matrix obtained} \\ \text{from } A \text{ is the identity matrix} \end{matrix} \right\}.$$

9.4 Matrices and Transformations

We now return to the subject of Section 5.4 (rotation of axes) and show
how the problem discussed there can be expressed in terms of matrices.
Moreover, we shall formulate the techniques in such a way that the solution
can be applied to more general cases.

As our starting point we take Equation [5.39],

$$Ax^2 + Bxy + Cy^2 + Dx + Ey + F = 0,$$

which, as we saw, includes all of the conic section curves. In Section 5.4 we
were concerned with a transformation of coordinates (a rotation) that would
eliminate the xy term. The linear terms can be removed by a translation of
axes, as already demonstrated, and we shall not be concerned with them.
Thus we are going to be interested in

$$Q(x, y) = ax^2 + 2bxy + cy^2, \tag{18}$$

which is an example of a *quadratic form*. The reason for the coefficient 2 will
soon be apparent.

We first point out that $Q(x, y)$ can be written in terms of matrices. Let
$\mathbf{v} = [x, y]$ be a vector. Then

$$Q(\mathbf{v}) = Q(x, y) = \mathbf{v} \begin{bmatrix} a & b \\ b & c \end{bmatrix} \mathbf{v}^t,$$

or

$$Q(\mathbf{v}) = \mathbf{v} A \mathbf{v}^t,$$

where

$$A = \begin{bmatrix} a & b \\ b & c \end{bmatrix}. \tag{19}$$

It is important to notice that A is symmetric, i.e., $A^t = A$.

For purposes of generalization, we shall use $\mathbf{x} = [x_1, x_2]$ instead of $\mathbf{v} = [x, y]$.

DEFINITION 17. *Given a symmetric 2×2 matrix A and a fixed coordinate system for $\mathbf{R}^2$, the* quadratic form *determined by A is the function $Q: \mathbf{R}^2 \to \mathbf{R}$ defined by*

$$Q(\mathbf{x}) = \mathbf{x}A\mathbf{x}^t. \qquad [20]$$

(Definition 17 could just as well have been formulated in terms of an $n \times n$ matrix and a function $Q: \mathbf{R}^n \to \mathbf{R}$; in that case $\mathbf{x} = [x_1, x_2, \ldots, x_n] \in \mathbf{R}^n$.)

Example 15. Let

$$A = \begin{bmatrix} 1 & 2 \\ 2 & 3 \end{bmatrix}$$

and let $\mathbf{x} = [x_1, x_2]$. Then

$$Q(\mathbf{x}) = [x_1 \quad x_2] \begin{bmatrix} 1 & 2 \\ 2 & 3 \end{bmatrix} \begin{bmatrix} x_1 \\ x_2 \end{bmatrix}$$

$$= [x_1 + 2x_2 \quad 2x_1 + 3x_2] \begin{bmatrix} x_1 \\ x_2 \end{bmatrix}$$

$$= [x_1^2 + 2x_1x_2 + 2x_1x_2 + 3x_2^2]$$

$$= [x_1^2 + 4x_1x_2 + 3x_2^2].$$

To be sure, as defined, $Q(\mathbf{x})$ is a 1×1 matrix. We shall make no distinction between a 1×1 matrix and its single element.

Still concerned with the problem of Section 5.4, we look at the equations of rotation used there:

$$\begin{cases} x = \cos \gamma x' - \sin \gamma y' \\ y = \sin \gamma x' + \cos \gamma y' \end{cases}. \qquad [5.43]$$

Recall that (x, y) represents a point P in terms of the original coordinate system and (x', y') represents the same point when the axes have been rotated through an angle γ.

We now point out that these equations can be represented in terms of matrices. We let $\mathbf{v} = [x, y]$, $\mathbf{v}' = [x', y']$, and

$$R = \begin{bmatrix} \cos \gamma & -\sin \gamma \\ \sin \gamma & \cos \gamma \end{bmatrix}. \qquad [21]$$

Then [5.43] becomes

$$\mathbf{v}^t = R(\mathbf{v}')^t. \qquad [22]$$

However, consistent with the modification we made for Q, we use $\mathbf{x} = [x_1, x_2]$ instead of $[x, y]$ and $\mathbf{y} = [y_1, y_2]$ instead of $[x', y']$. Then [22] becomes

$$\mathbf{x}^t = R\mathbf{y}^t. \tag{23}$$

We now make the important observation that, for every γ, the inverse of the matrix R is precisely its transpose:

$$R^{-1} = R^t = \begin{bmatrix} \cos\gamma & \sin\gamma \\ -\sin\gamma & \cos\gamma \end{bmatrix}. \tag{24}$$

(We leave it as an exercise to verify that this is indeed so.) This property is the characterizing feature of an *orthogonal matrix*.

DEFINITION 18.   *An $n \times n$ matrix R is* orthogonal $\Leftrightarrow R^{-1} = R^t$.

The reason for the name orthogonal is that any two distinct row (or column) vectors of such a matrix are orthogonal. Moreover, any row (or column) vector is a unit vector. We describe this property formally.

THEOREM 16.   *Let $R = [r_{ij}]$ be an $n \times n$ orthogonal matrix, i.e., $R^{-1} = R^t$. Then, for any $i, k = 1, \ldots, n$,*

$$\sum_{q=1}^{n} r_{iq}r_{kq} = \delta_{ik}; \tag{25}$$

and for any $j, k = 1, \ldots, n$,

$$\sum_{q=1}^{n} r_{qj}r_{qk} = \delta_{jk}. \tag{26}$$

   Proof.   We let $R^t = [r'_{ij}]$, where $r'_{ij} = r_{ji}$. Then from $RR^{-1} = I$, or, because R is orthogonal, $RR^t = I$, we have for every $i, k = 1, \ldots, n$,

$$\sum_{q=1}^{n} r_{iq}r'_{qk} = \delta_{ik}.$$

But $r'_{qk} = r_{kq}$, so this equation becomes [25].
   The proof of [26] is obtained by using $R^{-1}R = R^tR = I$. We omit the details. ∎
   Equation [25] says that if $k \neq i$ ($\delta_{ik} = 0$) $\mathbf{r}_i \cdot \mathbf{r}_k = 0$, or $\mathbf{r}_i \perp \mathbf{r}_k$, where $\mathbf{r}_i$ and $\mathbf{r}_k$ are, respectively, the ith and kth row vectors of R. And if $k = i$ ($\delta_{ik} = 1$), the same equation says that $|\mathbf{r}_i| = 1$. Similar remarks apply to [26] and the column vectors of R.
   We return to quadratic forms and recall that the definition involved a fixed coordinate system. What happens to a quadratic form upon a change of coordinates such as described by Equation [23], where R is orthogonal? Specifically, suppose that Q is defined by the symmetric matrix A in the

x-coordinate system (Equation [20]) and that a transformation from the **x** to the **y** system is made by means of [23], where R is orthogonal. Then, using P for a point in $\mathbf{R}^2$, we have

$$Q(P) = \mathbf{x}A\mathbf{x}^t.$$

Since $\mathbf{x}^t = R\mathbf{y}^t$, taking transposes gives $\mathbf{x} = \mathbf{y}R^t$, and we can evaluate Q in terms of **y** as

$$Q(P) = (\mathbf{y}R^t)A(R\mathbf{y}^t),$$

or

$$Q(P) = \mathbf{y}B\mathbf{y}^t, \tag{27}$$

where

$$B = R^tAR. \tag{28}$$

Notice that, because A is symmetric, so is B:

$$B^t = (R^tAR)^t = R^tA^t(R^t)^t = R^tAR = B.$$

We return to our original aim and (briefly) the notation of Section 5.4. We seek an orthogonal matrix R so that the coordinate change it produces transforms

$$Q(x, y) = ax^2 + 2bxy + cy^2$$

into

$$Q(x', y') = a'x'^2 + c'y'^2.$$

When we express this in terms of the more general notation we have introduced we make one further change so as to conform to common practice: we use λ_1 and λ_2 for a' and c', respectively. Thus, our aim is to find an orthogonal matrix R such that

$$Q(P) = Q(\mathbf{x}) = ax_1^2 + 2bx_1x_2 + cx_2^2$$

becomes, under the transformation $\mathbf{x}^t = R\mathbf{y}^t$,

$$Q(P) = Q(\mathbf{y}) = \mathbf{y}B\mathbf{y}^t = \lambda_1 y_1^2 + \lambda_2 y_2^2. \tag{29}$$

In order that Equation [29] hold it must be that the matrix $B = R^tAR$ have the form

$$B = \begin{bmatrix} \lambda_1 & 0 \\ 0 & \lambda_2 \end{bmatrix} \tag{30}$$

as is easily checked (exercise for student).

A matrix, such as B in [30], in which the elements off the main diagonal are zero, is called a *diagonal matrix*.

Specifically, to pursue this aim, we let A be a given symmetric matrix, we let $R = [r_{ij}]$ be orthogonal, and we let

$$B = \begin{bmatrix} \lambda_1 & 0 \\ 0 & \lambda_2 \end{bmatrix}.$$

We seek R and B so that

$$R^t A R = B = \begin{bmatrix} \lambda_1 & 0 \\ 0 & \lambda_2 \end{bmatrix}. \tag{31}$$

We begin by multiplying both sides of [31], on the left, by R:

$$RR^t A R = RB,$$

or, since $RR^t = RR^{-1} = I$ and $IAR = AR$,

$$AR = R \begin{bmatrix} \lambda_1 & 0 \\ 0 & \lambda_2 \end{bmatrix}. \tag{32}$$

We next let R_1 and R_2 be the column vectors of R, i.e.,

$$R_1 = \begin{bmatrix} r_{11} \\ r_{21} \end{bmatrix} \quad \text{and} \quad R_2 = \begin{bmatrix} r_{12} \\ r_{22} \end{bmatrix}.$$

Then [32] becomes

$$A[R_1, R_2] = [R_1, R_2] \begin{bmatrix} \lambda_1 & 0 \\ 0 & \lambda_2 \end{bmatrix}. \tag{33}$$

We now use Equation [10] (Exercise B6 after Section 9.2) on the left-hand side of [33]:

$$[AR_1, AR_2] = [\lambda_1 R_1, \lambda_2 R_2]. \tag{34}$$

[Verification that the right-hand side of [33] equals the right-hand side of [34] is left as an exercise for the student.]

A study of the two sides of [34] enables us to describe our aim as seeking numbers λ_1 and λ_2 and column vectors R_1 and R_2 such that

$$\begin{Bmatrix} AR_1 = \lambda_1 R_1 \\ AR_2 = \lambda_2 R_2 \end{Bmatrix}. \tag{35}$$

This is a commonly occurring problem in matrix theory. We pause to introduce the terminology that is used.

DEFINITION 19. *Let A be an $n \times n$ matrix. A number λ and a vector $\mathbf{v} \neq \mathbf{0}$, $\mathbf{v} \in \mathbf{R}^n$, are, respectively, an* eigenvalue *and associated* eigenvector *of $A \Leftrightarrow A\mathbf{v}^t = \lambda \mathbf{v}^t$.*

There is one property about eigenvectors that we shall need shortly: a (nonzero) scalar multiple of an eigenvector is also an eigenvector. We state this formally and more precisely.

THEOREM 17.   *Let λ be an eigenvalue for a matrix A, let $\mathbf{v}$ be an associated eigenvector, and let $c \neq 0$. Then $c\mathbf{v}$ is also an eigenvector associated with λ. In symbols,*

$$\left.\begin{array}{c} A\mathbf{v}^t = \lambda\mathbf{v}^t \\ c \neq 0 \end{array}\right\} \Rightarrow A(c\mathbf{v}^t) = \quad (c\mathbf{v}^t).$$

PROOF.   We have

$$A(c\mathbf{v}^t) = cA\mathbf{v}^t = c(\lambda\mathbf{v}^t) = \lambda(c\mathbf{v}^t). \quad \blacksquare$$

The problem of finding solutions for [35] now becomes the problem of finding eigenvalues and eigenvectors for A. Consider the following chain of equivalent statements (which, in fact, hold for any n):

$$A\mathbf{v}^t = \lambda\mathbf{v}^t \Leftrightarrow A\mathbf{v}^t - \lambda\mathbf{v}^t = 0$$
$$\Leftrightarrow A\mathbf{v}^t - \lambda I\mathbf{v}^t = 0 \Leftrightarrow$$
$$(A - \lambda I)\mathbf{v}^t = 0. \quad [36]$$

Now, in [36] the 0 on the right-hand side is the $n \times 1$ zero matrix. Thus, if $\mathbf{v} = [x_1, x_2, \ldots, x_n]$, then [36] is simply a homogeneous linear system in the n unknowns $x_1, \ldots, x_n$ with coefficient matrix $A - \lambda I$. By the definition of eigenvector, $\mathbf{v}^t \neq 0$, so we are looking for nontrivial solutions. And by a theorem from determinants we know that nontrivial solutions to an $n \times n$ homogeneous linear system exist $\Leftrightarrow$ the determinant of the coefficient matrix is zero. Thus, nontrivial solutions to [36] exist $\Leftrightarrow$

$$\det(A - \lambda I) = 0. \quad [37]$$

For the 2×2 case we are considering, the search for eigenvalues become a search for λ's such that

$$\begin{vmatrix} a - \lambda & b \\ b & c - \lambda \end{vmatrix} = 0, \quad [38]$$

or

$$(a - \lambda)(c - \lambda) - b^2 = 0,$$

or

$$f(\lambda) = \lambda^2 - (a + c)\lambda + ac - b^2 = 0. \quad [39]$$

Equation [39] is called the *characteristic equation* of the matrix A. Its roots, the eigenvalues, can be found by the quadratic formula:

$$\left\{\begin{array}{l} \lambda_1 = \tfrac{1}{2}(a + c + \sqrt{(a - c)^2 + 4b^2}) \\ \lambda_2 = \tfrac{1}{2}(a + c - \sqrt{(a - c)^2 + 4b^2}) \end{array}\right\}. \quad [40]$$

The essential fact is that λ_1 and λ_2 are real. It is a theorem that for every n the eigenvalues of an $n \times n$ symmetric matrix are real. We have just given a special proof for the special case $n = 2$. The general proof, for arbitrary n, involves complex numbers; we omit it.

To find the eigenvectors associated with the eigenvalues we return to Equations [35] and, for each of λ_1 and λ_2, solve the homogeneous system. This can be done, using the methods of Section 9.1, by reducing the matrix $A - \lambda_i I$ to echelon form. The condition of [37] guarantees the existence of nontrivial solutions.

It is time to illustrate these ideas.

Example 16.   Let

$$A = \begin{bmatrix} 1 & 2 \\ 2 & 1 \end{bmatrix}.$$

The characteristic equation (Equation [39]) is

$$\begin{vmatrix} 1 - \lambda & 2 \\ 2 & 1 - \lambda \end{vmatrix} = 0,$$

or $\lambda^2 - 2\lambda - 3 = 0$, the roots of which are $\lambda_1 = 3$, $\lambda_2 = -1$.

To find an eigenvector associated with λ_1 we find the echelon form of $A - \lambda_1 I$:

$$A - 3I = \begin{bmatrix} 1 - 3 & 2 \\ 2 & 1 - 3 \end{bmatrix} = \begin{bmatrix} -2 & 2 \\ 2 & -2 \end{bmatrix} \sim \begin{bmatrix} 1 & -1 \\ 2 & -2 \end{bmatrix} \sim \begin{bmatrix} 1 & -1 \\ 0 & 0 \end{bmatrix}.$$

We conclude that $x_1 - x_2 = 0$ or $x_1 = x_2$. Thus we could take as eigenvector $[1, 1]^t$, but the column vector R_1 should be a unit vector. Consequently we *normalize* the vector just found by multiplying by $1/\sqrt{2}$. By Theorem 17, the resulting vector is also an eigenvector associated with $\lambda_1 = 3$. Thus

$$R_1 = \begin{bmatrix} \dfrac{1}{\sqrt{2}} \\ \dfrac{1}{\sqrt{2}} \end{bmatrix}.$$

Similarly we find R_2 by considering $A - \lambda_2 I$, or

$$A - (-1)I = \begin{bmatrix} 2 & 2 \\ 2 & 2 \end{bmatrix} \sim \begin{bmatrix} 1 & 1 \\ 0 & 0 \end{bmatrix}.$$

This says that $x_1 + x_2 = 0$, or $x_2 = -x_1$. By taking a unit vector which satisfies this equation we find

$$R_2 = \begin{bmatrix} \dfrac{-1}{\sqrt{2}} \\ \dfrac{1}{\sqrt{2}} \end{bmatrix}.$$

The desired matrix $R = [R_1, R_2]$ is then

$$R = \begin{bmatrix} \dfrac{1}{\sqrt{2}} & \dfrac{-1}{\sqrt{2}} \\ \dfrac{1}{\sqrt{2}} & \dfrac{1}{\sqrt{2}} \end{bmatrix} = \frac{1}{\sqrt{2}} \begin{bmatrix} 1 & -1 \\ 1 & 1 \end{bmatrix}.$$

It is easily checked (exercise for student) that $R^t = R^{-1}$ and that

$$R^t A R = \begin{bmatrix} 3 & 0 \\ 0 & -1 \end{bmatrix} = B.$$

Does R correspond to a rotation of axes? If so, what is the angle γ?

Notice that, although we have shown that the columns of R will be the eigenvectors of A, we have not given any guarantee that R will be an orthogonal matrix. Theorem 17 assures us that the eigenvectors can be unit vectors but the orthogonality of these vectors is left open. There is another theorem, the proof of which is not accessible at this level, which asserts that a symmetric $n \times n$ matrix does have a set of n pairwise orthogonal eigenvectors.

This process of finding an orthogonal matrix R such that $R^t A R$ is a diagonal matrix is sometimes referred to as "diagonalizing A."

Example 17. We consider the quadratic form $Q(x, y) = 11x^2 + 24xy + 4y^2$ and endeavor to find a transformation to a new coordinate system with respect to which Q will have no crossproduct (xy) term.

The symmetric matrix A that determines Q in the xy-system is

$$A = \begin{bmatrix} 11 & 12 \\ 12 & 4 \end{bmatrix}.$$

The characteristic equation for A is $\det(A - \lambda I) = 0$, or

$$\begin{vmatrix} 11 - \lambda & 12 \\ 12 & 4 - \lambda \end{vmatrix} = 0,$$

or $\lambda^2 - 15\lambda - 100 = 0$, which has roots $\lambda_1 = 20$, $\lambda_2 = -5$.

We find the eigenvectors as we did in Example 17:

$$A - \lambda_1 I = \begin{bmatrix} 11 - 20 & 12 \\ 12 & 4 - 20 \end{bmatrix} = \begin{bmatrix} -9 & 12 \\ 12 & -16 \end{bmatrix} \sim \begin{bmatrix} 1 & -\frac{4}{3} \\ 12 & -16 \end{bmatrix}$$

$$\sim \begin{bmatrix} 1 & -\frac{4}{3} \\ 0 & 0 \end{bmatrix}.$$

Thus $x_1 - \frac{4}{3}x_2 = 0$. For a normalized (unit) vector we take

$$R_1 = \begin{bmatrix} \frac{4}{5} \\ \frac{3}{5} \end{bmatrix}$$

Similarly, considering $A - \lambda_2 I$, we have

$$\begin{bmatrix} 16 & 12 \\ 12 & 9 \end{bmatrix} \sim \begin{bmatrix} 1 & \frac{3}{4} \\ 12 & 9 \end{bmatrix} \sim \begin{bmatrix} 1 & \frac{3}{4} \\ 0 & 0 \end{bmatrix}.$$

This says $x_1 + \frac{3}{4} x_2 = 0$, and for a unit vector we take

$$R_2 = \begin{bmatrix} -\frac{3}{5} \\ \frac{4}{5} \end{bmatrix}.$$

The matrix R is then

$$R = \tfrac{1}{5} \begin{bmatrix} 4 & -3 \\ 3 & 4 \end{bmatrix}.$$

It is easy to verify that R is orthogonal and that

$$R^t A R = \begin{bmatrix} 20 & 0 \\ 0 & -5 \end{bmatrix}.$$

Thus, in the y_1, y_2-system, the quadratic form is $Q(y_1, y_2) = 20y_1^2 - 5y_2^2$.

We conclude this section with an example from three-dimensional geometry which illustrates the generality of the method discussed and, at the same time, some of the possible difficulties that may be encountered when $n > 2$.

Example 18. We consider the quadric surface defined by

$$2x^2 + 2xy + 2xz + 2y^2 + 2yz + 2z^2 = 1. \tag{41}$$

We seek a transformation of coordinates that will produce an equation free of crossproduct terms, i.e., we want to diagonalize the matrix A which determines the quadratic form

$$Q(x, y, z) = 2x^2 + 2xy + 2xz + 2y^2 + 2yz + 2z^2.$$

The symmetric matrix A is

$$A = \begin{bmatrix} 2 & 1 & 1 \\ 1 & 2 & 1 \\ 1 & 1 & 2 \end{bmatrix}.$$

The characteristic equation for A is

$$\begin{vmatrix} 2 - \lambda & 1 & 1 \\ 1 & 2 - \lambda & 1 \\ 1 & 1 & 2 - \lambda \end{vmatrix} = 0.$$

A commonly used way of expanding a 3×3 determinant (see Appendix 4) produces in this case

$$(2 - \lambda)^3 + 2 - 3(2 - \lambda) = 0,$$

or

$$(2 - \lambda)^3 - 3(2 - \lambda) + 2 = 0. \hspace{3cm} [42]$$

If we temporarily let $2 - \lambda = x$, so that [42] becomes $x^3 - 3x + 2 = 0$, we can see by inspection that one root is $x = 1$; it is then easy to find that the remaining roots are 1 and -2. It follows that the eigenvalues are $\lambda_1 = \lambda_2 = 1$ and $\lambda_3 = 4$. (This step, finding the roots of the characteristic equation, can be messy and time-consuming when $n > 2$.)

At this point we could stop. The theory we have described guarantees that there does exist an orthogonal transformation from the xyz-system to a y_1, y_2, y_3-system, say, that will take [41] into

$$y_1^2 + y_2^2 + 4y_3^2 = 1;$$

it follows that the quadric surface is an ellipsoid—in fact, a spheroid.

However, there may be some point in finding the orthogonal matrix R, partly because, in this case, there are only two distinct eigenvalues.

We find first the eigenvector associated with $\lambda_3 = 4$, i.e., we consider the matrix $A - 4I$:

$$A - 4I = \begin{bmatrix} -2 & 1 & 1 \\ 1 & -2 & 1 \\ 1 & 1 & -2 \end{bmatrix} \sim \begin{bmatrix} 1 & -2 & 1 \\ -2 & 1 & 1 \\ 1 & 1 & -2 \end{bmatrix} \sim \begin{bmatrix} 1 & -2 & 1 \\ 0 & -3 & 3 \\ 0 & 3 & -3 \end{bmatrix}$$

$$\sim \begin{bmatrix} 1 & -2 & 1 \\ 0 & 1 & -1 \\ 0 & 3 & -3 \end{bmatrix} \sim \begin{bmatrix} 1 & 0 & -1 \\ 0 & 1 & -1 \\ 0 & 0 & 0 \end{bmatrix}$$

This echelon form says that if $\mathbf{v}_3 = [x_1, x_2, x_3]$, then $x_1 - x_3 = 0$ and $x_2 - x_3 = 0$, i.e., $x_1 = x_2 = x_3$. For a unit vector the common value must be $1/\sqrt{3}$. Thus $R_3^t = (1/\sqrt{3})[1, 1, 1]$.

Now we consider the repeated root $\lambda_1 = \lambda_2 = 1$:

$$A - 1I = \begin{bmatrix} 1 & 1 & 1 \\ 1 & 1 & 1 \\ 1 & 1 & 1 \end{bmatrix} \sim \begin{bmatrix} 1 & 1 & 1 \\ 0 & 0 & 0 \\ 0 & 0 & 0 \end{bmatrix}.$$

This says that $x_1 + x_2 + x_3 = 0$, or $x_3 = -x_1 - x_2$. It is not hard to see that every vector obtained from this relation will be orthogonal to R_3. However, we need three columns for the matrix R, and it takes a little finagling (which we omit) to produce unit vectors R_1 and R_2 which are orthogonal. Two possibilities are

$$R_1 = \begin{bmatrix} \dfrac{1}{\sqrt{2}} \\ 0 \\ -\dfrac{1}{\sqrt{2}} \end{bmatrix} \quad \text{and} \quad R_2 = \begin{bmatrix} \dfrac{1}{\sqrt{6}} \\ \dfrac{-2}{\sqrt{6}} \\ \dfrac{1}{\sqrt{6}} \end{bmatrix}.$$

Then the desired orthogonal matrix can be written as

$$R = \frac{1}{\sqrt{6}} \begin{bmatrix} \sqrt{3} & 1 & \sqrt{2} \\ 0 & -2 & \sqrt{2} \\ -\sqrt{3} & 1 & \sqrt{2} \end{bmatrix}.$$

We leave it as an exercise to verify that $R^t = R^{-1}$ and that

$$R^t A R = \begin{bmatrix} 1 & 0 & 0 \\ 0 & 1 & 0 \\ 0 & 0 & 4 \end{bmatrix}.$$

Exercises

A. **1.** Verify that the matrix in [24] is the inverse of that in [21].

2. Verify that the matrix B in [30] produces the quadratic form in Equation [29].

3. Verify that the right-hand sides of Equations [33] and [34] are equal.

4. This refers to Example 16. Verify that

$$R^t A R = \begin{bmatrix} 3 & 0 \\ 0 & -1 \end{bmatrix}.$$

5. This refers to Example 18.
   (a) Show that $R^t = R^{-1}$.
   (b) Verify that

$$R^t A R = \begin{bmatrix} 1 & 0 & 0 \\ 0 & 1 & 0 \\ 0 & 0 & 4 \end{bmatrix}.$$

In Exercises 6–10 write the symmetric matrix A that determines the given quadratic form.

   6. $Q(x, y) = x^2 - 6xy + 2y^2$.
   7. $Q(x_1, x_2) = 3x_1^2 + 2x_1x_2 - x_2^2$.
   8. $Q(x_1, x_2) = 4x_1^2 + x_1x_2 - 2x_2^2$.

9. $Q(x, y) = 5x^2 - 2xy + 3y^2.$

10. $Q(x_1, x_2) = 4x_1^2 - 3x_1 x_2 + x_2^2.$

In Exercises 11–17 write the quadratic form $Q(x_1, x_2)$ determined by the matrix given.

11. $\begin{bmatrix} 1 & 4 \\ 4 & 1 \end{bmatrix}.$

12. $\begin{bmatrix} 2 & 4 \\ 4 & 2 \end{bmatrix}.$

13. $\begin{bmatrix} 3 & 2 \\ 2 & 0 \end{bmatrix}.$

14. $\begin{bmatrix} 5 & 6 \\ 6 & 0 \end{bmatrix}.$

15. $\begin{bmatrix} 8 & 12 \\ 12 & 1 \end{bmatrix}.$

16. $\begin{bmatrix} 2 & 2 \\ 2 & -1 \end{bmatrix}.$

17. $\begin{bmatrix} 3 & 6 \\ 6 & -2 \end{bmatrix}.$

In Exercises 18–24 diagonalize the matrices of Exercises 11–17, respectively, by finding their eigenvalues and eigenvectors.

25. Diagonalize A by finding its eigenvalues and eigenvectors.

$$A = \begin{bmatrix} 1 & -1 & 0 \\ -1 & 1 & 0 \\ 0 & 0 & 2 \end{bmatrix}.$$

C.   1. Prove that if P is orthogonal then P^t is orthogonal.

    2. Prove the assertion:

P and Q orthogonal $\Rightarrow PQ$ and QP orthogonal.

    3. Prove

$\left. \begin{array}{l} P \text{ orthogonal} \\ PQ \text{ orthogonal} \end{array} \right\} \Rightarrow Q \text{ orthogonal.}$

Hint: $Q = P^{-1}(PQ).$

    4. Let

$$A = \begin{bmatrix} a & b \\ c & d \end{bmatrix}$$

be orthogonal and suppose det $A = ad - bc = 1$. Show that either

$$A = \begin{bmatrix} \cos \gamma & -\sin \gamma \\ \sin \gamma & \cos \gamma \end{bmatrix} \quad \text{or} \quad A = \begin{bmatrix} \cos \gamma & \sin \gamma \\ -\sin \gamma & \cos \gamma \end{bmatrix}.$$

Hint: A orthogonal $\Rightarrow$

$a^2 + b^2 = c^2 + d^2 = a^2 + c^2 = b^2 + d^2 = 1,$
$ab + cd = ac + bd = 0.$

5. Let

$$A = \begin{bmatrix} a & b \\ c & d \end{bmatrix}$$

be orthogonal, let det $A = ad - bc = -1$. Discuss the nature of A.

6. Let

$$A = \begin{bmatrix} a & b \\ c & d \end{bmatrix}$$

be orthogonal. Prove det $A = \pm 1$.

Hint: $AA^t = AA^{-1} = I \Rightarrow det(AA^t) = det\ I = 1.$

Appendix 1
Sets

We define a set intuitively as a collection of objects, usually called *elements*. Sets may be described in different ways: (1) If the number of elements is not too large, one can simply list the elements; for example,

$$A = \{1, 2, 3, 4\}, \quad \text{or} \quad B = \{a, b, c, d, e\}.$$

(2) When listing is impracticable, a set may be defined by a property that characterizes the elements of the set; this is achieved by the following notational device:

$$C = \{x \in \mathbf{R} \mid 0 < x < 1\}.$$

The verbalization of the above is "*C* equals the set of *all* x in $\mathbf{R}$ satisfying the condition that (or, such that) x is greater than 0 and less than 1." This set is also known as the *open* interval—endpoints excluded—between 0 and 1 and will sometimes be indicated by $C = (0, 1)$. Some writers prefer to use a colon where we have used the vertical bar. Thus, they would describe a set as

$$D = \{x \in \mathbf{R} : 0 \leqslant x \leqslant 1\},$$

verbalized as "*D* equals the set of *all* x in $\mathbf{R}$ such that x is greater than or equal to 0 and less than or equal to 1." This set is the *closed*—endpoints included—interval between 0 and 1 and is also symbolized as $D = [0, 1]$.

To indicate that x is an element of a set X we write $x \in X$. Thus, in the examples above

$$2 \in A, \quad d \in B, \quad 0 \in D.$$

Note that 0 is *not* in C; we describe this by $0 \notin C$.

Different verbal descriptions may characterize the same set of elements (x is the Father of our Country, or x was the first president of the United States); thus

$$\{x \in \mathbf{R} \mid x^2 > 1\} \quad \text{and} \quad \{x \in \mathbf{R} \mid \text{either } x < -1 \text{ or } x > 1\}$$

will be seen to determine the same set.

In general, equality of sets is defined in terms of elements, *not* the verbal description. To say that two sets A and B are equal means that they contain precisely the same elements. This can be described more succinctly in the following way, using "$\Rightarrow$" to mean "implies" and "$\Leftrightarrow$" to mean "implies and is implied by," or "necessary and sufficient condition for," or "if and only if," or "is logically equivalent to":

$$A = B \Leftrightarrow \begin{cases} (1) \ x \in A \Rightarrow x \in B \\ \quad \text{and} \\ (2) \ y \in B \Rightarrow y \in A. \end{cases}$$

If we know only that condition (1) holds, that is, if $x \in A \Rightarrow x \in B$, then we say that A is a *subset* of B, symbolized as $A \subset B$. Notice that always $A \subset A$. If it should happen that $A \subset B$, but $A \neq B$, i.e., there is an element in B that is not in A, then A is said to be a *proper subset* of B. In the examples given earlier, C is a proper subset of D, since $x \in C \Rightarrow x \in D$ and $0 \in D$ but $0 \notin C$; similarly $1 \in D$, but $1 \notin C$.

Equality of sets can thus be described in terms of the subset relation:

$$A = B \Leftrightarrow \begin{cases} (1) \ A \subset B \\ \quad \text{and} \\ (2) \ B \subset A. \end{cases}$$

This provides an important and useful way of proving that two sets are equal: show that each is a subset of the other.

In addition to the two *relations* ($=$ and $\subset$) between sets, there are several *operations* which will be useful to us.

1. The *union* of the sets A and B is the set of all elements in either A or B:

$$A \cup B = \{x \mid x \in A \text{ or } x \in B\}.$$

2. The *intersection* of the sets A and B is the set of all elements in both A and B:

$$A \cap B = \{x \mid x \in A \text{ and } x \in B\}.$$

3. The *cartesian product* of the sets A and B is the set of all ordered pairs consisting of first element from A and second element from B:

$$A \times B = \{(a, b) \mid a \in A \text{ and } b \in B\}.$$

Finally, we mention that in order not to have to make exceptions, we define the *empty set* $\varnothing$ to be the set with no elements. In this way if two sets A and B have no elements in common (i.e., they are *disjoint*) we have $A \cap B = \varnothing$, a *set*.

Thus, if

$$A = \{1, 2, 3, 4\}, \quad B = \{3, 4, 5\}, \quad \text{and} \quad C = \{a, b\},$$

then

$A \cup B = \{1, 2, 3, 4, 5\}$
$A \cap B = \{3, 4\}$
$A \cup C = \{1, 2, 3, 4, a, b\},$
$A \cap C = \varnothing$
$A \times C = \{(1, a), (1, b), (2, a), (2, b), (3, a), (3, b), (4, a), (4, b)\}$
$C \times C = \{(a, a), (a, b), (b, a), (b, b)\}.$

The binary operations $\cup$ and $\cap$ are both associative (and commutative). It is possible, therefore, unambiguously to generalize them. Now, a different look at the definition of union discloses that an element is in the union of A and B precisely if it is in at least one of A and B. Then, if we have a collection of sets $A_1, A_2, \ldots, A_n$, we define

$$\bigcup_{i=1}^{n} A_i = \{x \mid x \in A_i, \text{ for at least one } i = 1, \ldots, n\}.$$

Similarly,

$$\bigcap_{i=1}^{n} A_i = \{x \mid x \in A_i, \text{ for every } i = 1, 2, \ldots, n\}.$$

The fact is that both of these definitions can be extended, in a natural way, to nonfinite collections of sets.

The cartesian product, also defined as a binary operation, is neither commutative nor, in the strictest sense, associative. Nevertheless, it also lends itself to generalization. If $A_1, A_2, \ldots, A_n$ are sets, then

$$A_1 \times A_2 \times \cdots \times A_n = \{(a_1, a_2, \ldots, a_n) \mid a_i \in A_i\},$$

where $(a_1, a_2, \ldots, a_n)$ stands for an ordered n-tuple.

If U is a universal set, i.e., if all sets $A, B, C, \ldots$, are subsets of U, then the following properties hold:

$$A \cup B = B \cup A \qquad\qquad A \cap B = B \cap A$$
$$A \cup (B \cup C) = (A \cup B) \cup C \qquad A \cap (B \cap C) = (A \cap B) \cap C$$
$$A \cup \varnothing = A \qquad\qquad A \cap U = A$$
$$A \cup U = U \qquad\qquad A \cap \varnothing = \varnothing$$
$$A \cup A = A \qquad\qquad A \cap A = A$$
$$A \subset A \cup B \qquad\qquad A \cap B \subset A$$
$$B \subset A \cup B \qquad\qquad A \cap B \subset B$$
$$A \cap (B \cup C) = (A \cap B) \cup (A \cap C)$$
$$A \cup (B \cap C) = (A \cup B) \cap (A \cup C).$$

Appendix 2
Theorems from Synthetic Geometry

1. (The Pythagorean Theorem) If a triangle with sides of length a, b, c is a right triangle, c being the length of the hypotenuse, then

$a^2 + b^2 = c^2$.

2. (Converse of the Pythagorean Theorem) If a triangle with sides of length a, b, c is such that $a^2 + b^2 = c^2$, then the triangle is a right triangle.

3. If two triangles are similar, then the lengths of corresponding sides are proportional. In symbols, if the triangles have angles A, B, C and A', B', C' and have sides a, b, c and a', b', c', then

$$\left.\begin{array}{l} \angle A = \angle A' \\ \angle B = \angle B' \\ \angle C = \angle C' \end{array}\right\} \Rightarrow \frac{a}{a'} = \frac{b}{b'} = \frac{c}{c'}.$$

4. An exterior angle of a triangle is equal to the sum of the two opposite interior angles.

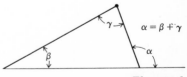

Figure 1

Appendix 3
The Sigma Notation

Expressions involving sums that obey a rule of formation occur frequently in mathematics; it is convenient to have a shorthand notation for such expressions. Consider, for example, expressions such as

$$1 + 2 + 3 + \cdots + n \tag{1}$$
$$1^2 + 2^2 + 3^2 + \cdots + n^2 \tag{2}$$
$$1 + 3 + 5 + \cdots + (2n - 1) \tag{3}$$
$$2 + 4 + 6 + \cdots + 2n. \tag{4}$$

These can be represented by using the Greek uppercase sigma, Σ, as follows:

$$1 + 2 + \cdots + n = \sum_{k=1}^{n} k \tag{5}$$

$$1^2 + 2^2 + \cdots + n^2 = \sum_{k=1}^{n} k^2 \tag{6}$$

$$1 + 3 + \cdots + (2n - 1) = \sum_{k=1}^{n} (2k - 1) \tag{7}$$

$$2 + 4 + \cdots + 2n = \sum_{k=1}^{n} (2k). \tag{8}$$

The scheme is to write the generic formula for the terms of the sum $(k, k^2, 2k - 1, 2k$ in [5]–[8], respectively) preceded by Σ, writing below and above Σ the range of the variable (k in the examples) used in writing the formula. The variable k is called a *dummy variable*; actually any letter or symbol could be used. Thus

$$\sum_{k=1}^{n} k^2 = \sum_{q=1}^{n} q^2 = 1^2 + 2^2 + \cdots + n^2.$$

The numbers 1 and n which appear below and above the Σ are the *limits* of the summation.

Examples

1. $\displaystyle\sum_{k=1}^{4} (3k - 1) = 2 + 5 + 8 + 11.$

2. $\displaystyle\sum_{q=1}^{5} \frac{1}{q(q + 1)} = \frac{1}{1 \cdot 2} + \frac{1}{2 \cdot 3} + \frac{1}{3 \cdot 4} + \frac{1}{4 \cdot 5} + \frac{1}{5 \cdot 6}.$

3. $\displaystyle\sum_{k=2}^{4} (4k - 3) = 5 + 9 + 13.$

In general, if $f(k)$ is a formula which produces a number for every $k \in \mathbf{N}$, then

$$\sum_{k=1}^{n} f(k) = f(1) + f(2) + \cdots + f(n). \tag{9}$$

There are three properties of the sigma notation that are useful.

LEMMA. *Let $f(k)$ and $g(k)$ be formulas which produce numbers for every $k \in \mathbf{N}$; let $c \in \mathbf{R}$. Then*

1. $\displaystyle\sum_{k=1}^{n} [f(k) + g(k)] = \sum_{k=1}^{n} f(k) + \sum_{k=1}^{n} g(k).$

2. $\displaystyle\sum_{k=1}^{n} cf(k) = c \sum_{k=1}^{n} f(k).$

3. $\displaystyle\sum_{k=1}^{n} c = nc.$

[*Note*: the first two of these assertions can be verbalized as "The sigma of a sum is the sum of the sigmas" and "The sigma of a constant times a function is the constant times the sigma of the function," respectively.]

PROOF.   To prove assertion 1 we simply write out the left-hand side and rearrange:

$$\sum_{k=1}^{n}[f(k) + g(k)] = [f(1) + g(1)] + [f(2) + g(2)] + \cdots + [f(n) + g(n)]$$
$$= [f(1) + f(2) + \cdots + f(n)] + [g(1) + g(2) + \cdots + g(n)]$$
$$= \sum_{k=1}^{n}f(k) + \sum_{k=1}^{n}g(k).$$

The proof of assertion 2 is similar:

$$\sum_{k=1}^{n}cf(k) = cf(1) + cf(2) + \cdots + cf(n)$$
$$= c[f(1) + f(2) + \cdots + f(n)]$$
$$= c\sum_{k=1}^{n}f(k).$$

The point of assertion 3 is that the sum consists of n terms, each of which is the number c. Obviously, then,

$$\sum_{k=1}^{n}c = nc. \quad \blacksquare$$

Appendix 4
Determinants

For every positive integer n it is possible to define a determinant of order n; in this book we need only determinants of order 2 and 3, and we limit this appendix to these simple cases.

Second-Order Determinants

If the system of equations

$$\begin{cases} ax + by = e \\ cx + dy = f \end{cases}$$ [1]

is solved by elementary methods (elimination or addition and subtraction), it can be found, on the assumption that $ad - bc \neq 0$, that

$$x = \frac{ed - bf}{ad - bc}, \quad y = \frac{af - ec}{ad - bc}.$$ [2]

The expression $ad - bc$ is known as the *determinant of the coefficients*.

DEFINITION 1. *The* determinant of order 2 *is defined by*

$$\begin{vmatrix} a & b \\ c & d \end{vmatrix} = ad - bc.$$ [3]

The number ad − bc is called the value of the determinant. Each of a, b, c, d is an element of the determinant. The first row consists of a, b; the first column of a, c.

For those familiar with matrices, we remark that the determinant is a function (of a very special sort) on the set of 2×2 (or, more generally, $n \times n$) matrices. When the discussion of determinants is within the context of matrices, we also use the notation det A for the determinant of the square matrix A. Thus

$$\det \begin{bmatrix} a & b \\ c & d \end{bmatrix} = \begin{vmatrix} a & b \\ c & d \end{vmatrix} = ad - bc.$$

The numerators in the expressions for x and y are also in the form of determinants; thus the solution of the system [1] can be written as

$$x = \frac{\begin{vmatrix} e & b \\ f & d \end{vmatrix}}{\begin{vmatrix} a & b \\ c & d \end{vmatrix}}, \quad y = \frac{\begin{vmatrix} a & e \\ c & f \end{vmatrix}}{\begin{vmatrix} a & b \\ c & d \end{vmatrix}}, \quad \begin{vmatrix} a & b \\ c & d \end{vmatrix} \neq 0. \qquad [4]$$

This assertion is a special case of what is known as *Cramer's Rule* for solving a system of n linear equations in n unknowns. The theorem says that if the determinant of the coefficients is nonzero, the unique solution is given by ratios of determinants such as in [4]. Notice that the determinants in the numerators are obtained by replacing with the constant terms the coefficients of the unknown being found.

In the denominator for x we have drawn arrows that show how the products in the two terms are formed. When the arrow goes from left to right the sign is plus; from right to left, minus.

We list now some of the important properties of 2×2 determinants. The proofs are easily obtained, using Definition 1, and will be left as exercises.

THEOREM 1. *Determinants of order 2 have the following properties:*

1. $\begin{vmatrix} a & c \\ b & d \end{vmatrix} = \begin{vmatrix} a & b \\ c & d \end{vmatrix} \quad \left(\det A^t = \det A, \text{ where } A = \begin{bmatrix} a & b \\ c & d \end{bmatrix} \right).$

If the rows and columns of a determinant are interchanged, the value of the determinant remains the same. Alternatively, the determinant of the transpose of a matrix equals the determinant of the matrix. The important implication of this result is that whenever an assertion is proven about, say, the rows of a determinant, one knows the corresponding assertion for the columns is also valid. Thus, although we state the following properties in terms of rows, they remain valid if row *is replaced by* column.

2. $\begin{vmatrix} c & d \\ a & b \end{vmatrix} = -\begin{vmatrix} a & b \\ c & d \end{vmatrix} \quad \left(\det \begin{vmatrix} c & d \\ a & b \end{vmatrix} = -\det A \right).$

If two rows (columns) are interchanged, the sign of the determinant is changed.

3. $\begin{vmatrix} a & b \\ a & b \end{vmatrix} = 0.$

If two rows (columns) are equal, the value of the determinant is zero.

4. $\begin{vmatrix} ka & kb \\ c & d \end{vmatrix} = \begin{vmatrix} a & b \\ kc & kd \end{vmatrix} = k\begin{vmatrix} a & b \\ c & d \end{vmatrix}.$

If a row (column) of a determinant is multiplied by a number k, the effect is to multiply the value of the determinant by k. Or, a factor common to the elements of a row (column) can be factored out.

5. $\begin{vmatrix} a & b \\ ka & kb \end{vmatrix} = \begin{vmatrix} kc & kd \\ c & d \end{vmatrix} = 0.$

If the elements of one row (column) are proportional to those in another, the value of the determinant is zero. (Notice that property 3 is a special case of property 5 with k = 1.)

6. $\begin{vmatrix} a_1 + a_2 & b_1 + b_2 \\ c & d \end{vmatrix} = \begin{vmatrix} a_1 & b_1 \\ c & d \end{vmatrix} + \begin{vmatrix} a_2 & b_2 \\ c & d \end{vmatrix},$

$\begin{vmatrix} a & b \\ c_1 + c_2 & d_1 + d_2 \end{vmatrix} = \begin{vmatrix} a & b \\ c_1 & d_1 \end{vmatrix} + \begin{vmatrix} a & b \\ c_2 & d_2 \end{vmatrix}.$

7. $\begin{vmatrix} a & b \\ c + ka & d + kb \end{vmatrix} = \begin{vmatrix} a + kc & b + kd \\ c & d \end{vmatrix} = \begin{vmatrix} a & b \\ c & d \end{vmatrix}.$

If one row (column) of a determinant is altered by adding to it a multiple of another row (column), the value of the determinant is unchanged.

8. $\det\left(\begin{bmatrix} a & b \\ c & d \end{bmatrix}\begin{bmatrix} e & f \\ g & h \end{bmatrix}\right) = \left(\det\begin{bmatrix} a & b \\ c & d \end{bmatrix}\right)\left(\det\begin{bmatrix} e & f \\ g & h \end{bmatrix}\right).$

The determinant of the product of two matrices equals the product of their determinants.

PROOF. Exercise for student. ∎

Third-Order Determinants

If the system

$$\begin{cases} a_{11}x_1 + a_{12}x_2 + a_{13}x_3 = b_1 \\ a_{21}x_1 + a_{22}x_2 + a_{23}x_3 = b_2 \\ a_{31}x_1 + a_{32}x_2 + a_{33}x_3 = b_3 \end{cases}$$

is solved by elementary methods, it will be found (after some simple but laborious calculations) that the solution can be written as

$$x_1 = \frac{N_1}{D}, \quad x_2 = \frac{N_2}{D}, \quad x_3 = \frac{N_3}{D},$$

where

$$D = a_{11}a_{22}a_{33} + a_{12}a_{23}a_{31} + a_{13}a_{21}a_{32} - a_{11}a_{23}a_{32} - a_{12}a_{21}a_{33}$$
$$- a_{13}a_{22}a_{31}$$
$$N_1 = b_1 a_{22}a_{33} + a_{12}a_{23}b_3 + a_{13}b_2 a_{32} - b_1 a_{23}a_{32} - a_{12}b_2 a_{33} - a_{13}a_{22}b_3$$
$$N_2 = a_{11}b_2 a_{33} + b_1 a_{23}a_{31} + a_{13}a_{21}b_3 - a_{11}a_{23}b_3 - b_1 a_{21}a_{33} - a_{13}b_2 a_{31}$$
$$N_3 = a_{11}a_{22}b_3 + a_{12}b_2 a_{31} + b_1 a_{21}a_{32} - a_{11}b_2 a_{32} - a_{12}a_{21}b_3 - b_1 a_{22}a_{31}.$$

One must assume, of course, that $D \neq 0$. This is Cramer's Rule for $n = 3$. The expression D is the *determinant* of the coefficients.

DEFINITION 2.   *The determinant of order 3 is defined by*

$$\begin{vmatrix} a_{11} & a_{12} & a_{13} \\ a_{21} & a_{22} & a_{23} \\ a_{31} & a_{32} & a_{33} \end{vmatrix} = a_{11}a_{22}a_{33} + a_{12}a_{23}a_{31} + a_{13}a_{21}a_{32} - a_{11}a_{23}a_{32}$$
$$- a_{12}a_{21}a_{33} - a_{13}a_{22}a_{31}. \quad [5]$$

The number on the right is the value *of the determinant.*

The following two schematic devices can be used to obtain the value of a determinant of order 3:

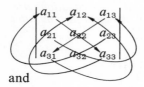

and

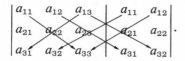

The products obtained going from left to right get a plus sign, those found by going from right to left get a minus sign. The student should check that these two schemes agree with each other and with Equation [5].

Warning.   The preceding schematic devices do *not* work for determinants of order n where $n > 3$.

We next remark that all parts of Theorem 1 remain valid for third-order determinants. The generalization to 3×3 determinants is easily obtained, except for property 6, by using the verbal description. For property 6 the following equation will suffice.

$$\begin{vmatrix} a'_{11} + a''_{11} & a'_{12} + a''_{12} & a'_{13} + a''_{13} \\ a_{21} & a_{22} & a_{23} \\ a_{31} & a_{32} & a_{33} \end{vmatrix} = \begin{vmatrix} a'_{11} & a'_{12} & a'_{13} \\ a_{21} & a_{22} & a_{23} \\ a_{31} & a_{32} & a_{33} \end{vmatrix} + \begin{vmatrix} a''_{11} & a''_{12} & a''_{13} \\ a_{21} & a_{22} & a_{23} \\ a_{31} & a_{32} & a_{33} \end{vmatrix}.$$

The proofs of these properties for third-order determinants are, in the case of some, a bit messier than those for second order. We shall omit them.

There are several additional properties for determinants of order $n > 2$ that are important and that we now mention. First we need some definitions.

DEFINITION 3. *The minor M_{ij} of the element a_{ij} is the 2×2 determinant obtained by deleting row i and column j. This applies to $i, j = 1, 2, 3$.*

The minors M_{11} and M_{23} are

$$M_{11} = \begin{vmatrix} a_{22} & a_{23} \\ a_{32} & a_{33} \end{vmatrix}, \quad M_{23} = \begin{vmatrix} a_{11} & a_{12} \\ a_{31} & a_{32} \end{vmatrix}.$$

DEFINITION 4. *The cofactor A_{ij} of element a_{ij} is*

$$A_{ij} = (-1)^{i+j} M_{ij}.$$

Thus

$$A_{11} = (-1)^2 M_{11} = M_{11}$$
$$A_{23} = (-1)^5 M_{23} = -M_{23}.$$

We can now state the properties.

THEOREM 2. *For a third-order determinant the following equations are valid:*

1. *For every $i = 1, 2, 3$*

$$\sum_{j=1}^{3} a_{ij} A_{ij} = det\ A.$$

2. *For every $j = 1, 2, 3$*

$$\sum_{i=1}^{3} a_{ij} A_{ij} = det\ A.$$

3. *For any i and $k = 1, 2, 3, k \neq i$,*

$$\sum_{j=1}^{3} a_{ij} A_{kj} = 0.$$

4. *For any j and $k = 1, 2, 3, k \neq j$,*

$$\sum_{i=1}^{3} a_{ij} A_{ik} = 0.$$

PROOF. We prove assertion 1 for the case $i = 1$. All the other proofs are similar. We have

$$a_{11}A_{11} + a_{12}A_{12} + a_{13}A_{13} = a_{11}M_{11} - a_{12}M_{12} + a_{13}M_{13}$$

$$= a_{11}\begin{vmatrix} a_{22} & a_{23} \\ a_{32} & a_{33} \end{vmatrix} - a_{12}\begin{vmatrix} a_{21} & a_{23} \\ a_{31} & a_{33} \end{vmatrix}$$

$$+ a_{13}\begin{vmatrix} a_{21} & a_{22} \\ a_{31} & a_{32} \end{vmatrix}$$

$$= a_{11}(a_{22}a_{33} - a_{23}a_{32})$$
$$- a_{12}(a_{21}a_{33} - a_{23}a_{31})$$
$$+ a_{13}(a_{21}a_{32} - a_{22}a_{31})$$
$$= \det A,$$

as is seen by comparison with the right-hand side of Equation [5]. (This illustrates what is called expansion by the cofactors of the first row.) ∎

Example. We use the technique of this proof to evaluate $\det A$, where

$$A = \begin{bmatrix} 1 & 5 & 2 \\ 3 & -6 & 4 \\ -2 & 3 & -5 \end{bmatrix}.$$

Thus

$$\det A = (1)\begin{vmatrix} -6 & 4 \\ 3 & -5 \end{vmatrix} - 5\begin{vmatrix} 3 & 4 \\ -2 & -5 \end{vmatrix} + 2\begin{vmatrix} 3 & -6 \\ -2 & 3 \end{vmatrix}.$$

$$= (30 - 12) - 5(-15 + 8) + 2(9 - 12)$$
$$= 18 - 5(-7) + 2(-3) = 18 + 35 - 6$$
$$= 47.$$

We also evaluate $\det A$ by a technique that is useful for determinants of order n where $n > 3$.

We use property 7 of Theorem 1 to get zeros in the 21 and 31 positions, first multiplying row 1 by -3 and adding to row 2 and then adding twice row 1 to row 3:

$$\begin{vmatrix} 1 & 5 & 2 \\ 3 & -6 & 4 \\ -2 & 3 & -5 \end{vmatrix} = \begin{vmatrix} 1 & 5 & 2 \\ 0 & -21 & -2 \\ -2 & 3 & -5 \end{vmatrix} = \begin{vmatrix} 1 & 5 & 2 \\ 0 & -21 & -2 \\ 0 & 13 & -1 \end{vmatrix}.$$

Now we can easily expand by the first *column*, for there will be only one nonzero term:

$$1 \cdot \begin{vmatrix} -21 & -2 \\ 13 & -1 \end{vmatrix} = 21 + 26 = 47.$$

We conclude this brief discussion by mentioning (without proof) three theorems that, like the other theorems given, are valid for determinants of all orders.

THEOREM 3. *A square matrix A has an inverse $\Leftrightarrow \det A \neq 0$.*

THEOREM 4. *The system of n linear equations in n unknowns*

$$\sum_{j=1}^{n} a_{ij}x_j = b_i, \qquad i = 1, \ldots, n,$$

has a unique solution $\Leftrightarrow \det A \neq 0$, where $\det A$ is the determinant of the coefficients.

THEOREM 5. *The homogeneous system of n linear equations in n unknowns*

$$\sum_{j=1}^{n} a_{ij}x_j = 0, \qquad i = 1, \ldots, n,$$

has a nontrivial solution $\Leftrightarrow \det A = 0$. (A nontrivial solution is one for which at least one $x_i \neq 0$.)

Appendix 5
Trigonometry

Trigonometry originated as a tool for solving triangles, perhaps with the Babylonians or the Egyptians. In any case, we owe to the Babylonians the scheme of dividing the circle into 360 degrees. The triangle-solving aspect of trigonometry is important, but with the growing importance of abstract functions and with the use of trigonometric functions in calculus it became necessary to have a broader definition of the trigonometric functions than that needed for solving triangles, and it became advisable to have a different system of angular measurement than degrees, minutes, and seconds. We take up first the second of these matters.

Perhaps the simplest unit of angular measurement is a *revolution*; as the reader knows, this unit is widely used, but it is not convenient for the analytic study of the trigonometric functions. For reasons grounded in calculus, not easily explained outside that context, the most satisfactory angular unit for our purposes is the *radian*, the angle subtended at the center of a circle by a length of arc on the circumference equal to the radius (see Figure 1).

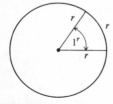

Figure 1

The relation between radians and degrees can be obtained by noting that the circumference equals $2\pi r$, i.e., one revolution equals 2π radians. Thus we have

one revolution $= 360° = 2\pi$ radians.

From this fundamental relation we can easily derive many others. Those listed below are among the more useful ones, with which the student should become familiar.

π rad $= 180°$ $\qquad \dfrac{2\pi}{3}$ rad $= 120°$

$\dfrac{\pi}{2}$ rad $= 90°$ $\qquad \dfrac{3\pi}{4}$ rad $= 135°$

$\dfrac{\pi}{3}$ rad $= 60°$ $\qquad \dfrac{3\pi}{2}$ rad $= 270°$

$\dfrac{\pi}{4}$ rad $= 45°$ $\qquad\qquad$ etc.

$\dfrac{\pi}{6}$ rad $= 30°$

$$1 \text{ rad} = \left(\frac{180}{\pi}\right)° \approx 57°.$$

Now we turn to a definition of the trigonometric functions, which is suitable from the point of view of analytic geometry and calculus. Because of the definition of radian in terms of length of arc of a circle the trigonometric functions will also be defined in terms of arc length of a circle. We make an explicit assumption, showing the manner in which our development depends on geometry.

Assumption

1. The circumference of a circle of radius r is $2\pi r$. Thus the circumference of a circle of radius 1 is 2π.
2. If $\mathscr{C}_1$ and $\mathscr{C}_r$ are concentric circles of radius 1 and r, respectively, and if two half-lines from the common center cut off arcs of length s_1 and s_r, respectively, then $s_r = rs_1$ (see Figure 2).

We shall initially focus attention on the sine and cosine. Once the definitions and basic properties of these functions have been given and

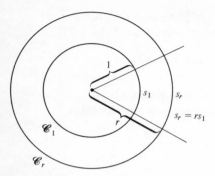

Figure 2

developed it will be routine to obtain the corresponding properties of the other four trigonometric functions.

DEFINITION 1. *Let C be the unit circle, i.e., the set of points in the plane determined by the equation $x^2 + y^2 = 1$. Let ϕ be any real number, and let P_ϕ be the point on C determined by the property that the length of arc on C from $(1, 0)$ to P_ϕ is ϕ; if $\phi > 0$, the direction from $(1, 0)$ to P_ϕ is counterclockwise; if $\phi < 0$, the direction is clockwise. If P_ϕ has coordinates (x, y), then by definition*

$$\cos \phi = x$$
$$\sin \phi = y$$

(see Figure 3).

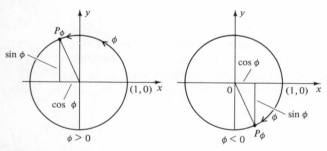

Figure 3

There are a few properties of sine and cosine that follow immediately from the definition. We list them in a theorem.

THEOREM 1.

1. $\sin^2 \phi + \cos^2 \phi = 1$,   *all $\phi \in \mathbf{R}$.*
2. $-1 \leqslant \sin \phi \leqslant 1$,   *all $\phi \in \mathbf{R}$.*
3. $-1 \leqslant \cos \phi \leqslant 1$,   *all $\phi \in \mathbf{R}$.*

4. $\sin 0 = \sin \pi = \sin 2\pi = 0$, $\sin \dfrac{\pi}{2} = 1$, $\sin \dfrac{3\pi}{2} = -1$.

5. $\cos 0 = \cos 2\pi = 1$, $\cos \dfrac{\pi}{2} = \cos \dfrac{3\pi}{2} = 0$, $\cos \pi = -1$.

PROOF.   Obvious (especially if you stop and think about it). ∎
It is frequently convenient to be able to work with a circle with a radius $r \neq 1$. This can easily be done in the following way.

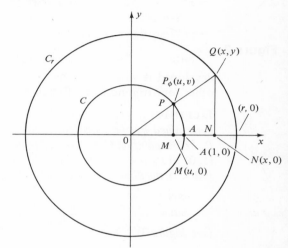

Figure 4

THEOREM 2.   *Let $\mathscr{C}$ and $\mathscr{C}_r$ be circles of radii 1 and $r \neq 1$, respectively, and let ϕ be any number. Let the radial line through $P_\phi(u, v)$ on $\mathscr{C}$ (determined as in Definition 1), extended if necessary, intersect $\mathscr{C}_r$ at $Q(x, y)$. Then*

$$\cos \phi = \frac{x}{r}, \quad \sin \phi = \frac{y}{r}.$$

PROOF.   See Figure 4. Using the similar triangles OMP and ONQ, we have

$$\frac{|\overline{ON}|}{|\overline{OM}|} = \frac{|\overline{OQ}|}{|\overline{OP}|} \quad \text{or} \quad \frac{x}{u} = \frac{r}{1} \quad \text{or} \quad \frac{x}{r} = u = \cos \phi.$$

Also

$$\frac{|\overline{NQ}|}{|\overline{MP}|} = \frac{|\overline{OQ}|}{|\overline{OP}|} \quad \text{or} \quad \frac{y}{v} = \frac{r}{1} \quad \text{or} \quad \frac{y}{r} = v = \sin \phi. \quad ∎$$

It follows from this result that if one wishes to identify ϕ with the central angle between the positive x-axis and the radius $\overline{OQ}$ and if it should happen that $0 < \phi < \pi/2$, then the familiar designations of sin ϕ as "opposite over hypotenuse" and of cos ϕ as "adjacent over hypotenuse" are applicable.

We now list a few additional properties of the sine and cosine.

THEOREM 3.

1. $\sin(\phi + 2n\pi) = \sin \phi$, $\cos(\phi + 2n\pi) = \cos \phi$, $n = 0, \pm 1, \pm 2, \ldots$.
2. $\sin(\phi + \pi) = -\sin \phi$, $\cos(\phi + \pi) = -\cos \phi$.
3. $\sin(-\phi) = -\sin \phi$, $\cos(-\phi) = \cos \phi$.

PROOF.   We refer to Figure 5.

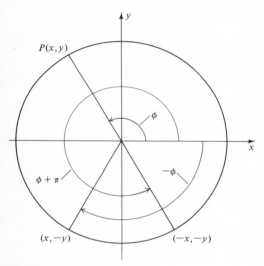

Figure 5

1. Assertion 1 is equivalent to the geometric assertion that if, starting from any point P on C, one describes an integral number of revolutions, in either direction, then one ends at the same point P.
2. If P has coordinates (x, y), then the diametrically opposite point, obtained by increasing the arc length by π units, has coordinates $(-x, -y)$. Thus

$$\sin(\phi + \pi) = -y = -\sin \phi$$
$$\cos(\phi + \pi) = -x = -\cos \phi.$$

3. If P has coordinates (x, y), then the point obtained by measuring

from $(1, 0)$ $|\phi|$ units along C in the direction opposite to that used for ϕ will have coordinates $(x, -y)$. Thus

$$\sin(-\phi) = -y = -\sin \phi.$$
$$\cos(-\phi) = x = \cos \phi. \quad \blacksquare$$

Two remarks about Theorem 3 are in order. Statement 1 says that the sine and cosine functions are *periodic with period 2π*. A function f is *periodic* if and only if there exists a number p such that

$$f(x + p) = f(x)$$

for all x such that x and $x + p$ are in the domain, of f. The minimum p for which this equation holds is *the period* of f. The fact that many physical phenomena are periodic suggests (and correctly so) that the trigonometric functions would be important in the application of mathematics to physical problems.

Statement 3 of Theorem 3 says that the sine is an *odd function* and the cosine is an *even function*.

For our next result we need the familiar law of cosines from the triangle-solving part of trigonometry. We now derive it.

LEMMA 1 (LAW OF COSINES). *If a triangle has sides of lengths a, b, c, and if the angle between sides a and b is θ (angle opposite side c), then*

$$c^2 = a^2 + b^2 - 2ab \cos \theta.$$

PROOF. We introduce a coordinate system such that side a lies along the positive x-axis and the angle θ is at the origin, and we consider a circle C of radius b (see Figure 6).

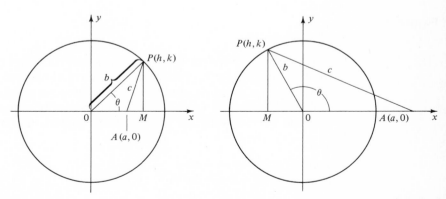

Figure 6

Using the distance formula, we have

$$c^2 = \overline{AP}^2 = (a - h)^2 + k^2$$
$$= a^2 - 2ah + h^2 + k^2$$
$$= a^2 + b^2 - 2ah,$$

since $P(h, k)$ lies on C_b. But, by Theorem 2, $\cos\theta = h/b$, so $h = b\cos\theta$; thus

$$c^2 = a^2 + b^2 - 2ab\cos\theta. \quad \blacksquare$$

Note that, although it would usually be the case that the θ in Lemma 1 would satisfy $0 < \theta < \pi$, the result of the lemma still applies if $\theta = 0$ or if $\theta = \pi$ (see Figure 7).

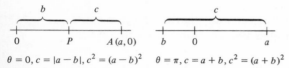

$\theta = 0, c = |a - b|, c^2 = (a - b)^2 \qquad \theta = \pi, c = a + b, c^2 = (a + b)^2$

Figure 7

We now derive an identity that will open a veritable treasure chest of other wonderful relationships.

THEOREM 4.   *For every $\phi_1, \phi_2 \in \mathbf{R}$ it is true that*

$$\cos(\phi_1 - \phi_2) = \cos\phi_1 \cos\phi_2 + \sin\phi_1 \sin\phi_2.$$

PROOF.   We first remark that it is always possible to find an integer n and a number θ, $0 \leqslant \theta \leqslant \pi$, such that $\phi_1 - \phi_2 = 2n\pi \pm \theta$. Then

$$\cos(\phi_1 - \phi_2) = \cos(2n\pi \pm \theta)$$
$$= \cos(\pm\theta) \qquad \text{(by 1 of Theorem 3)}$$
$$= \cos\theta \qquad \text{(by 3 of Theorem 3).}$$

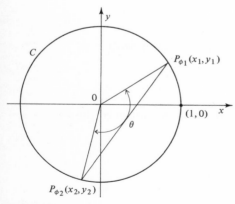

Figure 8

Next we consider the unit circle C with P_{ϕ_1} and P_{ϕ_2} determined in the usual way and we describe the distance $|\overline{P_{\phi_1}P_{\phi_2}}|$ by using both the distance formula and the law of cosines of Lemma 1 (see Figure 8). Thus,

$$|\overline{P_{\phi_1}P_{\phi_2}}|^2 = (x_1 - x_2)^2 + (y_1 - y_2)^2$$

and

$$|\overline{P_{\phi_1}P_{\phi_2}}|^2 = |\overline{OP_{\phi_1}}|^2 + |\overline{OP_{\phi_2}}|^2 - 2|\overline{OP_{\phi_1}}||\overline{OP_{\phi_2}}| \cos \theta.$$

Equating the right-hand sides of the preceding two equations, and using the fact that C has radius 1, we find

$$x_1^2 - 2x_1x_2 + x_2^2 + y_1^2 - 2y_1y_2 + y_2^2 = 2 - 2 \cos \theta,$$

or, since $x_1^2 + y_1^2 = x_2^2 + y_2^2 = 1$,

$$-2x_1x_2 - 2y_1y_2 = -2 \cos \theta.$$

Thus

$$\cos \theta = \cos \phi_1 \cos \phi_2 + \sin \phi_1 \sin \phi_2,$$

But $\cos \theta = \cos(\phi_1 - \phi_2)$, as remarked above, so

$$\cos(\phi_1 - \phi_2) = \cos \phi_1 \cos \phi_2 + \sin \phi_1 \sin \phi_2. \quad \blacksquare$$

COROLLARY. *For all $\phi \in \mathbf{R}$ it is true that*

1. $\cos\left(\dfrac{\pi}{2} - \phi\right) = \sin \phi.$

2. $\sin\left(\dfrac{\pi}{2} - \phi\right) = \cos \phi.$

PROOF. For assertion 1 we use Theorem 4 with $\phi_1 = \pi/2$, $\phi_2 = \phi$:

$$\cos\left(\frac{\pi}{2} - \phi\right) = \cos \frac{\pi}{2} \cos \phi + \sin \frac{\pi}{2} \sin \phi$$

$$= \sin \phi, \quad \text{(by Theorem 1).}$$

For assertion 2 we use the result of assertion 1 with ϕ replaced by $(\pi/2) - \phi$; thus

$$\sin\left(\frac{\pi}{2} - \phi\right) = \cos\left[\frac{\pi}{2} - \left(\frac{\pi}{2} - \phi\right)\right] = \cos \phi. \quad \blacksquare$$

We are now able to obtain, very quickly, three more identities of the same type as that of Theorem 4.

THEOREM 5. *For all $\phi_1, \phi_2 \in \mathbf{R}$ it is true that*

1. $\cos(\phi_1 + \phi_2) = \cos \phi_1 \cos \phi_2 - \sin \phi_1 \sin \phi_2.$
2. $\sin(\phi_1 + \phi_2) = \sin \phi_1 \cos \phi_2 + \cos \phi_1 \sin \phi_2.$
3. $\sin(\phi_1 - \phi_2) = \sin \phi_1 \cos \phi_2 - \cos \phi_1 \sin \phi_2.$

PROOF.

1. $\cos(\phi_1 + \phi_2) = \cos[\phi_1 - (-\phi_2)]$
$$= \cos \phi_1 \cos(-\phi_2)$$
$$+ \sin \phi_1 \sin(-\phi_2) \qquad \text{(Theorem 4)}$$
$$= \cos \phi_1 \cos \phi_2 - \sin \phi_1 \sin \phi_2 \qquad \text{(3 of Theorem 3)}.$$

2. $\sin(\phi_1 + \phi_2) = \cos\left[\dfrac{\pi}{2} - (\phi_1 + \phi_2)\right] \qquad \text{(corollary)}$

$$= \cos\left[\left(\frac{\pi}{2} - \phi_1\right) - \phi_2\right]$$

$$= \cos\left(\frac{\pi}{2} - \phi_1\right) \cos \phi_2$$

$$+ \sin\left(\frac{\pi}{2} - \phi_1\right) \sin \phi_2 \qquad \text{(Theorem 4)}$$

$$= \sin \phi_1 \cos \phi_2 + \cos \phi_1 \sin \phi_2 \qquad \text{(corollary)}.$$

3. $\sin(\phi_1 - \phi_2) = \sin[\phi_1 + (-\phi_2)]$
$$= \sin \phi_1 \cos(-\phi_2) + \cos \phi_1 \sin(-\phi_2)$$
$$= \sin \phi_1 \cos \phi_2 - \cos \phi_1 \sin \phi_2 \qquad \text{(Theorem 3)}. \quad \blacksquare$$

For the sake of reference we list, in slightly different form, the identities just derived:

1. $\sin(\phi + \theta) = \sin \phi \cos \theta + \cos \phi \sin \theta$.
2. $\sin(\phi - \theta) = \sin \phi \cos \theta - \cos \phi \sin \theta$.
3. $\cos(\phi + \theta) = \cos \phi \cos \theta - \sin \phi \sin \theta$.
4. $\cos(\phi - \theta) = \cos \phi \cos \theta + \sin \phi \sin \theta$.

We now give some of the immediate consequences of the above formulas:

5. $\sin 2\phi = 2 \sin \phi \cos \phi \qquad$ (set $\theta = \phi$ in 1).
6. $\cos 2\phi = \cos^2 \phi - \sin^2 \phi \qquad$ (set $\theta = \phi$ in 3)
$$= 2 \cos^2 \phi - 1 \qquad \text{(use Theorem 1)}$$
$$= 1 - 2 \sin^2 \phi \qquad \text{(use Theorem 1)}.$$
7. $\sin \phi \cos \theta = \frac{1}{2}[\sin(\phi + \theta) + \sin(\phi - \theta)] \qquad$ (add 1 and 2).
8. $\cos \phi \cos \theta = \frac{1}{2}[\cos(\phi + \theta) + \cos(\phi - \theta)] \qquad$ (add 3 and 4).
9. $\sin \phi \sin \theta = \frac{1}{2}[-\cos(\phi + \theta) + \cos(\phi - \theta)] \qquad$ (subtract 3 from 4).
10. $\sin^2 \phi = \frac{1}{2}(1 - \cos 2\phi)$ ⎫
11. $\cos^2 \phi = \frac{1}{2}(1 + \cos 2\phi)$ ⎬ (use 6 in this list).

12. $\sin^2 \dfrac{\theta}{2} = \dfrac{1}{2}(1 - \cos \theta)$ ⎫

13. $\cos^2 \dfrac{\theta}{2} = \dfrac{1}{2}(1 + \cos \theta)$ ⎬ (set $\theta = 2\phi$ in 10 and 11).

It is now a straightforward process to define the remaining four functions and determine their properties.

The names of the functions we are about to define are *tangent, cotangent, secant,* and *cosecant.* These are usually abbreviated tan, cot, sec, and csc, respectively.

DEFINITION 2.

$$\tan \phi = \frac{\sin \phi}{\cos \phi}, \qquad \phi \neq \frac{\pi}{2} + n\pi, n = 0, \pm 1, +2, \ldots$$

$$\cot \phi = \frac{\cos \phi}{\sin \phi}, \qquad \phi \neq n\pi, n = 0, \pm 1, \pm 2, \ldots$$

$$\sec \phi = \frac{1}{\cos \phi}, \qquad \phi \neq \frac{\pi}{2} + n\pi, n = 0, \pm 1, \pm 2, \ldots$$

$$\csc \phi = \frac{1}{\sin \phi}, \qquad \phi \neq n\pi, n = 0, \pm 1, \pm 2, \ldots.$$

We remark that the restrictions on the domains of the above functions are, of course, because of the zeros of the sine and cosine. Also, it is evident that the tangent and cotangent are reciprocal functions.

A further observation is that the newly defined functions are all periodic as a consequence of their definitions and the periodicity of the sine and cosine. What is not immediately obvious is the fact that tan and cot have period π. For, in the case of tan,

$$\tan(\phi + \pi) = \frac{\sin(\phi + \pi)}{\cos(\phi + \pi)} = \frac{-\sin \phi}{-\cos \phi}$$

$$= \tan \phi.$$

A similar proof holds for cot. The period of sec and csc is 2π.

We should point out that, in terms of the coordinates of a point $P(x, y)$ on a circle of radius r (see Figure 4) the values of the tangent, etc., can be obtained from

$$\tan \phi = \frac{y}{x}$$

$$\cot \phi = \frac{x}{y}$$

$$\sec \phi = \frac{r}{x}$$

$$\csc \phi = \frac{r}{y}.$$

These expressions follow immediately from Definition 2 and the fact that $\sin \phi = y/r$, $\cos \phi = x/r$ (Theorem 2).

A few other properties of these functions are also immediate consequences of their definitions and corresponding properties of sin and cos. For example, sec is an even function [since $\sec(-\phi) = 1/[\cos(-\phi)] = 1/(\cos \phi) = \sec \phi$], whereas tan, cot, and csc are odd functions. And, since $|\sin \phi| \leqslant 1$, $|\cos \phi| \leqslant 1$, all $\phi \in \mathbf{R}$, it follows that $|\csc \phi| \geqslant 1$ and $|\sec \phi| \geqslant 1$, all ϕ in the domains of these functions.

With regard to identities involving the functions of Definition 2, we can list the most important ones and give a proof of one or two, but leave for the reader the proofs of the rest. These equations hold for all ϕ and θ for which the functions involved are defined.

14. $\tan^2 \phi + 1 = \sec^2 \phi$.

15. $1 + \cot^2 \phi = \csc^2 \phi$.

16. $\tan(\phi + \theta) = \dfrac{\tan \phi + \tan \theta}{1 - \tan \phi \tan \theta}$.

17. $\tan(\phi - \theta) = \dfrac{\tan \phi - \tan \theta}{1 + \tan \phi \tan \theta}$.

18. $\tan 2\phi = \dfrac{2 \tan \phi}{1 - \tan^2 \phi}$.

19. $\tan \dfrac{1}{2}\phi = \pm \sqrt{\dfrac{1 - \cos \phi}{1 + \cos \phi}} = \dfrac{\sin \phi}{1 + \cos \phi} = \dfrac{1 - \cos \phi}{\sin \phi}$.

PROOFS.

14. Since $\sin^2 \phi + \cos^2 \phi = 1$ (Theorem 1), we obtain identity 14 by dividing both sides by $\cos^2 \phi$:

$\tan^2 \phi + 1 = \sec^2 \phi$.

16.

$$\tan(\phi + \theta) = \frac{\sin(\phi + \theta)}{\cos(\phi + \theta)} = \frac{\sin \phi \cos \theta + \cos \phi \sin \theta}{\cos \phi \cos \theta - \sin \phi \sin \theta}.$$

If, now, numerator and denominator of this last fraction are divided by $\cos \theta \cos \phi$, we find

$$\tan(\phi + \theta) = \frac{\dfrac{\sin \phi}{\cos \phi} + \dfrac{\sin \theta}{\cos \theta}}{1 - \dfrac{\sin \phi}{\cos \phi} \dfrac{\sin \theta}{\cos \theta}},$$

or

$$\tan(\phi + \theta) = \frac{\tan \phi + \tan \theta}{1 - \tan \phi \tan \theta}.$$

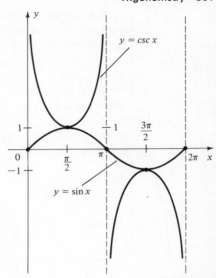

Figure 9

From the properties already studied it is an easy matter to obtain the graphs of the six trigonometric functions. We show one period of each in Figures 9 through 12.

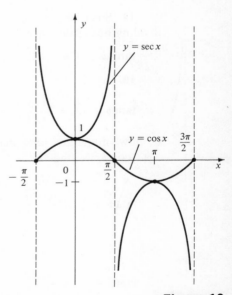

Figure 10

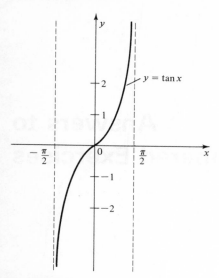

Figure 11

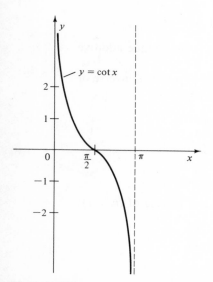

Figure 12

Answers to
Odd-Numbered Exercises

1.2

B. **1.** (Follow proof of Theorem 1). Suppose $a \in F$ has two inverses a^{-1} and b; i.e., $aa^{-1} = ab = 1$. Will show $b = a^{-1}$:

$$b = b \cdot 1 = b \cdot (aa^{-1}) = (ba)a^{-1} = (ab)a^{-1} = 1 \cdot a^{-1} = a^{-1}.$$

3. *Part 3.* Since $a + (-a) = (-a) + a = 0$, a is the unique additive inverse of $(-a)$, i.e., $a = -(-a)$.

Part 4. Show first that $(-a)(-b)$ is the (unique) additive inverse of $-(ab)$; then, by part 3, $(-a)(-b) = ab$. For the first assertion,

$$
\begin{aligned}
-(ab) + (-a)(-b) &= a(-b) + (-a)(-b) & \text{part 2} \\
&= (-b)(a) + (-b)(-a) & \text{M}_2 \\
&= (-b)(a + (-a)) & \text{D} \\
&= (-b)0 & \text{A}_5 \\
&= 0 & \text{Theorem 2.}
\end{aligned}
$$

Part 6. Show that $(-b) + (-c)$ is the additive inverse of $(b + c)$:

$$
\begin{aligned}
(b + c) + (-b) + (-c) &= (b + c) + (-c) + (-b) \\
&= b + (c + (-c)) + (-b) \\
&= b + 0 + (-b) \\
&= b + (-b) \\
&= 0.
\end{aligned}
$$

Part 8. $a - (b + c) = a + (-(b + c))$
$$= a + (-b) + (-c), \quad \text{by part 6.}$$

Part 13.
$$
\begin{aligned}
(a/c) \pm (b/c) &= ac^{-1} \pm bc^{-1} && \text{def. of } a/b \\
&= c^{-1}a \pm c^{-1}b && \text{M}_2 \\
&= c^{-1}(a \pm b) && \text{D} \\
&= (a \pm b)c^{-1} && \text{M}_2 \\
&= (a \pm b)/c && \text{def. of } a/b.
\end{aligned}
$$

Part 16. Remark: $c^{-1}d^{-1}$ is the multiplicative inverse of cd, i.e., $c^{-1}d^{-1} = (cd)^{-1}$, unique, by Exercise B1. For,

$$
\begin{aligned}
(cd)(c^{-1}d^{-1}) &= (cd)(d^{-1}c^{-1}) && \text{M}_2 \\
&= c(dd^{-1})c^{-1} && \text{M}_3 \\
&= c \cdot 1 \cdot c^{-1} && \text{M}_5 \\
&= 1 && \text{M}_4.
\end{aligned}
$$

Now,

$$
\begin{aligned}
(1/c)(1/d) &= (1 \cdot c^{-1})(1 \cdot d^{-1}) && \text{def. of } a/b \\
&= c^{-1}d^{-1} && \text{M}_4 \\
&= (cd)^{-1} && \text{above remark} \\
&= 1 \cdot (cd)^{-1} && \text{M}_4 \\
&= 1/(cd) && \text{def. of } a/b.
\end{aligned}
$$

Part 17.
$$
\begin{aligned}
(ac)/(bc) &= (ac)(bc)^{-1} && \text{def. of } a/b \\
&= (ac)(b^{-1}c^{-1}) && \text{remark in proof of part 16} \\
&= (ac)(c^{-1}b^{-1}) && \text{M}_2 \\
&= a(cc^{-1})b^{-1} && \text{M}_3 \\
&= a \cdot 1 \cdot b^{-1} && \text{M}_5 \\
&= ab^{-1} && \text{M}_4 \\
&= a/b && \text{def. of } a/b.
\end{aligned}
$$

Part 20. $a/b = c/d \Leftrightarrow ab^{-1} = cd^{-1} \Leftrightarrow (ab^{-1})(bd) = (cd^{-1})(bd) \Leftrightarrow a(b^{-1}b)d = (cd^{-1})(db) \Leftrightarrow a \cdot 1 \cdot d = c(d^{-1}d)b \Leftrightarrow ad = cb \Leftrightarrow ad = bc.$

Part 21.
$$
\begin{aligned}
(a/b) \pm (c/d) &= (ad)/(bd) \pm (bc)/(bd) && \text{part 17} \\
&= (ad \pm bc)/(bd) && \text{part 13.}
\end{aligned}
$$

5. In **N**, axioms A_4, A_5, and M_5 are not satisfied. In **Z**, axiom M_5 is not satisfied.

7. Axioms A_1, M_1, A_2, M_2, A_4, M_4, A_5, and M_5 follow immediately from Equations [1.1]—note that $-1 = 1^{-1} = 1$. Axioms A_3 and M_3 can be proved by considering the different possibilities for a, b, and c. To prove axiom D, first let $a = 1$; then

$$a(b + c) = 1 \cdot (b + c) = b + c = 1 \cdot b + 1 \cdot c.$$

Similarly, if $a = 0$,

$$a(b + c) = 0(b + c) = 0 = 0 + 0 = 0 \cdot b + 0 \cdot c.$$

9. Show that $(b + d) - (a + c) > 0$ and use [1.2] of Exercise B8. Thus

$$\begin{aligned} (b + d) - (a + c) &= b + d - a - c \\ &= (b - a) + (d - c) \\ &> 0 + 0 = 0, \end{aligned}$$

since $b > a$ and $d > c$, by hypothesis.

11. Suppose first that $-c = 0$; then

$$0 = c + (-c) = c + 0 = c,$$

which contradicts the hypothesis that $c < 0$. Next, try $-c < 0$. We use axiom O_2:

$$\left.\begin{array}{c} c < 0 \\ -c < 0 \end{array}\right\} \Rightarrow 0 = c + (-c) < 0,$$

again a contradiction (why?). By axiom O_1, it must follow that $-c > 0$.

13. If $0 < 1$, then, by axiom O_3

$$0 + 1 < 1 + 1 \quad \text{or} \quad 1 < 0;$$

using axiom O_2 on $0 < 1$ and $1 < 0$ gives $0 < 0$, impossible. On the other hand,

$$1 < 0 \Rightarrow 1 + 1 < 0 + 1, \quad \text{or } 0 < 1.$$

Using axiom O_2 on $1 < 0$ and $0 < 1$ gives $1 < 1$, also impossible.

1.3

A.   **1.** $S = \{x \mid x < 3\}$.
  3. $S = \{x \mid 0 < x < 3\}$.
  5. $S = \{x \mid x < -4\} \cup \{x \mid x > 2\}$.
  7. $S = \{x \mid x < -6\} \cup \{x \mid x > -3\}$.
  9. $S = \{x \mid 1 < x < 2\} \cup \{x \mid x > 3\}$.
  11. $S = \varnothing$.
  13. $S = \{x \mid -2 < x < 3\}$.
  15. $S = \mathbf{R}$.
  17. $S = \mathbf{R}$.
  19. $S = \{x \mid -2 < x < 2\}$.
  21. $S = \{x \mid -9 < x < 1\}$.
  23. $S = \{x \mid -\frac{7}{2} < x < 2\}$.
  25. $S = \{x \mid x < -2\} \cup \{x \mid x > 2\}$.
  27. $S = \{x \mid x \leqslant -9\} \cup \{x \geqslant 1\}$.
  29. $S = \mathbf{R}$.

B.   **1.** (a)   ⊟ Suppose that $ab > 0$ and $a > 0$. We show that the assumption that $b \leqslant 0$ leads to a contradiction; by the Law of the Trichotomy, $b > 0$. Clearly $b = 0 \Rightarrow ab = 0$, contradicting $ab > 0$. Also,

$$b < 0 \Rightarrow -b > 0 \qquad\qquad \text{[Equation (1.4)]}$$
$$\Rightarrow a(-b) = -(ab) > 0 \qquad (O_4)$$
$$\Rightarrow ab < 0,$$

contradicting $ab > 0$.

   Next suppose $ab > 0$ and $a < 0$. We show that the assumption that $b \geqslant 0$ leads to a contradiction; this implies that $b < 0$. Again, if $b = 0$, $ab = 0$, contradicting $ab > 0$. And

$$\left.\begin{array}{l} a < 0 \Rightarrow -a > 0 \\ b > 0 \end{array}\right\} \Rightarrow (-a)b = -(ab) > 0$$

$$\Rightarrow ab < 0,$$

contradicting $ab > 0$.

   ⊟ . First,

$$\left.\begin{array}{l} a > 0 \\ b > 0 \end{array}\right\} \Rightarrow ab > 0.$$

Next

$$\left.\begin{array}{l} a < 0 \\ b < 0 \end{array}\right\} \Rightarrow \left\{\begin{array}{l} -a > 0 \\ -b > 0 \end{array}\right\} \Rightarrow (-a)(-b) = ab > 0.$$

(b)   ⊟ The hypothesis is that $ab < 0$.
   (i) Suppose $a > 0$ and assume $b \geqslant 0$. Then $ab \geqslant 0$, contradicting the hypothesis. Thus, if $a > 0$, then $b < 0$.
   (ii) Suppose $a < 0$ and assume $b \leqslant 0$. Then

$$\left.\begin{array}{l} -a > 0 \\ -b \geqslant 0 \end{array}\right\} \Rightarrow (-a)(-b) = ab \geqslant 0,$$

contradicting the hypothesis. Thus, if $a < 0$, then $b > 0$.
   ⊟ We use Equation [1.5] in Exercise B12 after Section 1.2.

(i) $\left.\begin{array}{l} a > 0 \\ b < 0 \end{array}\right\} \Rightarrow ab < 0.$

(ii) $\left.\begin{array}{l} b > 0 \\ a < 0 \end{array}\right\} \Rightarrow ab < 0.$

2.2
A.   **3.** (a) x-axis.
   (b) y-axis.

(c) Line parallel to and 2 units above x-axis.

(d) Line parallel to and 1 unit to left of y-axis.

(e) Line through origin in quadrants I and III, making $45°$ angle with x-axis.

7. (a) $\{(x, y) \mid x < 0, y > 0\}$.

(b) $\{(x, y) \mid y < 0\}$.

(c) $\{(x, y) \mid x \geqslant 0\}$.

B. 1. $y = 0$.

3. $y = c \ (y = -c)$.

2.3

A. 1. (a) $|\overline{AC}| = |\overline{BC}| = 5, |\overline{AB}| = 5\sqrt{2}$.

(b) $m_{AC} = \frac{4}{3}, m_{BC} = -3/4, m_{AB} = \frac{1}{7}$.

(c) $M_{AC} = (\frac{9}{2}, 0), M_{BC} = (1, -1/2), M_{AB} = (\frac{5}{2}, \frac{3}{2})$.

(d) $(\frac{8}{3}, -\frac{2}{3})$

3. (a) $|\overline{AB}| = \sqrt{20}, |\overline{BC}| = \sqrt{40}, |\overline{CD}| = \sqrt{40}, |\overline{DE}| = \sqrt{68},$
$|\overline{EA}| = \sqrt{40}$.

(b) $m_{AB} = -2, m_{BC} = \frac{1}{3}, m_{CD} = 3, m_{DE} = -\frac{1}{4}, m_{EA} = 3$.

(c) $S(5, 2), T(1, 3), U(-3, -1), V(0, -5), W(5, -3)$.

(d) $m_{ST} = -1/4, m_{TU} = 1, m_{UV} = -4/3, m_{VW} = \frac{2}{5}, m_{WS}$ does not exist.

(e) No.

5. (a) $x^2 + y^2 + 10x - 14y + 54 = 0$.

(b) $3x^2 + 3y^2 + 40x + 26y + 83 = 0$.

(c) $x^2 + y^2 + 8x + 12y + 12 = 0$.

(d) $x^2 + y^2 - 20 = 0$.

C. 1. Show that slopes of opposite sides are equal.

3. Let the vertices of the quadrilateral be $(0, 0), (a, 0), (b, c)$, and (d, e). Then the condition is

$$(a - d)^2 + e^2 = b^2 + c^2.$$

5. No.

7. Some disadvantages of m':

(a) More cumbersome to compute.

(b) Depends on the order in which points are taken.

(c) Consider m' for $\overline{OP_2}$ and $\overline{OP'_2}$, where $P_2(x_2, y_2), P'_2(-x_2, y_2)$.

2.4

A. 1. (a) $X = \mathbf{R}, f[X] = \{y \mid y \geqslant -\frac{1}{4}\}$.

(b) $X = f[X] = \mathbf{R} - \{0\}$.

(c) $X = \mathbf{R}, f[X] = \{y \mid -\frac{1}{2} \leqslant y \leqslant \frac{1}{2}\}$.

(d) $X = \{x \mid x \geqslant 2\}, f[X] = \{y \mid y \geqslant 0\}$.

    (e) $X = \{x \mid -1 \leqslant x \leqslant 1\}, f[X] = \{y \mid 0 \leqslant y \leqslant 1\}$.

    (f) $X = \mathbf{R} - \{1\} = f[X]$.

    (g) $X = f[X] = \mathbf{R}$.

    (h) $X = \mathbf{R}, f[X] = \{y \mid y \geqslant -\frac{1}{4}\}$.

    (i) $X = \mathbf{R}, f[X] = \{4\}$.

    (j) $X = f[X] = \mathbf{R}$.

    (k) $X = \{x \mid x \leqslant -1\} \cup \{x \mid x \geqslant 1\}, f[X] = \{y \mid y \geqslant 0\}$.

5. (a) No.

    (b) Yes.

    (c) No.

    (d) Yes.

    (e) No.

    (f) Yes.

B.   **1.** The points in (a) and (d) are symmetric with respect to l; those in (b) and (c) are not.

    3. The functions in (a), (c), (e), and (g) are even; those in (b), (d), and (f) are not.

    5. $\dfrac{x_1 + x_2}{2} = 0 \Leftrightarrow x_2 = -x_1$

    $\dfrac{y_1 + y_2}{2} = 0 \Leftrightarrow y_2 = -y_1$.

    7. The functions in (b), (e), (f) are odd; those in (a), (c), and (d) are not.

    9. (a) $(f \circ g)(x) = |x|, \quad (g \circ f)(x) = x$.

    (b) $(f \circ g)(x) = x, \quad (g \circ f)(x) = |x|$.

    (c) $(f \circ g)(x) = \sin\dfrac{x}{x^2 + 1}, \quad (g \circ f)(x) = (\sin x)/(\sin^2 x + 1)$.

    (d) $(f \circ g)(x) = (g \circ f)(x) = x$.

    (e) $(f \circ g)(x) = -x^2 - 11, \quad (g \circ f)(x) = \sqrt{x^4 + 14x^2 + 53}$.

    (f) $(f \circ g)(x) = 2x^2/(x^4 + 1), \quad (g \circ f)(x) = (x^4 + 1)/-2x^2$.

2.5

A.   **1.** Intercepts: $(0, -6), (-3, 0), (2, 0)$.

Extent: all $x \in \mathbf{R}, y \geqslant -\frac{25}{4}$.

Symmetry: w.r.t. $x = -\frac{1}{2}$.

$x < -3 \Rightarrow y > 0; -3 < x < 2 \Rightarrow y < 0; x > 2 \Rightarrow y > 0$.

No asymptote.

    3. Intercepts: $(-3, 0), (0, 0), (2, 0)$.

Extent: all $x \in \mathbf{R}$, all $y \in \mathbf{R}$.

$x < -3 \Rightarrow y < 0; \quad -3 < x < 0 \Rightarrow y > 0; \quad 0 < x < 2 \Rightarrow y < 0; \quad x > 2 \Rightarrow y > 0$.

No asymptote.

5. Intercepts: $(-1, 0)$, $(0, 0)$, $(1, 0)$.
Extent: all $x \in \mathbf{R}$, all $y \in \mathbf{R}$.
Symmetry: w.r.t. origin.
$x < -1 \Rightarrow y < 0$; $-1 < x < 0 \Rightarrow y > 0$; $0 < x < 1 \Rightarrow y < 0$; $x > 1 \Rightarrow y > 0$.
No asymptote.
7. Intercept: $(4, 0)$.
Extent: $x \geqslant 4$, $y \geqslant 0$.
9. Intercepts: $(8, 0)$, $(0, -2)$
Extent: all $x \in \mathbf{R}$, all $y \in \mathbf{R}$.
Symmetry: w.r.t. $(8, 0)$.
$x < 8 \Rightarrow y < 0$; $x > 8 \Rightarrow y > 0$.
11. Intercept: $(0, 0)$
Extent: $x \neq 1$, $y \neq 1$.
Symmetry: w.r.t. $(1, 1)$.
$x < 0 \Rightarrow 0 < y < 1$; $0 < x < 1 \Rightarrow y < 0$; $x > 1 \Rightarrow y > 1$.
Asymptotes: $x = 1$, $y = 1$.
13. Intercepts: $(-3, 0)$, $(3, 0)$, $(0, -\frac{9}{2})$.
Extent: $x \neq 1, 2$.
$x < -3 \Rightarrow y > 0$; $-3 < x < 1 \Rightarrow y < 0$; $1 < x < 2 \Rightarrow y > 0$; $2 < x < 3 \Rightarrow y < 0$; $x > 3 \Rightarrow y > 0$.
Asymptotes: $x = 1$, $x = 2$, $y = 1$.
Note: $x = \frac{11}{3} \Rightarrow y = 1$; $x > \frac{11}{3} \Rightarrow y > 1$.
15. Intercept: $(0, -1)$.
Extent: $x \neq -1, 1$; $y \leqslant -1$, $y > 0$.
Symmetry: w.r.t. y-axis.
$x < -1 \Rightarrow y > 0$; $-1 < x < 1 \Rightarrow y < 0$; $x > 1 \Rightarrow y > 0$.
Asymptotes: $x = -1$, $x = 1$, $y = 0$.
17. Intercepts: $(-3, 0)$, $(3, 0)$, $(0, 3)$.
Extent: $-3 \leqslant x \leqslant 3$, $0 \leqslant y \leqslant 3$.
Symmetry: w.r.t. y-axis.
19. Intercept: $(1, 0)$.
Extent: $x \neq 0$.
$x < 1 \Rightarrow y < 0$; $x > 1 \Rightarrow y > 0$.
Asymptotes: $x = 0$; $y = x$.
Note: $(2, 2)$ is on curve; $x > 2 \Rightarrow y > x$.
21. The three curves are congruent and differ only in vertical position.
25. Range $= \mathbf{R} - \{y \mid 0 < y \leqslant 1\}$.

B.   **3.** Changing $|a|$ effects "rate of opening up"; sign of a determines whether curve has minimum point $(a > 0)$ or maximum point $(a < 0)$. Changing b changes lateral position. Changing c changes vertical position.

C.   **1.** $m = n + 1$, $a_0 = b_0$, $a_1 = b_1$.

3.1

A.   **1.** (a) Right angle at B. Angle A = angle C.
  (b) Right angle at C.
  (c) Right angle at C.
  (d) Right angle at B.

3. (a) $P_3(11, -1)$.
  (b) $P_3(2, 12)$.
  (c) $P_3(8, 12)$.
  (d) $P_3(9, -12)$.

B.   **1.** (a) $\alpha = 180° \Rightarrow$ the line is horizontal with positive direction to the left.
  (b) No; $\tan 90°$ does not exist.
  (d) Label the lines so that $\alpha_2 > \alpha_1$. Then

$$l_1 \perp l_2 \Leftrightarrow \alpha_2 - \alpha_1 = 90° \Leftrightarrow \tan(\alpha_2 - \alpha_1) \text{ not defined}$$
$$\Leftrightarrow \frac{m_2 - m_1}{1 + m_1 m_2} \text{ not defined}$$
$$\Leftrightarrow m_1 m_2 + 1 = 0.$$

C.   **1.** Use (a) Pythagorean Theorem and (b) slopes.

3. (a) $\left. \begin{array}{l} f(x) = ax + b \\ f(f(x)) = x \end{array} \right\} \Rightarrow a(ax + b) + b = x$

$\Rightarrow (a^2 - 1)x + ab + b = 0$

$\Rightarrow \left\{ \begin{array}{l} a = \pm 1 \\ (a + 1)b = 0 \end{array} \right\} \Rightarrow \left\{ \begin{array}{l} \text{(i) } a = 1, b = 0, \text{ or } y = x \\ \text{(ii) } a = -1, \text{ or } x + y = b. \end{array} \right.$

  (b) $\left. \begin{array}{l} f(x) = ax^2 + bx + c \\ f(f(x)) = x \end{array} \right\} \Rightarrow a^3 x^4 + \text{ terms in } x^3, x^2, x, x^0 = 0$

$\Rightarrow a = 0 \Rightarrow f$ is not quadratic.

  (c) Guess:

$\left. \begin{array}{l} p \text{ polynomial} \\ p(p(x)) = x \end{array} \right\} \Rightarrow p(x) = x \quad \text{or} \quad p(x) = -x + b.$

  (d) (i) $a + d = 0$, $a^2 + bc \neq 0$, i.e., $f(x) = (ax + b)/(cx - a)$, where $a^2 + bc \neq 0$.
  (ii) $b = c = 0$, $d = a \neq 0$, i.e., $f(x) = x$.

3.2

A.   **1.** $x + 3y - 1 = 0$.
  3. $x + y - 2 = 0$.
  5. $2x - 3y + 13 = 0$.
  7. $x = 2$.

9. $2x - 5y + 10 = 0$.

11. $x - 5y + 22 = 0$.

13. $2x + y + 5 = 0$.

15. $3x + 2y + 18 = 0$.

17. (a) Same y-intercept: $b = -\frac{3}{2}$.

    (b) Same x-intercept: $(-\frac{3}{4}, 0)$.

    (c) Same slope: $m = -2$.

19. $2x + y - 4 = 0$.

21. On and above the line $y = x + 1$.

23. $\{(x, y) \mid y > x - 1\}$.

25. Two parallel lines: $x - y - 2 = 0$, $x - y + 2 = 0$.

B.   **3.** (b) The point of intersection of $3x - y - 1 = 0$ and $2x - 5y + 8 = 0$ lies on every line of the family.

    5. (a) y-intercept: $b = 2$.

      (b) Slope: $m = 2$.

      (c) x-intercept: $(-2, 0)$; $x = -2$ not included.

      (d) x-intercept: $(-2, 0)$; $x = -2$ not included. If $b = 0$, the equation gives $y = 0$, the x-axis.

C.   **3.** (a) $-\frac{3}{5}x + \frac{4}{5}y - 2 = 0$; $\cos \omega = -\frac{3}{5}$, $\sin \omega = \frac{4}{5}$, $p = 2$.

      (b) $\frac{5}{13}x + \frac{12}{13}y - 2 = 0$; $\cos \omega = \frac{5}{13}$, $\sin \omega = \frac{12}{13}$, $p = 2$.

      (c) $(-1/\sqrt{2})x - (1/\sqrt{2})y - (1/\sqrt{2}) = 0$; $\cos \omega = -1/\sqrt{2}$, $\sin \omega = -1/\sqrt{2}$, $p = -(1/\sqrt{2})$.

      (d) $-\frac{3}{5}x + \frac{4}{5}y = 0$; $\cos \omega = -\frac{3}{5}$, $\sin \omega = \frac{4}{5}$, $p = 0$.

      (e) $(1/\sqrt{5})x + (2/\sqrt{5})y = 0$; $\cos \omega = 1/\sqrt{5}$, $\sin \omega = 2/\sqrt{5}$, $p = 0$.

      (f) $(-\frac{4}{5})x - \frac{3}{5}y - 3 = 0$; $\cos \omega = -\frac{4}{5}$, $\sin \omega = -\frac{3}{5}$, $p = 3$.

3.3

A.   **1.** $\frac{3}{14}$.

    3. $\frac{1}{13}$.

    5. $\tan \theta = -\cot \alpha_2 = -(1/m_2) = \frac{1}{2}$.

    7. $\theta = \pi/2$.

    9. Lines are parallel.

    11. 0.

    13. $25/\sqrt{85}$.

    15. $\frac{2}{3}$.

    17. 0.

    19. $\sqrt{2}$.

    21. From A: $64/\sqrt{74}$; from B: $32/\sqrt{26}$; from C: $64/\sqrt{58}$.

    23. $S = \{(x, y) \mid 5x + 12y + 31 = 0\} \cup \{(x, y) \mid 5x + 12y - 47 = 0\}$.

Two lines parallel to $5x + 12y - 8 = 0$.

3.4

A. **1.** The quarter-plane above $3x + 5y = 15$ and below $x - y + 3 = 0$; vertex of angle at $(0, 3)$.

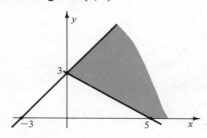

3. The strip between the parallel lines $x + y = 1$ and $x + y = -3$.

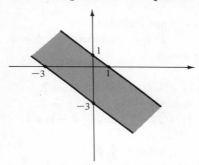

5. The quarter-plane above $x - 2y = 4$ and to the left of and on $x = 4$; vertex of angle at $(4, 0)$.

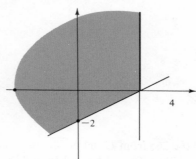

7. The interior of the triangle with vertices at $(0, 3)$, $(-5, -2)$, and $(\frac{25}{3}, -2)$.

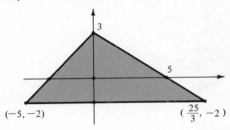

9. The quarter-plane above $5x - 9y + 11 = 0(l_1)$ and below $2x + 7y + 15 = 0(l_2)$; vertex of angle at $(-4, -1)$.

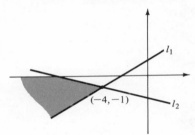

11. The strip on and between the parallel lines $x + 2y = 4$ and $2x + 4y = -11$, but to the left of—and on—$x - y = 4$; corners at $(\frac{5}{6}, -\frac{19}{6})$ and $(4, 0)$.

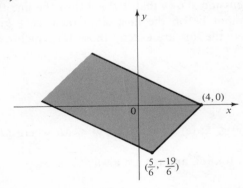

13. The quarter-plane above $x + 2y = 4$ and below $x - y = 4$; vertex of angle at $(4, 0)$.

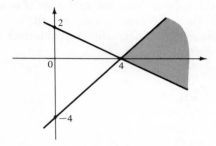

15. Number the regions as in the figure. Then the regions are given by the following inequalities: $0(>, >, <)$, $1(<, >, >)$, $2(<, >, <)$, $3(<, <, <)$, $4(>, <, <)$, $5(>, <, >)$, $6(>, >, >)$.

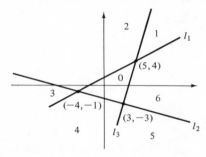

C. **1.** (a) 4; (b) 8; (c) 2^n; (d) $(<, <, >)$ gives $\varnothing$.

3. The proof of assertion 1 of Theorem 7 is complete. The discussion showed that if a point P is above the line, then $ax + by + c > 0$. Conversely, suppose $P(x, y)$ satisfies $ax + by + c > 0$ and P is below the line. This is a contradiction, because the discussion shows that if P is below the line then $ax + by + c < 0$. Also, P cannot be on the line, since then $ax + by + c = 0$. Thus the points P above the line are exactly those for which $ax + by + c > 0$.

3.5
A. **3.** $-23 \leqslant L(x, y) \leqslant 41$.
5. $-1 \leqslant L(x, y) \leqslant 3$.
7. (a) –(d): $-5 \leqslant L(x, y) \leqslant 5$; (e) $-M \leqslant L(x, y) \leqslant M$, where $M = \max(|a|, |b|)$.
9. The figures in (a), (b), (c), (e), and (g) are always convex.

B. **1.** Let the minimum and maximum for L on S occur at (x_1, y_1) and (x_2, y_2), respectively. Then $(x, y) \in S \Rightarrow L(x_1, y_1) \leqslant L(x, y) \leqslant L(x_2, y_2) \Leftrightarrow$

$ax_1 + by_1 + c \leqslant ax + by + c \leqslant ax_2 + by_2 + c \Leftrightarrow ax_1 + by_1 \leqslant ax + by \leqslant ax_2 + by_2 \Leftrightarrow L_0(x_1, y_1) \leqslant L_0(x, y) \leqslant L_0(x_2, y_2)$.

    3. (a) If P_0 is a vertex, the result follows from the definition of m and M. If P_0 is not a vertex, then Theorem 12 can be used.

       (b) Because S is convex the extended segment must intersect the boundary of S exactly once.

       (e) Yes. No.

4.1

    1. $x^2 + (y + 2)^2 = 4$.

    3. $(x + 3)^2 + (y + 4)^2 = 25$.

    5. $x^2 + y^2 + 4x - 2y - 20 = 0$; $C(-2, 1)$, $a = 5$.

    7. $(x + 1)^2 + (y - 3)^2 = 34$, $C(-1, 3)$, $a = \sqrt{34}$.

    9. $(x + 2)^2 + (y - 4)^2 = 25$, $C(-2, 4)$, $a = 5$.

    11. $(x + 4)^2 + (y + 1)^2 = 13^2$.

    13. $(x - 5)^2 + (y - 4)^2 = 25$.

    15. $(x - 4)^2 + (y - 4)^2 = 18$.

    17. $x^2 + y^2 + 2x = 0$.

    19. $C(2, -1)$, $a = \sqrt{8}$.

    21. $C(2, -3)$, $a = 0$.

    23. $C(1, -\frac{1}{2})$, $a = \sqrt{\frac{31}{12}}$.

    25. $C(0, 1)$, $a = 1$.

C.   **1.** (a) (i) $y - y_0 = m(x - x_0)$.

          (iii) $(m^2 + 1)x^2 + 2(my_0 - m^2x_0^2)x + (m^2 - 1)x_0^2 - 2mx_0y_0 = 0$.

       (b) The equation for m in step (v) of part (a) has no solution if $y_0 = 0$.

       (d) The quadratic equation for m in step (v) of part (a) has two equal roots, i.e., a unique solution.

    3. Translate coordinates so that center of circle is at the origin; use Theorem 2. If $y_0 \neq 0$, then

$$m_r = \frac{y_0}{x_0}, \quad m_t = \frac{-x_0}{y_0};$$

if $y_0 = 0$, the radius is horizontal, the tangent vertical.

    5. Use Theorem 5 in Exercise C4.

4.2

A.   **1.** (a) RA: $7x - 6y + 15 = 0$; LC: $6x + 7y - 19 = 0$.

       (b) RA: $16x - y + 14 = 0$; LC: $x + 16y - 19 = 0$.

       (c) RA: $x = 2$; LC: $y = 0$.

       (d) RA: $18x + 26y - 33 = 0$; LC: $26x - 18y + 50 = 0$.

3. Centers on $y = 1$. The point $(0, 1)$ is on every member.

5. All go through $(0, 0)$.

7. $x^2 + y^2 - 4 + k(x^2 + y^2 - 2x) = 0$.

9. $x^2 + y^2 + 2x - \frac{8}{3}y + k(x^2 + y^2 + 8x + 6y - 11) = 0$.

11. $x^2 + y^2 - 2hx + 10h - 26 = 0$.

13. $(x - h)^2 + (y - k)^2 = (\sqrt{h^2 + k^2} - 1)^2$.

15. $x^2 + y^2 - 2hx - 2ky + k^2 = 0$.

C. **1.** The centers

$$C\left(\frac{-D_1 - kD_2}{2(1 + k)}, \frac{-E_1 - kE_2}{2(1 + k)}\right)$$

all lie on

$$(E_1 - E_2)x - (D_1 - D_2)y - \tfrac{1}{2}(D_1E_2 - D_2E_1) = 0.$$

4.3

1. Intercept $(0, 0)$; symmetry with respect to both axes and origin; no values of x or y excluded; graph is the union of the lines $y = x$ and $y = -x$.

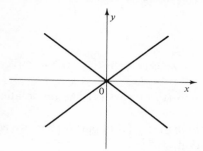

3. Intercept $(1, 0)$; symmetry with respect to the x-axis; must have $x \geqslant 1$.

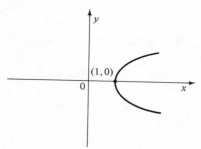

5. Intercept $(0, 0)$; symmetry with respect to origin; no values of x or y excluded.

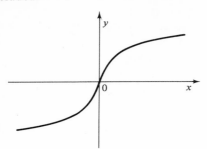

7. The graph is the set of points on and outside the circle of radius 2 with center at the origin.

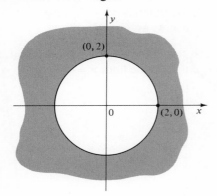

9. Intercept $(0, 0)$; symmetry with respect to the x-axis; must have $x \geqslant 0$.

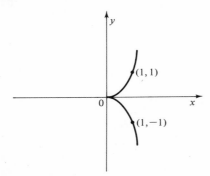

11. Intercept $(0, 0)$; symmetry with respect to the x-axis; values of x, $0 < x \leqslant 2$, excluded; $x \leqslant 0 \Rightarrow -1 < y < 1$; $x > 2 \Rightarrow y^2 > 1$; asymptotes: $x = 2$, $y = \pm 1$.

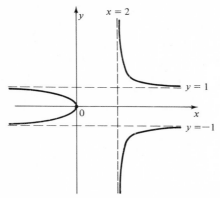

13. Intercepts $(-2, 0)$, $(\pm \sqrt{2}/2, 0)$; symmetry with respect to the x-axis; values of x must satisfy $-2 \leqslant x < 4$; asymptote: $x = 4$.

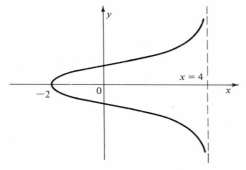

15. Intercepts $(\pm 2, 0)$; symmetry with respect to both axes and origin; x must satisfy $0 < x^2 \leqslant 4$; asymptote: $x = 0$.

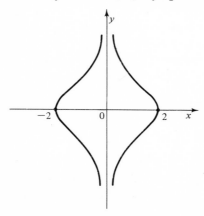

C. **1.** The relations in Exercises A5 and 8 are functions of x; those in A2, 3, 5, 9, 10, 11, 12, and 13 can be expressed as functions of y.

5.1

A. **3.** (a) Increasing $|p|$ causes a wider, more open, curve near the vertex.
  (b) The parabola opens toward the right when $p > 0$.
  (c) The parabola opens toward the left when $p < 0$.
5. $(x + 2)^2 = y + 4$, $F(-2, -15/4)$, directrix: $y = -17/4$.
7. $(x - 1)^2 = -\frac{1}{2}(y + 2)$, $F(1, -17/8)$, directrix $y = -15/8$.
9. $(y - 2)^2 = -\frac{5}{3}(x - 4)$, $F(\frac{43}{12}, 2)$, directrix: $x = \frac{53}{12}$.
11. $(x - 1)^2 = y + 1$, $F(1, -3/4)$, directrix: $y = -\frac{5}{4}$.
13. $(y - 1)^2 = -x$, $F(-\frac{1}{4}, 1)$, directrix: $x = \frac{1}{4}$.
15. $(x - 3)^2 = -3y$.
17. $(y + 2)^2 = -8(x + 2)$.
19. $(x - 3)^2 = 4(y + 2)$.
21. $y^2 = 8(x + 2)$.
23. (a) $2x^2 - 5x + y + 2 = 0$.
  (b) $2y^2 + 3x + y - 6 = 0$.

B. **1.** (b) 5. 1.
      6. 2.
      7. $\frac{1}{2}$.
      8. 1.
      9. $\frac{5}{3}$.
     10. 1.
     11. 1.
     12. 1.
     13. 1.
     14. 1.

5.2

A. **1.** (b) Values of e: $\sqrt{99}/10 \approx 0.99$, $\sqrt{24}/5 \approx 0.98$, $\sqrt{21}/5 \approx 0.92$,
     $\frac{4}{5} = 0.8$, $\frac{3}{5} = 0.6$, $\sqrt{19}/10 \approx 0.436$.
  (c) The vertices of all members are at $(\pm 5, 0)$.
3. $e = \frac{1}{2}$, $V(\pm 2, 0)$, $F(\pm 1, 0)$.
5. $e = \sqrt{2}/2$, $V(0, \pm 1)$, $F(0, \pm \sqrt{2}/2)$.
7. $e = (2\sqrt{2})/3$, $V(3 \pm 3, 0)$, $F(3 \pm 2\sqrt{2}, 0)$.
9. $e = \frac{1}{4}$, $V(0, -8 \pm 8)$, $F(0, -8 \pm 2)$.
11. Point ellipse: locus consists of $(2, 1)$.
13. $(y^2/16) + (x^2/7) = 1$.
15. $9(x - 5)^2 + 8(y - 3)^2 = 72$.
17. $16x^2 + 12(y - 4)^2 = 192$.
19. $16(x - 1)^2 + 12(y - 3)^2 = 192$.

21. $8(x + 5)^2 + 9y^2 = 81$, $9(x + 5)^2 + 8y^2 = 81$.
23. $144x^2 + 135(y - 3)^2 = (144)(135)$.

C. **3.** The light ray will be reflected through the other focus.

5.3
A. **1.** (b) Values of e: $\frac{1}{5}\sqrt{26} \approx 1.02$, $\frac{1}{5}\sqrt{41} \approx 1.28$, $\sqrt{2} \approx 1.41$, 2.6.
  (c) The vertices of all members are at $(\pm 5, 0)$.
  5. $C(0, 0)$, $V(\pm \sqrt{3}, 0)$, $F(\pm \sqrt{7}, 0)$, $e = \frac{1}{3}\sqrt{21}$.
  7. $C(0, 0)$, $V(0, \pm 2\sqrt{3})$, $F(0, \pm \sqrt{19})$, $e = \frac{1}{6}\sqrt{57}$.
  9. $C(2, 0)$, $V(2 \pm 2, 0)$, $F(2 \pm \sqrt{13}, 0)$, $e = \frac{1}{2}\sqrt{13}$.
  11. $C(5, 0)$, $V(5 \pm 5, 0)$, $F(5 \pm 5\sqrt{2}, 0)$, $e = \sqrt{2}$.
  13. $C(-2, 1)$, $V(-2, 1 \pm 3)$, $F(-2, 1 \pm \sqrt{13})$, $e = \frac{1}{3}\sqrt{13}$.
  15. $C(1, -2)$, $V(1 \pm 2, -2)$, $F(1 \pm \sqrt{5}, -2)$, $e = \frac{1}{2}\sqrt{5}$.
  17. $7x^2 - 9y^2 = 63$.
  19. $9(x - 4)^2 - 16(y + 2)^2 = 144$.
  21. $(x + 3)^2 - 3(y - 2)^2 = 12$.
  23. $3(y - 3)^2 - (x + 2)^2 = 27$.
  25. $4(x + 2)^2 - (y - 1)^2 = 4$; $(y - 1)^2 - 4(x + 2)^2 = 4$.
  27. $(x + 2)^2 - y^2 = \pm 9$.

5.4
A. **1.** Hyperbola.
  3. Ellipse.
  5. Hyperbola.
  7. Parabola.
  9. No. The line $x + y = 0$.
  11. $\gamma = \pi/4$; $3x'^2 - y'^2 = 1$.
  13. $\sin \gamma = 2/\sqrt{13}$; $11x'^2 - 2y'^2 = 4$.
  15. $\sin \gamma = 1/\sqrt{5}$; $4x'^2 - y'^2 = 8$.
  17. $x^2 + 2xy + y^2 + 1 = 0$.
  19. No. $\Delta > 0 \Rightarrow$ represents a hyperbola or a pair of intersecting lines.
  21. See answer to Exercise A19.

6.1
A. **3.** Circle of radius 2, center at pole.
  5. Vertical and horizontal lines, respectively.

6.2
A. **1.** Circle.
  3. Cardioid.
  9. Four-leaved rose.
  13. Parabola.

15. Lemniscate.

17. Limaçon.

B.   **1.** The point (r, θ) and $(-r, -\theta)$ are symmetric with respect to the $\pi/2$-axis.

6.3

A.   **1.** $x^2 + y^2 = 4y$.

   3. $x = 2$.

   5. $(x^2 + y^2)^3 = (x^2 - y^2)^2$.

   7. $y = x + 2$.

   9. $y^2 = 2x + 1$.

   11. $r = 9 \csc \theta \cot \theta$.

   13. $r = 2 \sin \theta$.

   15. $r = 4/(3 \sin \theta - 2 \cos \theta)$.

   17. $r^2 = \cos 2\theta$.

   19. $\theta = 3\pi/4$.

6.4

   1. Ellipse.

   3. Parabola.

   5. Ellipse.

   7. Ellipse.

   9. Hyperbola.

   11. Hyperbola.

   13. $r = 3/(1 + \sin \theta)$.

   15. $r = 4/(100 - 4 \sin \theta)$.

   17. $r = 2/(3 - \sin \theta)$.

   19. $r = 20/(3 - 5 \cos \theta)$.

7.1

A.   **1.** $|\overrightarrow{AB}| = \sqrt{73}$, $\cos \alpha = (-8)/\sqrt{73}$, $\cos \beta = (-3)/\sqrt{73}$.

   3. $|\overrightarrow{AB}| = 8$, $\cos \alpha = 1$, $\cos \beta = 0$.

   5. $|\overrightarrow{AB}| = 4\sqrt{2}$, $\cos \alpha = \cos \beta = (-1)/\sqrt{2}$.

   7. $|\overrightarrow{AB}| = 0$.

   9. $\cos \alpha = (-4)/5$, $\cos \beta = \frac{3}{5}$, $B(-2, 2)$.

   11. $\cos \alpha = 1$, $\cos \beta = 0$, $B(0, 0)$.

   13. $\cos \alpha = a/\sqrt{a^2 + b^2}$, $\cos \beta = b/\sqrt{a^2 + b^2}$, $B(0, 0)$.

   15. $\cos \alpha = \frac{3}{5}$, $\cos \beta = (-4)/5$, $B(5, -4)$.

B.   **3.** $\boxminus$ $\overrightarrow{AB} = \overrightarrow{CD} \Rightarrow |\overrightarrow{AB}| = |\overrightarrow{CD}| \Rightarrow (b_1 - a_1)^2 + (b_2 - a_2)^2 = (d_1 - c_1)^2 + (d_2 - c_2)^2 = q^2, q > 0$.

$$\vec{AB} = \vec{CD} \Rightarrow \begin{cases} \dfrac{b_1 - a_1}{q} = \dfrac{d_1 - c_1}{q} \\ \dfrac{b_2 - a_2}{q} = \dfrac{d_2 - c_2}{q} \end{cases} \Rightarrow \begin{cases} b_1 - a_1 = d_1 - c_1 \\ b_2 - a_2 = d_2 - c_2 \end{cases}.$$

For ⇐ reverse the steps.

7.2

A.   **1.** (a) $\mathbf{a} + \mathbf{b} = [9, 11]$.
  (b) $(\mathbf{a} + \mathbf{b}) + \mathbf{c} = \mathbf{a} + (\mathbf{b} + \mathbf{c}) = [12, 6]$.
  (c) $(-1)\mathbf{a} = [-5, -9]$.
  (d) $\mathbf{a} - \mathbf{b} = [1, 7]$, $\mathbf{b} - \mathbf{a} = [-1, -7]$.
  (e) $2\mathbf{a} + 3\mathbf{b} = [22, 24]$.
  (f) $3\mathbf{a} - 4\mathbf{b} = [-1, 19]$.
  (g) $\mathbf{a} - 2\mathbf{b} + \mathbf{c} = [0, 0]$.
  (h) $2\mathbf{b} - \mathbf{c} = [5, 9] = \mathbf{a}$.
  3. (a) $c_1 = 2$, $c_2 = -1$.
  (b) $c_1 = (-5)/3$, $c_2 = \frac{7}{3}$.
  (c) $c_1 = 3$, $c_2 = 1$.
  (d) $c_1 = c_2 = -\frac{4}{3}$.
  5. $c_1 = 2$, $c_2 = 1$.
  7. (a) $P_0(0, 4)$.
  (b) $P_0(1, 5)$.
  (c) $P_0(11, 10)$.

B.   **1.** 2. $\mathbf{a} + \mathbf{b} = [a_1, a_2] + [b_1, b_2] = [a_1 + b_1, a_2 + b_2]$
      $= [b_1 + a_1, b_2 + a_2] = \mathbf{b} + \mathbf{a}$.
  3. $\mathbf{a} + (\mathbf{b} + \mathbf{c}) = (\mathbf{a} + \mathbf{b}) + \mathbf{c} = [a_1 + b_1 + c_1, a_2 + b_2 + c_2]$.
  8. $(r + s)\mathbf{a} = (r + s)[a_1, a_2] = [(r + s)a_1, (r + s)a_2]$
      $= [ra_1 + sa_1, ra_2 + sa_2] = [ra_1, ra_2] + [sa_1, sa_2]$
      $= r[a_1, a_2] + s[a_1, a_2] = r\mathbf{a} + s\mathbf{a}$.
  3. c_1 and c_2 can be determined $\Leftrightarrow \mathbf{v}_2 \neq k\mathbf{v}_1$.

C.   **1.** $(3, -6)$ and $(-9, 10)$.

7.3

A.   **1.** $(-11)/(\sqrt{10}\sqrt{29})$.
  3. 0.
  5. $(-2)/\sqrt{13}$.
  7. 0.
  9. $(-4)/5$.
  11. $\cos A = 58/(\sqrt{61}\sqrt{73})$, $\cos B = 5/(\sqrt{2}\sqrt{73})$, $\cos C = 1/(\sqrt{2}\sqrt{61})$.
  13. $c = (48 + 25\sqrt{3})/11 \approx 8.3$.
  15. $\mathbf{b} = \pm\frac{1}{5}[4, 3]$.

B.   **3.** (c) $(-33)/13, (-33)/5.$
(e) $\mathbf{v} = 0.$

C.   **1.** (a) $h = \dfrac{(\mathbf{a} \cdot \mathbf{v})(\mathbf{b} \cdot \mathbf{b}) - (\mathbf{a} \cdot \mathbf{b})(\mathbf{b} \cdot \mathbf{v})}{(\mathbf{a} \cdot \mathbf{a})(\mathbf{b} \cdot \mathbf{b}) - (\mathbf{a} \cdot \mathbf{b})^2}$

$k = \dfrac{(\mathbf{a} \cdot \mathbf{a})(\mathbf{b} \cdot \mathbf{v}) - (\mathbf{a} \cdot \mathbf{b})(\mathbf{a} \cdot \mathbf{v})}{(\mathbf{a} \cdot \mathbf{a})(\mathbf{b} \cdot \mathbf{b}) - (\mathbf{a} \cdot \mathbf{b})^2}.$

(c) $h = \dfrac{(\mathbf{a} \cdot \mathbf{v}) - (\mathbf{a} \cdot \mathbf{b})(\mathbf{b} \cdot \mathbf{v})}{1 - (\mathbf{a} \cdot \mathbf{b})^2}$

$k = \dfrac{(\mathbf{b} \cdot \mathbf{v}) - (\mathbf{a} \cdot \mathbf{b})(\mathbf{a} \cdot \mathbf{v})}{1 - (\mathbf{a} \cdot \mathbf{b})^2}.$

7.4
A.   **1.** The line segment from $(1, -1)$ to $(2, 0)$.

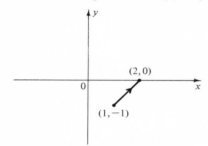

3. The line $y = x - 2$, directed upward.
5. The lower half of the circle $x^2 + y^2 = 4$; the positive direction is counterclockwise from $(-2, 0)$ to $(2, 0)$.
7. The line segment from $(1, 0)$ to $(0, 1)$, directed upward.
9. The *semicubical parabola* $y^2 = x^3$; the positive direction is upward.

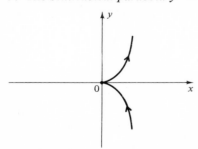

11. The curve $\sqrt{x} + \sqrt{y} = \sqrt{a}$ (a portion, including the vertex, of a parabola), directed from $(a, 0)$ toward $(0, a)$.

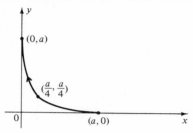

13. That part of the curve $x^{2/3} + y^{2/3} = a^{2/3}$ which lies in the first quadrant. The positive direction is from $(a, 0)$ to $(0, a)$.

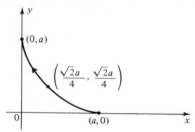

15. (a) The arc in quadrant III, directed toward $(0, -1)$.
(b) The arc in quadrant IV, directed from $(0, -1)$ toward $(1, 0)$.
(c) The arc in quadrant I, directed toward $(0, 1)$.
(d) The arc in quadrant II; positive direction is counterclockwise.

17. In each of (a) and (b) the curve is $y = x^3$, directed upward. The curve in (c) is the portion of the same curve—use the identity $\cos 3t = 4\cos^3 t - 3\cos t$—between $(1, 1)$ and $(-1, -1)$, directed downward.

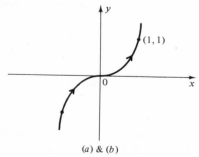

(a) & (b)

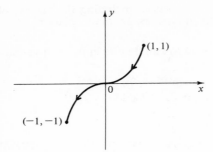

19. $\mathbf{r}(t) = (-3 + 2t)\mathbf{i} + (2 - t)\mathbf{j}$.

B.   **1.** $\mathbf{r}(t) = (a + ht)\mathbf{i} + (b + kt)\mathbf{j}$.

C.   **1.** $y = x - 2$.
3. $x^3 = y^2$.
5. $y = x^2$.
7. $y = abx/(x^2 + a^2)$.

7.5
A.   **1.** (b)

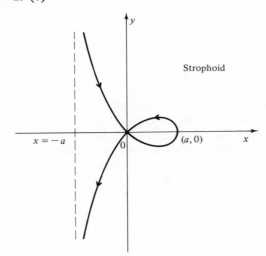

Strophoid

8.1
A.   **1.** (a) Half-space above the xy-plane.
(b) The first octant, the octant below the first octant, and the two octants symmetric to these with respect to the z-axis.
(c) The positive x-axis.

    (d) The z-axis.

    (e) Circle of radius 1, center on z-axis, in plane parallel to and 1 unit above xy-plane.

    (f) Straight line in plane parallel to and 2 units in front of yz-plane, through $(2, 1, 0)$ and $(2, 0, 1)$.

    (g) Line parallel to z-axis, through $(2, 1, 0)$.

  3. (a) Sphere; radius 1, center $(1, 0, 0)$.

    (b) Sphere; radius $\sqrt{2}$, center $(1, 1, 0)$.

    (c) Sphere; radius 2, center $(1, -2, 4)$.

    (d) Right circular cylinder; radius 1, axis parallel to z-axis and through $(1, 0, 0)$.

    (e) Plane through z-axis, bisecting first octant.

  5. $x - z = 0$; plane through y-axis, bisecting first octant.

  7. $x^2 + z^2 = 4$.

B.   **3.** (a) $\begin{cases} x_0 = (1 - \lambda)x_1 + \lambda x_2 \\ y_0 = (1 - \lambda)y_1 + \lambda y_2 \\ z_0 = (1 - \lambda)z_1 + \lambda z_2 \end{cases}, \quad 0 < \lambda < 1.$

    (b) $\begin{cases} x_0 = \frac{1}{2}(x_1 + x_2) \\ y_0 = \frac{1}{2}(y_1 + y_2) \\ z_0 = \frac{1}{2}(z_1 + z_2) \end{cases}.$

    (c) $P_0(3, 1, 1)$.

8.2

A.   **1.** $\mathbf{i} - 2\mathbf{j} + 2\mathbf{k}$; $\cos \alpha = \frac{1}{3}$, $\cos \beta = -\frac{2}{3}$, $\cos \gamma = \frac{2}{3}$.

  3. $\mathbf{i} + \mathbf{j} + \mathbf{k}$; $\cos \alpha = \cos \beta = \cos \gamma = 1/\sqrt{3}$.

  5. $\mathbf{i} + \mathbf{k}$; $\cos \alpha = \cos \gamma = 1/\sqrt{2}$, $\cos \beta = 0$.

  7. $-3\mathbf{i} - 4\mathbf{j} - 5\mathbf{k}$; $\cos \alpha = (-3)/(2\sqrt{5})$, $\cos \beta = (-4)/(2\sqrt{5})$, $\cos \gamma = (-5)/(2\sqrt{5})$.

  9. $-4\mathbf{j} + 3\mathbf{k}$; $\cos \alpha = 0$, $\cos \beta = (-4)/5$, $\cos \gamma = \frac{3}{5}$.

  11. (a) $\cos \theta = (-7)/(15\sqrt{2})$.

    (b) $\cos \theta = 0$.

    (c) $\cos \theta = (-2)/(3\sqrt{21})$.

  13. $\mathbf{P_1P_2} = \mathbf{P_3P_4} = 4\mathbf{i} + 6\mathbf{j} - 8\mathbf{k}$, $\mathbf{P_1P_3} = \mathbf{P_2P_4} = 3\mathbf{i} - 3\mathbf{j} + 6\mathbf{k}$; $\mathbf{P_1P_2} \cdot \mathbf{P_1P_3} = -54 \neq 0$.

  15. (a) $\mathbf{v}$ is parallel to the xy-plane.

    (b) $\mathbf{v}$ is parallel to the x-axis.

    (c) $\mathbf{v}$ is parallel to the yz-plane.

    (d) $\mathbf{v}$ is parallel to the z-axis.

    (e) $\mathbf{v} = \mathbf{0}$.

8.3

A. **1.** (a) $\mathbf{a} \times \mathbf{b} = [3, -5, -6]$.
  (b) $\mathbf{a} \times \mathbf{b} = [9, 19, 2]$.
  (c) $\mathbf{a} \times \mathbf{b} = 14\mathbf{i} + 2\mathbf{j} + 10\mathbf{k}$.
  (d) $\mathbf{a} \times \mathbf{b} = 5\mathbf{i} - 4\mathbf{j} - 21\mathbf{k}$.
  (e) $\mathbf{a} + \mathbf{b} = [1, 1, -2]$.
  3. (a) 3.
  (b) 12.
  (c) 0.
  (d) 0.
  5. (a) $6/\sqrt{29}$.
  (b) $12/\sqrt{42}$.
  (c) 0.
  7. The triples in (a) and (b) are right-handed.

B. **1.** Since θ lies in the interval $0 \leqslant \theta \leqslant \pi$, $\sin \theta \geqslant 0$ and $\sqrt{\sin^2 \theta} = \sin \theta$.
  5. ⇨ Suppose $\mathbf{a}$ and $\mathbf{b}$ are not parallel and $\mathbf{c}$ lies in the plane of $\mathbf{a}$ and $\mathbf{b}$; then $\mathbf{c} = h\mathbf{a} + k\mathbf{b}$ and $\mathbf{a} \times \mathbf{b} \cdot \mathbf{c} = \mathbf{a} \times \mathbf{b} \cdot (h\mathbf{a} + k\mathbf{b}) = h(\mathbf{a} \times \mathbf{b} \cdot \mathbf{a}) + k(\mathbf{a} \times \mathbf{b} \cdot \mathbf{b}) = 0$. If $\mathbf{a}$ and $\mathbf{b}$ are parallel, then $\mathbf{b} = h\mathbf{a}$, $\mathbf{a} \times \mathbf{b} = \mathbf{0}$, and $\mathbf{a} \times \mathbf{b} \cdot \mathbf{c} = 0$.

  ⇦ $\mathbf{a} \times \mathbf{b} \cdot \mathbf{c} = 0 \Rightarrow \mathbf{a} \times \mathbf{b}$ is perpendicular to $\mathbf{c}$. Since $\mathbf{a} \times \mathbf{b}$ is perpendicular to the plane of $\mathbf{a}$ and $\mathbf{b}$, $\mathbf{c}$ lies in the plane of $\mathbf{a}$ and $\mathbf{b}$.

C. **1.** (a) $(\mathbf{a} \times \mathbf{b}) \times \mathbf{c}$ is perpendicular to $\mathbf{a} \times \mathbf{b}$, which, in turn, is perpendicular to the plane of $\mathbf{a}$ and $\mathbf{b}$. Thus $(\mathbf{a} \times \mathbf{b}) \times \mathbf{c}$ is in the plane of $\mathbf{a}$ and $\mathbf{b}$.
  (b) $\mathbf{a} \times (\mathbf{b} \times \mathbf{c})$ is perpendicular to $\mathbf{b} \times \mathbf{c}$, which, in turn, is perpendicular to the plane of $\mathbf{b}$ and $\mathbf{c}$. Thus $\mathbf{a} \times (\mathbf{b} \times \mathbf{c})$ is in the plane of $\mathbf{b}$ and $\mathbf{c}$.

8.4

A. **1.** (a) $ax + by + cz = 0$.
  (b) $2x - 4y + z = -7$.
  (c) $x + y = 2$.
  (d) $z = 3$.
  (e) $x = 0$.
  (f) $y - z = 0$.
  3. $3x - 7y + z = 28$.
  5. The plane $x + y + 3z = 7$.
  7. $y + 4z = 28$.
  9. $x = y$.
  11. $x + y = 2$.

C. **1.** $b = 0$, $d \neq 0$.

3. If $d \neq 0$, then distance $= |d|/\sqrt{a^2 + b^2 + c^2}$; if $d = 0$, then distance $= 0$.

8.5

A. **1.** (a) $\mathbf{r}(t) = [4, -5, 2] + t[-2, 12, -5] = (4 - 2t)\mathbf{i} + (-5 + 12t)\mathbf{j} + (2 - 5t)\mathbf{k}$,

$$\begin{cases} x = 4 - 2t \\ y = -5 + 12t \\ z = 2 - 5t \end{cases}, \quad \frac{x-4}{-2} = \frac{y+5}{12} = \frac{z-2}{-5}.$$

(b) $\mathbf{r}(t) = [3, -3, 6] + t[2, 0, -4] = (3 + 2t)\mathbf{i} + (-3)\mathbf{j} + (6 - 4t)\mathbf{k}$,

$$\begin{cases} x = 3 + 2t \\ y = -3 \\ z = 6 - 4t \end{cases}, \quad \frac{x-3}{2} = \frac{y+3}{0} = \frac{z-6}{-4}.$$

(c) $\mathbf{r}(t) = [-1, 0, 8] + t[3, 5, -12] = (-1 + 3t)\mathbf{i} + (5t)\mathbf{j} + (8 - 12t)\mathbf{k}$,

$$\begin{cases} x = -1 + 3t \\ y = 5t \\ z = 8 - 12t \end{cases}, \quad \frac{x+1}{3} = \frac{y}{5} = \frac{z-8}{-12}.$$

(d) $\mathbf{r}(t) = [3, 5, 2] + t[3, 0, 0] = (3 + 3t)\mathbf{i} + 5\mathbf{j} + 2\mathbf{k}$,

$$\begin{cases} x = 3 + 3t \\ y = 5 \\ z = 2 \end{cases}, \quad \frac{x-3}{3} = \frac{y-5}{0} = \frac{z-2}{0}.$$

(e) $\mathbf{r}(t) = [4, -1, 7] + t[0, 3, -2] = 4\mathbf{i} + (-1 + 3t)\mathbf{j} + (7 - 2t)\mathbf{k}$,

$$\begin{cases} x = 4 \\ y = -1 + 3t \\ z = 7 - 2t \end{cases}, \quad \frac{x-4}{0} = \frac{y+1}{3} = \frac{z-7}{-2}.$$

3. (a) $\begin{cases} x = -\frac{1}{8} + t \\ y = \frac{19}{8} - 11t \\ z = 8t \end{cases}.$

(b) $\begin{cases} x = -2t \\ y = -22 - 19t \\ z = 6 + 5t \end{cases}.$

(c) $\begin{cases} x = \frac{1}{5} - 14t \\ y = -\frac{1}{5} - 16t \\ z = -5t \end{cases}.$

(d) $\begin{cases} x = \frac{9}{2} + t \\ y = 2t \\ z = \frac{1}{2} + t \end{cases}$.

5. (a) $\begin{cases} x = 5 + t \\ y = -4 - t \\ z = 2 - t \end{cases}$.

(b) $\begin{cases} x = 1 - 4t \\ y = 1 - t \\ z = 1 + 3t \end{cases}$.

7. (a) $(-3, 1, 2)$.
(b) No intersection.

C. **1.** The vector $[a, b, c]$ is a unit vector in the positive direction along the line.

8.6

A. **1.** Traces: $z = 0, x^2 + y^2 = 4; y = 0, z = 4 - x^2; x = 0, z = 4 - y^2$.
Symmetry with respect to: z-axis, yz-plane, zx-plane.
Extent: $z \leqslant 4$.
  3. Traces: $z = 0, x + y = 0; y = 0, z = x; x = 0, z = y$.
Plane through origin, normal vector $\mathbf{n} = [1, 1, -1]$.
  5. Traces: $z = 0, x = \frac{1}{2} \pm n, n = 0, 1, 2, \ldots; x = 0, z = 1; y = 0,$
$z = \cos^2 \pi x$.
Extent: $0 \leqslant z \leqslant 1$.
  7. Traces: $x = 0, y = \pm 2; y = 0, x = \pm 2$.
Symmetry with respect to: z-axis, xy-plane, yz-plane, zx-plane.
Right circular cylinder, radius 2.
  9. Traces: $z = 0, y = (3\pi)/2 \pm 2n, n = 0, 1, 2, \ldots; y = 0, z = 1;$
$x = 0, z = 1 + \sin y$.
Extent: $0 \leqslant z \leqslant 2$.
  11. Traces: $z = 0$, lines $x = 2$ and $y = 3; y = 0, z = 1 - \frac{1}{2}x; x = 0,$
$z = 1 - \frac{1}{3}y$.
  13. Traces: $z = 0, x^2 + y^2 = 4; y = 0, x^2 + 4z^2 = 4; x = 0, y^2 + 4z^2 = 4$.
Symmetry with respect to all coordinate axes and all coordinate planes.
Extent: $-2 \leqslant x \leqslant 2, -2 \leqslant y \leqslant 2, -1 \leqslant z \leqslant 1$.
  15. Traces: $z = 0, x^2 + y^2 = 1; y = 0, x^2 - z^2 = 1; x = 0, y^2 - z^2 = 1$.
Symmetry with respect to all coordinates axes and all coordinate planes.
  17. Traces: $x = 0, z = 1/y^2; y = 0, z = 1/x^2$.
Symmetry with respect to: z-axis, yz-plane, zx-plane. Extent: $z > 0$.

19. $y = 0$, $x^2 + z^2 = 1$; $z = 0$, $y = 1 - x^2$; $x = 0$, $y = 1 - z^2$. Symmetry with respect to: y-axis, xy-plane, yz-plane. Extent: $y \leqslant 1$.

B.   **1.** (a) The line segment $\overline{P_1 P_2}$ is perpendicular to the xy-plane and the midpoint of $\overline{P_1 P_2}$ is on the xy-plane.
   (b) $x_2 = x_1$, $y_2 = y_1$, $z_2 = -z_1$.
   (c) $(x, y, z) \in S \Rightarrow (x, y, -z) \in S$.

8.7

A.   **11.** $x^2 + y^2 = z^4$.
   13. $x^2 + y^2 = z^2$.
   15. $y^2 + z^2 = \frac{1}{4}x^2$.
   17. $y^2 + z^2 = (1 - x)^2$.
   19. $1 - z = x^2 + y^2$.
   21. Yes. The base curve is a line.

8.8

A.   **1.** Ellipsoid.
   3. Hyperboloid of two sheets.
   5. Paraboloid of revolution.
   7. Hyperbolic paraboloid.
   9. Two planes through the z-axis: $y = \pm \sqrt{2}x$.
   11. Cone.
   13. Paraboloid of revolution.
   15. Hyperbolic paraboloid.
   17. $x^2 - 4y^2 + z^2 = 0$.
   19. $4x^2 + 4y^2 - z^2 = 4$.
   21. $4x^2 + y^2 + 4z^2 = 4$.
   23. $x^2 + y^2 + z^2 = 1$.
   25. $x^2 - 4y^2 + z^2 = 4$.

9.1

A.   **1.** $x = 4$, $y = 1$.
   3. $S = \{[2 - \frac{1}{5}z, -1 + \frac{7}{5}z, z] \mid z \in \mathbf{R}\}$.
   5. $S = \{[3y - 2, y] \mid y \in \mathbf{R}\}$.
   7. $S = \{[3 - 5y, y] \mid y \in \mathbf{R}\}$.
   9. $S = \{[3, -2, 4]\}$.
   11. $S \neq \varnothing$.
   13. $S = \left\{ \left[\dfrac{23 - 7z}{10}, \dfrac{-1 + 19z}{10}, z \right] \,\Big|\, z \in \mathbf{R} \right\}$.
   15. $S = \varnothing$.
   17. (a) 1, (b) 3, (c) 2, (d) 2, (e) 4, (f) 4, (g) 6.

B. **3.** (a) $\begin{bmatrix} 1 & 0 & 0 \\ 0 & 1 & 0 \\ 0 & 0 & 1 \end{bmatrix}$. (b) $\begin{bmatrix} 1 & 0 & 0 & \cdots & 0 \\ 0 & 1 & 0 & \cdots & 0 \\ \vdots & \vdots & & \vdots \\ 0 & 0 & 0 & \cdots & 1 \end{bmatrix}$.

C. **1.** (a) Obvious.

(b) $L_1 \sim L_2 \Rightarrow S_1 = S_2 \Rightarrow S_2 = S_1 \Rightarrow L_2 \sim L_1$.

(c) $\left.\begin{matrix} L_1 \sim L_2 \\ L_2 \sim L_3 \end{matrix}\right\} \Rightarrow \left\{\begin{matrix} S_1 = S_2 \\ S_2 = S_3 \end{matrix}\right\} \Rightarrow S_1 = S_3 \Rightarrow L_1 \sim L_3$.

3. The other five:

$$\begin{bmatrix} 0 & 1 & a \\ 0 & 0 & 0 \end{bmatrix}, \begin{bmatrix} 0 & 0 & 1 \\ 0 & 0 & 0 \end{bmatrix}, \begin{bmatrix} 1 & 0 & a \\ 0 & 1 & a \end{bmatrix}, \begin{bmatrix} 0 & 1 & 0 \\ 0 & 0 & 1 \end{bmatrix}, \begin{bmatrix} 1 & 0 & 0 \\ 0 & 0 & 1 \end{bmatrix}.$$

9.2

A. **1.** (a) $A + B = \begin{bmatrix} 3 & 3 \\ 2 & 2 \end{bmatrix}$, $-A = \begin{bmatrix} -2 & -3 \\ 1 & -4 \end{bmatrix}$

$AB = \begin{bmatrix} 11 & -6 \\ 11 & -8 \end{bmatrix}$, $BA = \begin{bmatrix} 2 & 3 \\ 8 & 1 \end{bmatrix}$

$A^t = \begin{bmatrix} 2 & -1 \\ 3 & 4 \end{bmatrix}$, $B^t = \begin{bmatrix} 1 & 3 \\ 0 & -2 \end{bmatrix}$.

(b) $A + B = \begin{bmatrix} 5 & 1 & 3 \\ 1 & -1 & 9 \\ 6 & -3 & 4 \end{bmatrix}$, $-A = \begin{bmatrix} -1 & 0 & -3 \\ -2 & 1 & -7 \\ -3 & 2 & -2 \end{bmatrix}$

$AB = \begin{bmatrix} 13 & -2 & 6 \\ 30 & -5 & 12 \\ 20 & 1 & 0 \end{bmatrix}$, $BA = \begin{bmatrix} 6 & -1 & 19 \\ 5 & -4 & 1 \\ 7 & -3 & 6 \end{bmatrix}$

$A^t = \begin{bmatrix} 1 & 2 & 3 \\ 0 & -1 & -2 \\ 3 & 7 & 2 \end{bmatrix}$, $B^t = \begin{bmatrix} 4 & -1 & 3 \\ 1 & 0 & -1 \\ 0 & 2 & 2 \end{bmatrix}$.

3. (a) $A^2 = \begin{bmatrix} 0 & 0 & 1 \\ 0 & 0 & 0 \\ 0 & 0 & 0 \end{bmatrix}$, (b) $A^3 = \begin{bmatrix} 0 & 0 & 0 \\ 0 & 0 & 0 \\ 0 & 0 & 0 \end{bmatrix}$.

5.

$$A^2 = \begin{bmatrix} 1 & 2 & 3 & 4 \\ 0 & 1 & 2 & 3 \\ 0 & 0 & 1 & 2 \\ 0 & 0 & 0 & 1 \end{bmatrix}, \quad A^3 = \begin{bmatrix} 1 & 3 & 6 & 10 \\ 0 & 1 & 3 & 6 \\ 0 & 0 & 1 & 3 \\ 0 & 0 & 0 & 1 \end{bmatrix},$$

$$A^4 = \begin{bmatrix} 1 & 4 & 10 & 20 \\ 0 & 1 & 4 & 10 \\ 0 & 0 & 1 & 4 \\ 0 & 0 & 0 & 1 \end{bmatrix}, \quad A^5 = \begin{bmatrix} 1 & 5 & 15 & 35 \\ 0 & 1 & 5 & 15 \\ 0 & 0 & 1 & 5 \\ 0 & 0 & 0 & 1 \end{bmatrix},$$

$$A^n = \begin{bmatrix} 1 & n & S_n & T_n \\ 0 & 1 & n & S_n \\ 0 & 0 & 1 & n \\ 0 & 0 & 0 & 1 \end{bmatrix},$$

where

$$S_n = \sum_{k=1}^{n} k = \frac{n(n+1)}{2}$$

$$T_n = \frac{n(n+1)(n+2)}{6}.$$

B. **1.** $B_{n \times p}, C_{n \times p}, D_{p \times q}.$
3. (a) $p = n$ and $q = m.$
(b) $q = p = m = n.$
(c) Yes.
7. $A = [a_{ij}]$ skew-symmetric $\Rightarrow a_{ji} = -a_{ij}, i, j = 1, \ldots, n.$ If $j = i,$
then $a_{ii} = -a_{ii},$ or $a_{ii} = 0, i = 1, \ldots, n.$

C. **1.** (a) Let $A^2 = B = [b_{ij}];$ then

$$b_{ij} = \sum_{k=1}^{n} a_{ik}a_{kj} = \sum_{k=1}^{n} a_{kj}a_{ik} = \sum_{k=1}^{n} a_{jk}a_{ki} \quad (A \text{ sym.})$$

$$= b_{ji}.$$

Therefore B is symmetric.
(b) Let $A^2 = C = [c_{ij}];$ then

$$c_{ij} = \sum_{k=1}^{n} a_{ik}a_{kj} = \sum_{k=1}^{n} a_{kj}a_{ik} = \sum_{k=1}^{n} (-a_{jk})(-a_{ki}) \quad (A \text{ sk.-sym.})$$

$$= \sum_{k=1}^{n} a_{jk}a_{ki} = c_{ji}.$$

Therefore C is symmetric.

9.3

A. **1.** $\dfrac{1}{23}\begin{bmatrix} 5 & 3 \\ 1 & -4 \end{bmatrix}$.

3. $\begin{bmatrix} -5 & 3 \\ 2 & -1 \end{bmatrix}$.

5. $\dfrac{1}{48}\begin{bmatrix} 5 & 20 & -1 \\ -2 & -8 & 10 \\ 15 & 12 & -3 \end{bmatrix}$.

7. $\dfrac{1}{31}\begin{bmatrix} -2 & 9 & -4 \\ -16 & 10 & -1 \\ 5 & -7 & 10 \end{bmatrix}$.

9. $\dfrac{1}{38}\begin{bmatrix} -1 & 5 & -5 \\ 8 & -2 & 40 \\ 8 & -2 & 2 \end{bmatrix}$.

11. $\dfrac{1}{148}\begin{bmatrix} 16 & 22 & -43 & 61 \\ -20 & 28 & 26 & -30 \\ 8 & -26 & -3 & 49 \\ 28 & 20 & 8 & -32 \end{bmatrix}$.

B. **1.** $C = CI = CAB = IB = B.$

9.4

A. **7.** $\begin{bmatrix} 3 & 1 \\ 1 & -2 \end{bmatrix}$.

9. $\begin{bmatrix} 5 & -1 \\ -1 & 3 \end{bmatrix}$

11. $Q(x_1, x_2) = x_1^2 + 8x_1x_2 + x_2^2.$
13. $Q(x_1, x_2) = 3x_1^2 + 4x_1x_2.$
15. $Q(x_1, x_2) = 8x_1^2 + 24x_1x_2 + x_2^2.$
17. $Q(x_1, x_2) = 3x_1^2 + 12x_1x_2 - 2x_2^2.$
19. $\lambda_1 = -2, \quad \lambda_2 = 6, \quad R_1 = \dfrac{1}{\sqrt{2}}\begin{bmatrix} 1 \\ -1 \end{bmatrix}, \quad R_2 = \dfrac{1}{\sqrt{2}}\begin{bmatrix} 1 \\ 1 \end{bmatrix}, \quad \begin{bmatrix} -2 & 0 \\ 0 & 6 \end{bmatrix}$

21. $\lambda_1 = -4$, $\lambda_2 = 9$, $R_1 = \dfrac{1}{\sqrt{13}}\begin{bmatrix} 2 \\ -3 \end{bmatrix}$, $R_2 = \dfrac{1}{\sqrt{13}}\begin{bmatrix} 3 \\ 2 \end{bmatrix}$, $\begin{bmatrix} -4 & 0 \\ 0 & 9 \end{bmatrix}$

23. $\lambda_1 = -2$, $\lambda_2 = 3$, $R_1 = \dfrac{1}{\sqrt{5}}\begin{bmatrix} 1 \\ -2 \end{bmatrix}$, $R_2 = \dfrac{1}{\sqrt{5}}\begin{bmatrix} 2 \\ 1 \end{bmatrix}$, $\begin{bmatrix} -2 & 0 \\ 0 & 3 \end{bmatrix}$.

25. $\lambda_1 = \lambda_2 = 2$, $\lambda_3 = 0$, $R_1 = \dfrac{1}{\sqrt{3}}\begin{bmatrix} 1 \\ -1 \\ 1 \end{bmatrix}$, $R_2 = \dfrac{1}{\sqrt{6}}\begin{bmatrix} 1 \\ -1 \\ -2 \end{bmatrix}$,

$R_3 = \dfrac{1}{\sqrt{2}}\begin{bmatrix} 1 \\ 1 \\ 0 \end{bmatrix}$, $\begin{bmatrix} 2 & 0 & 0 \\ 0 & 2 & 0 \\ 0 & 0 & 0 \end{bmatrix}$.

C. **1.** P orthogonal $\Rightarrow PP^t = P^tP = I \Rightarrow P^t$ orthogonal.

3. P orthogonal $\Rightarrow P^{-1} = P^t$ orthogonal, by Exercise C1. Therefore, since P^{-1} and PQ orthogonal (hypothesis), $Q = P^{-1}(PQ)$ orthogonal, by Exercise C2.

5. Either

$$A = \begin{bmatrix} \cos\theta & \sin\theta \\ \sin\theta & -\cos\theta \end{bmatrix},$$

or

$$A = \begin{bmatrix} \cos\theta & -\sin\theta \\ -\sin\theta & -\cos\theta \end{bmatrix},$$

where $0 \leqslant \theta \leqslant \pi$. Geometrically, the first form represents a rotation of the x-axis through an angle θ and a rotation of the y-axis through an angle θ followed by a reflection in the x-axis.

Index